DESIGN OF PLATED STRUCTURES

ECCS Eurocode Design Manuals

ECCS Editorial Board
Luís Simões da Silva (ECCS)
António Lamas (Portugal)
Jean-Pierre Jaspart (Belgium)
Reidar Bjorhovde (USA)
Ulrike Kuhlmann (Germany)

Design of Steel Structures
Luís Simões da Silva, Rui Simões and Helena Gervásio

Fire Design of Steel Structures
Jean-Marc Franssen and Paulo Vila Real

Design of Plated Structures
Darko Beg, Ulrike Kuhlmann, Laurence Davaine and Benjamin Braun

Available Soon

Design of Cold-Formed Steel Structures
Dan Dubina, Viorel Ungureanu and Raffaele Landolfo

Fatigue Design of Steel and Composite Structures
Alain Nussbaumer, Luís Borges and Laurence Davaine

Design of Joints in Steel and Composite Structures
Jean-Pierre Jaspart, Klaus Weynand and Jurgen Kuck

Information and Ordering Details

For price, availability, and ordering visit our website **www.steelconstruct.com**.
For more information about books and journals visit **www.ernst-und-sohn.de**

DESIGN OF PLATED STRUCTURES

Eurocode 3: Design of Steel Structures
Part 1-5 – Design of Plated Structures

Darko Beg
Ulrike Kuhlmann
Laurence Davaine
Benjamin Braun

Design of Plated Structures

1st Edition, 2010

Published by:
ECCS – European Convention for Constructional Steelwork
publications@steelconstruct.com
www.steelconstruct.com

Sales:
Wilhelm Ernst & Sohn Verlag für Architektur und technische Wissenschaften GmbH & Co. KG, Berlin

All rights reserved. No parts of this publication may be reproduced, stored in a retrieval system, or transmitted in any form or by any means, electronic, mechanical, photocopying, recording or otherwise, without the prior permission of the copyright owner.

ECCS assumes no liability with respect to the use for any application of the material and information contained in this publication.

Copyright © 2010 ECCS – European Convention for Constructional Steelwork

ISBN (ECCS): 978-92-9147-100-3
ISBN (Ernst & Sohn): 978-3-433-02980-0
Legal dep.: 320032/10 - Printed in Multicomp Lda, Mem Martins, Portugal
Photo cover credits: Vincent de Ville de Goyet

TABLE OF CONTENTS

FOREWORD vii

PREFACE ix

SYMBOLS xi

Chapter 1
INTRODUCTION 1
1.1. Plate buckling in steel structures 1
1.2. Purpose of this book 2
1.3. Structure of this book 3

Chapter 2
OVERVIEW OF DESIGN RULES 5
2.1. Introduction 5
2.2. Basis of design and modelling 5
    2.2.1. General 5
    2.2.2. Effective width models for global analysis 6
    2.2.3. Uniform and non uniform members 7
    2.2.4. Reduced stress method 8
2.3. Shear lag in member design 8
    2.3.1. Phenomenon 8
    2.3.2. Shear lag in global analysis (calculation of internal forces and moments) 10
    2.3.3. Elastic shear lag in section analysis (calculation of stresses at SLS and fatigue ULS) 11
    2.3.4. Elastoplastic shear lag in section analysis (calculation of stresses at ULS) 14
    2.3.5. Interaction between shear lag and plate buckling at ULS 15

2.3.6. Design examples	16
2.4. Plate buckling effects due to direct stresses (including annexes A and E where applicable)	22
2.4.1. Introduction	22
2.4.2. Effective width method	25
2.4.2.1. General requirements	25
2.4.2.2. Principles of effective width calculation	27
2.4.2.3. Hybrid girders	30
2.4.2.4. Plate-like and column-like buckling	31
2.4.3. Plate-like buckling	32
2.4.3.1. Unstiffened plates	32
2.4.3.2. Longitudinally stiffened plates	36
2.4.4. Column-like buckling	42
2.4.4.1. Unstiffened plates	42
2.4.4.2. Longitudinally stiffened plates	43
2.4.5. Interpolation between plate-like and column-like buckling	45
2.4.6. Verification of the cross section resistance in ultimate limit states	48
2.4.7. Verification of plated structural elements in the serviceability limit states	50
2.4.8. Design examples	51
2.5. Resistance to shear (including annex A where applicable)	83
2.5.1. Collapse behaviour	83
2.5.2. Design according to section 5, EN 1993-1-5	84
2.5.3. Design example	92
2.6. Resistance to transverse loading	93
2.6.1. Collapse behaviour	93
2.6.2. Design according to section 6, EN 1993-1-5	94
2.6.3. Design example	102
2.7. Interaction	109
2.7.1. Interaction between bending moment and shear force in a web panel	109

2.7.2. Interaction between axial force, bending moment and shear force in a web panel ... 112

2.7.3. Interaction between axial force, bending moment and shear force in a flange panel ... 112

2.7.4. Interaction between axial force, bending moment and transverse force ... 113

2.7.5. Interaction between shear force and transverse force in a web panel ... 115

2.7.6. Design examples ... 117

2.8. Flange induced buckling ... 118

2.9. Stiffeners and detailing ... 121

   2.9.1. Introduction ... 121

   2.9.2. Transverse stiffeners ... 124

      2.9.2.1. Direct stresses ... 124

      2.9.2.2. Shear ... 127

      2.9.2.3. Simultaneous action of direct stresses and shear ... 131

      2.9.2.4. Introduction of reaction forces and other large transverse forces ... 134

   2.9.3. Longitudinal stiffeners ... 135

      2.9.3.1. Direct stresses ... 135

      2.9.3.2. Shear ... 137

   2.9.4. Torsional buckling of stiffeners ... 137

   2.9.5. Structural detailing related to plate buckling ... 140

      2.9.5.1. Transverse welds in the plate ... 140

      2.9.5.2. Cut-outs in stiffeners ... 141

      2.9.5.3. Welds ... 142

   2.9.6. Design examples ... 143

2.10. Reduced stress method (including Annexes A and B where applicable) ... 160

   2.10.1. General ... 160

   2.10.2. Choice of reduction factors ... 164

2.11. FEM ... 166

   2.11.1. Introduction ... 166

TABLE OF CONTENTS

2.11.2. Modelling	168
2.11.3. Definition of initial imperfections in the FE model	168
2.11.4. Definition of material behaviour in the FE model	172
2.11.5. Design examples	173

Chapter 3
CRANE RUNWAY BEAM EXAMPLE — 181

3.1. Description of the crane	181
3.2. Description of the crane runway beam	182
3.2.1. Geometry	182
3.2.2. Material properties and material partial factors	184
3.2.3. Cross section classification	184
3.3. Actions and load partial factors	186
3.3.1. General	186
3.3.2. Crane actions	187
3.4. Internal forces and stresses	189
3.4.1. General	189
3.4.2. Transverse forces and stresses	190
3.4.3. Maximum bending moments and stresses	192
3.4.4. Maximum shear forces and stresses	193
3.5. Verifications in general	194
3.6. Buckling verifications according to sections 4 to 7, EN 1993-1-5	194
3.6.1. Resistance to shear forces	195
3.6.2. Resistance to transverse forces	197
3.6.3. Interaction checks	199
3.7. Buckling verifications according to section 10, EN 1993-1-5	200
3.8. Flange induced buckling verification	204
3.9. Stiffener verifications	205
3.9.1. Bearing stiffeners	205

Chapter 4
BOX-GIRDER BRIDGE EXAMPLE — 209

4.1. Description of the bridge	209

- 4.1.1. Longitudinal elevation — 209
- 4.1.2. Cross section of the composite deck — 209
- 4.1.3. Material properties and partial factors — 210
  - *4.1.3.1. Structural steel* — 210
  - *4.1.3.2. Reinforced concrete* — 211
  - *4.1.3.3. Partial factors* — 211
- 4.1.4. Structural steel distribution — 211
- 4.2. Internal forces and moments, Stresses — 214
  - 4.2.1. Actions and load partial factors — 214
  - 4.2.2. Transient design situation (launching phase) — 215
  - 4.2.3. Permanent design situation — 215
- 4.3. Web buckling verification for the launching phase — 217
  - 4.3.1. Patch loading verification — 218
    - *4.3.1.1. Resistance load for a single wheel ($s_s = 0$)* — 220
    - *4.3.1.2. Resistance load for a patch length $s_s = 1500$ mm* — 220
    - *4.3.1.3. Patch loading verification* — 221
  - 4.3.2. Interaction between patch loading and bending moment — 221
- 4.4. Effective cross section of the stiffened bottom flange at internal support P1 (uniform compression) — 222
  - 4.4.1. First step: shear lag effect according to EN1993-1-5, 3.2 and 3.3 — 222
  - 4.4.2. Second step: Critical plate buckling stress according to EN1993-1-5, Annex A — 223
  - 4.4.3. Third step: Effective cross section — 225
    - *4.4.3.1. Step A: Local buckling of sub-panels* — 225
    - *4.4.3.2. Step B: Global buckling of the whole stiffened bottom flange* — 227
- 4.5. Effective cross section of the stiffened web at internal support P1 (bending) — 230
  - 4.5.1. Local buckling of sub-panels — 232
  - 4.5.2. Global buckling of the whole stiffened web in bending — 234
    - *4.5.2.1. Column like behaviour* — 234

4.5.2.2. Plate like behaviour	236
4.5.2.3. Interpolation between plate like and column like behaviour	237
4.5.3. Torsional buckling of the longitudinal web stiffener	238
4.6. Checking of the box-girder section under bending at support P1	239
4.7. Shear resistance of the stiffened web panel closest to the internal support P1	240
4.8. Interaction between bending and shear at support P1	246
4.9. Intermediate transverse stiffener design	247
4.9.1. Transverse web stiffeners	247
4.9.1.1. Axial forces from the tension field action	247
4.9.1.2. Transverse deviation forces from adjacen compressed panels	247
4.9.1.3. Verification of the transverse stiffener	248
4.9.2. Lower flange transverse stiffeners	250
4.9.2.1. Cross section class check	251
4.9.2.2. Strength and stiffness check of the stiffener	252
4.9.2.3. Shear resistance of the stiffener web	253
4.10. Buckling verifications at internal support P1 according to section 10, EN 1993-1-5	254
4.10.1. General	254
4.10.2. Stiffened bottom flange	254
4.10.2.1. General	254
4.10.2.2. Determination of ρ_{loc} to account for local buckling	256
4.10.2.3. Determination of ρ_c to account for global buckling	257
4.10.3. Stiffened bottom flange	260
4.10.3.1. General	260
4.10.3.2. Determination of ρ_{loc} to account for local buckling	261
4.10.3.3. Determination of ρ_c to account for global buckling	263
REFERENCES	267

FOREWORD

Plated structures are large steel structures commonly made from steel plates welded together. A typical use is for bridge girders and girders for heavy overhead cranes. Compared to steel structures of rolled profiles, plated structures are more prone to local buckling and therefore require design rules to cover such phenomena. In Eurocode 3 such rules are collected in Part 1-5 "Plated structures", EN 1993-1-5. I was the convener of the project team that wrote the standard, and this team was made up of some very knowledgeable specialists. We spent many years on comparing and finding the best methods of dealing with the most common buckling phenomena. These have attracted a lot of research efforts not only due to some spectacular bridge failures, but also because buckling of plates, and particularly stiffened plates, are scientifically interesting and have attracted the attention of many sharp brains. The result of our efforts was published as a standard in 2006, but the implementation in the different member countries of CEN follows different time tables.

Already before the standard was published we had many requests for background information. The reason was probably that the project team had collected design rules from different sources and chosen the ones that best fitted available information. Some of those were unfamiliar to many engineers and the requests of background information were reasonable. The contract with the EU commission did not include the task of delivering background documents but the academic participants in the project team decided to write one on their own expense. This document can be found on the ECCS web site with the URL http://www.steelconstruct.com/. It is described as a commentary to EN 1993-1-5 and includes background to the design rules and some explanations. There are also some design examples.

As a third step, ECCS has taken on the task of publishing the present manual that you have in your hands. It is intended for engineers who shall apply the rules of EN 1993-1-5 and I have to admit that it is needed. That does not

Foreword

mean that I think we did a bad job with the standard but that the text in the standard is quite brief and in order to interpret it correctly one needs experience and insight in the problems to be dealt with. This manual will be of great importance for engineers to aid them to apply the standard correctly thanks to its explanations and design examples. The authors have done a very good job and after reviewing the text I fully support it as a proper interpretation of the standard.

Bernt Johansson
Professor Emeritus Steel Structures

PREFACE

Plate buckling related problems in steel structures are inherently linked to complex solution strategies and design procedures. They involve stability analysis in the post-critical state, interaction of different failure modes, imperfection sensitivity, etc.

Eurocode standard EN 1993-1-5 gives a unique opportunity to deal with these problems, at least for typical geometrically more or less regular structural components, by means of fairly simple and consistent set of design procedures, suitable for hand calculations. The main advantage of these design procedures is that generally they were derived from available test results and despite their relative simplicity very often they can be more reliable than advanced numerical simulations. The latter heavily depend on the quality of the applied software tool, the way of modelling, experience of the user, correct interpretation of the results, etc. But even when an experienced design engineer applies advanced numerical simulations for plate buckling problems, a check by means of EN 1993-1-5 design procedures provides comfort and confidence in the results.

The main aim of this Design Manual is to provide practical advice to designers of plated structures for correct and efficient application of EN 1993-1-5 design rules, including several design examples. No deeper theoretical background is given and in this respect the reader is directed to other literature.

The initiative for this Design Manual came from the ECCS that included this Manual into the comprehensive action of preparing the ECCS Eurocode Design Manuals.

The four authors: Darko Beg (University of Ljubljana, Slovenia), Laurence Davaine (SNCF – French National Railway Service), Ulrike Kuhlmann and Benjamin Braun (University of Stuttgart, Germany) worked in close

Preface

cooperation helping each other and carefully proof-reading parts of the text prepared by other authors. Nonetheless, the leading authors of individual chapters are:

> Chapters 2.2, 2.4, 2.9 and all short numerical examples in Chapter 2: Darko Beg
> Chapters 1, 2.5, 2.6, 2.10, 3: Ulrike Kuhlmann and Benjamin Braun
> Chapters 2.3, 2.7, 2.8, 2.11: Laurence Davaine
> Chapter 4: Laurence Davaine and Benjamin Braun

It should be mentioned that Franci Sinur and Blaž Čermelj helped in the preparation of the short numerical examples of Chapter 2 and Primož Može and Mojca Jelančič helped at the final editing of the text, all four coming from the University of Ljubljana.

At the end of this short Preface it is important to express strong wishes and expectations of the authors that this Manual will find a place on the working desks of design engineers helping them design excellent plated structures. In the authors' opinion the manual will also be helpful to students of structural engineering on their way of getting familiar with plated structures.

Darko Beg
Ulrike Kuhlmann
Laurence Davaine
Benjamin Braun

SYMBOLS

a	length of a stiffened or unstiffened plate
b	width of a stiffened or unstiffened plate
b_f	flange width
$b_{c,loc,i}$	width of the compressed part of each individual sub-panel i
b_{eff}	effective width (for elastic shear lag or local plate buckling)
b_1	height of the loaded sub-panel taken as the clear distance between the loaded flange and the longitudinal stiffener
b_w	clear width between welds
c	distance between plastic hinges in the flanges
e_{max}	maximum distance from the edge of the stiffener to the centroid of the stiffener
f_y	yield strength of steel
f_{yf}	flange yield strength
f_{yw}	web yield strength
h_f	distance between mid-planes of flanges
h_w	clear web depth between flanges
h_{wi}	clear height of sub-panel i
k_F	buckling coefficient for transverse loading
$k_{\sigma,p}$	plate buckling coefficient
k_τ	shear buckling coefficient of the web between flanges
$k_{\tau,i}$	shear buckling coefficient of sub-panel i
$k_{\tau s\ell}$	shear buckling coefficient of a web stiffened with longitudinal stiffeners
ℓ_y	effective loaded length
s_s	length of stiff bearing
t	thickness of the plate
t_f	flange thickness
t_w	web thickness
w_{el}	elastic deflection of the stiffener
w_0	equivalent geometric imperfection of the stiffener

SYMBOLS

A_s	gross cross sectional area of the stiffener
A_{sl}	total area of all the longitudinal stiffeners of a stiffened plate
A_{st}	gross cross sectional area of one transverse stiffener
A_{eff}	effective cross sectional area
$A_{c,eff}$	effective area of the compression zone of the stiffened or unstiffened plate
$A_{c,eff,loc}$	effective section areas of all the stiffeners and sub-panels that are fully or partially in the compression zone
$A_{sl,eff}$	sum of the effective sections of all longitudinal stiffeners with gross area A_{sl} located in the compression zone
$A_{sl,1}$	gross cross sectional area of the stiffener and the adjacent parts of the plate
$A_{sl,1,eff}$	effective cross sectional area of the stiffener and adjacent parts of the plate with due allowance for plate buckling of sub-panels
E	elastic modulus of steel
F_{Ed}	design transverse force
F_{Rd}	design resistance to transverse loading
F_{cr}	elastic critical load at transverse loading
F_y	yield load at transverse loading
G	shear elastic modulus
I_p	polar second moment area of the stiffener alone around the edge fixed to the plate
I_{st}	minimum required second moment of the area of a transverse stiffener to be considered as rigid
I_t	St. Venant torsional constant of the stiffener alone (without contributing plating)
I_w	warping cross section constant of the stiffener alone around the edge fixed to the plate
L_{eff}	effective length for resistance to transverse forces
$I_{s\ell}$	sum of the second moment of area of all longitudinal stiffeners
$I_{s\ell,1}$	second moment of area of the gross cross section of the stiffener and the adjacent parts of the plate, relative to the out-of-plane bending of the plate

I_{st}	second moment of the area of a stiffener for a cross section for the axis parallel to the web plate
$I_{st,act}$	actual second moment of area of the transverse stiffener
M_{Ed}	applied design bending moment
$M_{pl,Rd}$	design plastic moment resistance of the cross section (irrespective of cross section class)
$M_{f,Rd}$	design plastic moment resistance of a cross section consisting of the flanges only
N_{Ed}	design axial force
$N_{st,ten}$	axial force in the intermediate stiffener imposed by the tension field action
N_{cr}	Euler elastic critical force
$N_{cr,st}$	Euler elastic critical force of the stiffener
V_{Ed}	design shear force including shear from torque
$V_{bw,Rd}$	contribution from the web to the design shear resistance
$V_{bf,Rd}$	contribution from the flanges to the design shear resistance
$V_{b,Rd}$	design shear resistance
W_{eff}	effective elastic section modulus
$\alpha_{ult,k}$	minimum load amplifier for the design loads to reach the characteristic value of the resistance
α_{cr}	minimum load amplifier for the design loads to reach the elastic critical value of the plate
β	effective width factor for elastic shear lag
β_{ult}	effective width factor for the effect of shear lag at the ultimate limit state
χ_c	reduction factor due to column buckling
χ_F	reduction factor for transverse loading
χ_w	reduction factor for shear buckling

$$\varepsilon = \sqrt{\frac{235}{f_y\,[MPa]}}$$

γ_M	partial safety factor
η	factor depending on the steel grade
η_1	utilisation level of the design resistance to direct stresses
η_2	utilisation level of the design resistance to transverse loading

SYMBOLS

η_3	utilisation level of the design shear resistance
$\overline{\lambda}_F$	slenderness for transverse loading (in EN 1993-1-5 the term "modified slenderness" is used according the Corrigendum (April 2009). In this document a shorter version, i.e. "slenderness", is systematically used for the sake of simplicity)
$\overline{\lambda}_p$	plate slenderness
$\overline{\lambda}_{p,red}$	reduced plate slenderness
$\overline{\lambda}_w$	web slenderness for shear
ν	Poisson coefficient of steel
ρ	plate buckling reduction factor
$\rho_x; \rho_z$	reduction factors
$\rho_{loc,i}$	reduction factor for each sub-panel i
$\sigma_{cr,p}$	elastic critical plate buckling stress
$\sigma_{cr,c}$	elastic critical column buckling stress
$\sigma_{cr,sl}$	elastic critical column buckling stress of a single stiffener
$\sigma_{com,Ed}$	maximum design compressive stress
$\sigma_{eq,Ed}$	equivalent design stress
σ_E	Euler stress
$\sigma_{cr,x}; \sigma_{cr,z}; \tau_{cr}$	elastic critical buckling stress
$\sigma_{x,Ed}; \sigma_{z,Ed}; \tau_{Ed}$	design stresses
τ_{cr}	elastic critical shear buckling stress
ψ	stress ratio along edges

Chapter 1

INTRODUCTION

1.1 PLATE BUCKLING IN STEEL STRUCTURES

State-of-the-art steel structures are characterised by a lightweight, slender and fabrication-optimised design. Especially the progress in welding technology since the 1930s has facilitated the increased application of steel plated structures, see Fig. 1.1. The significant knowledge gained since then has clearly influenced the design as well as the development of the design standards. With the Eurocodes, harmonised European rules have been established of which standard EN 1993-1-5 "Design of steel structures – Plated structural elements" (CEN, 2006a) deals with the design of plated structural elements in steel structures.

Fig. 1.1: Assembly of Haseltal road bridge near Suhl, Germany

1. INTRODUCTION

Based on EN 1993-1-5 the designer can choose, considering national allowance, mainly between two different types of design methods according to Fig. 1.2. The effective width method, also comprising resistance models for shear force and transverse force, is very efficient for standard geometries because it accounts not only for the post-critical reserve in a single plate element but also for load shedding between cross sectional elements. The reduced stress method abstains from load shedding between cross sectional elements, but it fully accounts for the post-critical reserve in a single plate element. Beyond that, its general format facilitates its use for serviceability verifications and for the design of non-uniform members such as haunched beams, beam webs with openings and plates with non-orthogonal stiffeners. In addition, a verification methodology based on the finite element method is given in section 2.11. It is the most versatile verification method, however, it requires a lot of experience. It can be used for the determination of the "real" buckling resistance by means of a nonlinear analysis considering imperfections and for the calculation of elastic critical stress values by means of a linear bifurcation analysis.

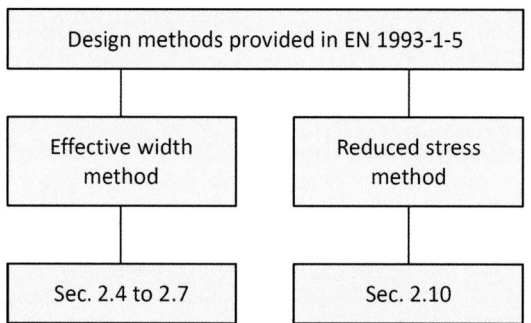

Fig. 1.2: Overview of design methods in EN 1993-1-5 and their references to the sections in this book

1.2 PURPOSE OF THIS BOOK

This book intends to provide the designer of steel plated structures with a practically oriented guide to assess EN 1993-1-5 (CEN, 2006a). This design manual is part of a comprehensive series of ECCS publications dealing with accompanying documentation to the Eurocodes. Its aim is to complement the comprehensive theoretical background given in the

Commentary to EN 1993-1-5 (Johansson *et al*, 2007) with practical knowledge for daily usage. Nevertheless, fundamental knowledge of structural mechanics is expected.

This book gives explanations and examples, advice and warnings, all of which intend to give the user considerably more insight and confidence in applying the rules of EN 1993-1-5. In order not to prejudice the use of EN 1993-1-5 where national choices are possible, Eurocode recommendations have been adopted throughout. This has to be kept in mind and, if required, the nationally determined parameters have to be adjusted when applying EN 1993-1-5 in the various member states.

1.3 STRUCTURE OF THIS BOOK

The layout of this book deliberately follows the layout of EN 1993-1-5 in order to allow for easy navigation and reference.

Chapter 2 gives a concise overview of the stability behaviour of plates in steel structures and the corresponding design rules in EN 1993-1-5. Relevant knowledge and terms about load-carrying mechanisms in plates and plated structures under direct stress, shear stress and transverse stress are introduced in order to ease the understanding of the design rules. The main components of Chapter 2 are the explanations of the verification methods which correspond to sections in this book as shown in Fig. 1.2. In this book, small design examples in each section address specific issues of these design rules.

In addition, chapters 3 and 4 present two comprehensive design examples of a crane runway beam and a box-girder bridge. In both examples not only the verification methods are illustrated, but also the big picture of the whole design is given. Besides general information on geometry and material properties, firstly loads and governing internal forces are determined. Based on cross section classification, and while adhering to the objective of this book, the examples finally focus on the plate buckling verifications.

1. Introduction

Chapter 2

OVERVIEW OF DESIGN RULES

2.1 INTRODUCTION

Chapter 2 gives a commented overview of the EN 1993-1-5 design rules following the structure of the standard. At the end of each main section short numerical examples illustrate practical application of the design rules. The Contents of the Annexes are included in the corresponding sections of chapter 2, except that FEM analysis (Annex C of EN 1993-1-5) is given in section 2.11 and that plate girders with corrugated webs (Annex D of EN 1993-1-5) are not addressed in this Manual.

2.2 BASIS OF DESIGN AND MODELLING

2.2.1 General

When designing plated structures the effects of shear lag, plate buckling and interaction of both effects should be taken into account at the ultimate, serviceability or fatigue limit states. Possible simplifications for global analysis are given in section 2.2.2. EN 1993-1-5 (CEN, 2006a), as a generic Eurocode standard does not provide the values of partial factors γ_{M0} and γ_{M1}. These values should be taken from relevant application parts of Eurocode standards or National Annexes to these standards, whenever the values are different from the recommended ones. This means that for example for buildings γ_{M0} and γ_{M1} should be taken from EN 1993-1-1 (CEN, 2005), in bridge design from EN 1993-2 (CEN, 2006b) and for crane runway

2. OVERVIEW OF DESIGN RULES

girders from EN 1993-6 (CEN, 2007).

Three approaches to the analysis of plated structures are covered by EN 1993-1-5:

- Effective width method (sub-chapter 2.3-2.9 of this publication)
- Reduced stress method (sub-chapter 2.10 of this publication)
- Finite element analysis (FEA) (sub-chapter 2.11 of this publication)

For effective width and reduced stress methods very detailed design procedures are given, while for FEA only general principles are described. The first two methods are meant to be predominantly used in the design of plated structures and the FEA may be successfully used to calculate elastic critical stresses to be used in the first two approaches. A complete design by FEA is possible but requires experience, appropriate software and a very careful interpretation of results.

In relation to the effective width method, EN 1993-1-5 introduces three different designations for three types of effective widths:

- Effective^s width – shear lag effects
- Effective^p width – local buckling of plates
- Effective width – interaction of shear lag and local buckling

2.2.2 Effective width models for global analysis

Shear lag and plate buckling reduce the stiffness of plated structures and should in principle be accounted for in the global analysis.

The effect of shear lag of flanges in global analysis may be taken into account by means of the effective width method. For simplicity this effective^s width may be taken as constant over the length of each span, see Fig. 2.1.

The effect of plate buckling in elastic global analysis may also be taken into account by means of the effective^p width method (see section 2.4.2 and 2.4.7 and references Johansson *et al* (2007), Sedlacek *et al* (2008)). This effect may be neglected when the effective cross sectional area of an element in compression in the ultimate limite state is larger than ρ_{lim} times the gross cross sectional area of the same element. The recommended value is $\rho_{lim} = 0.5$, but different values may be given in the National Annex. Only very slender plates will violate this criterion.

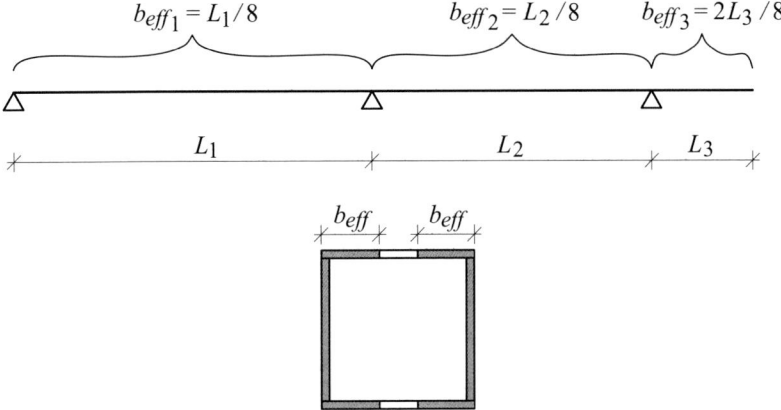

Fig. 2.1: Effective^s widths for global analysis

2.2.3 Uniform and non-uniform members

The design procedures for plate buckling that are based on the effective width method (see sub-chapter 2.3 to 2.9) were developed for web or flange panels of uniform width. Usually these panels are stiffened or unstiffened plates between rigid transverse stiffeners. The panels may be considered as uniform when:

- The shape of the panel is rectangular or almost rectangular. In the latter case the angle α (see Fig. 2.2) should not exceed 10°.
- The diameter of any unstiffened hole or cut-out does not exceed 0.05 b, where b is the width of the panel.

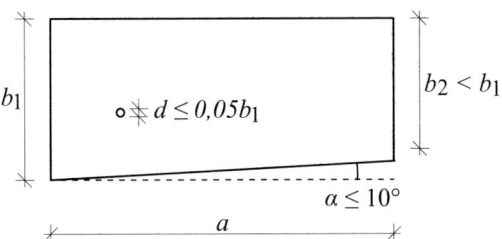

Fig. 2.2: Nominally uniform panels

2. OVERVIEW OF DESIGN RULES

If angle α is larger than 10°, then the panel may be conservatively treated as rectangular with the width equal to the larger of widths on both ends of the panel (Fig. 2.3).

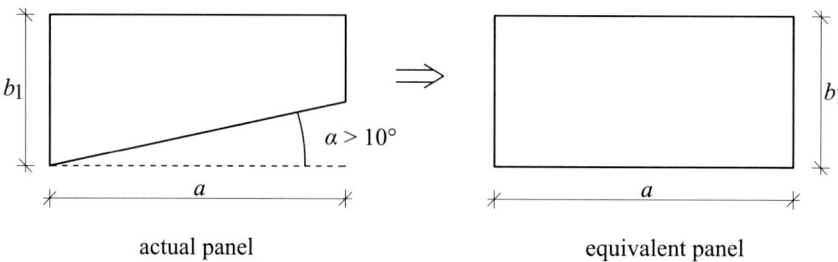

Fig. 2.3: Non-uniform panel transformed to equivalent uniform panel

Another more general possibility for non-uniform members (e.g. haunched members, not rectangular panels) or members with large openings is to take advantage of sub-chapter 2.10 or to apply FE analysis.

For the calculation of stresses at the serviceability and fatigue limit states only the effective[s] area due to shear lag, which is based on purely elastic assumption, may be used if parameter $\rho_{lim} > 0.5$. For the ultimate limit state the effective area due to combined effects of shear lag and plate buckling (see section 2.3.5) should be used.

2.2.4 Reduced stress method

When the reduced stress method is applied, the stresses in each panel should not exceed the limiting values calculated according to sub-chapter 2.10 and the cross sections may be treated as Class 3 sections.

2.3 SHEAR LAG IN MEMBER DESIGN

2.3.1 Phenomenon

When the flange width of an I-girder or box-girder is not negligible compared to the girder span, the transverse distribution of the longitudinal normal stresses is no more uniform over the whole width of the flange due to shear deformation. In a given cross section the value of maximum normal stress in the flange is reached at the junction between the web and the flange and this stress progressively decreases when moving transversally away across the flange width. See Fig. 2.4.

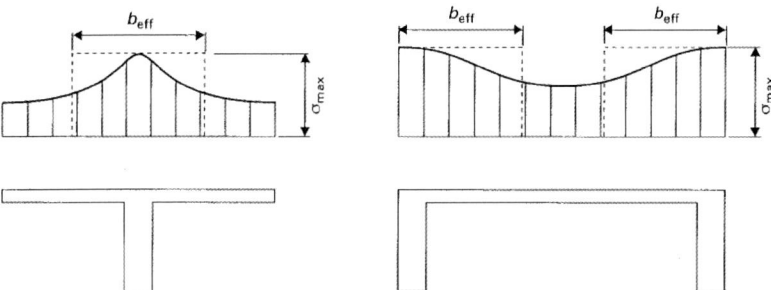

Fig. 2.4: Transverse distribution of the longitudinal normal stresses in a wide flange compared to the span length

In EN1993-1-5, the concept of taking shear lag into account is based on an effective^s width of the flange. This effective^s width is defined in order to have the same total normal force in the gross flange subjected to the real transverse stress distribution as in the effective flange subjected to a uniform stress equal to the maximum stress of the real transverse distribution:

$$\int_{b_f} \sigma_x(y) \cdot t_f \cdot dy = b_{eff} t_f \cdot \sigma_{x,max} \qquad (2.1)$$

Then the following aspects should be highlighted:

- Shear lag effects should be taken into account for the global analysis as well as for the section analysis.
- Shear lag effects are a first order effect (no out-of-plane deformations in the flange) that should not be confused with the second order plate buckling effect (also dealt with in EN1993-1-5 through the definition of an effective^p width).
- As a consequence of the previous comment, shear lag can occur in tension flange as well as in compression flange. In compression flange, interaction should be considered between shear lag and plate buckling effects.
- Shear lag should be considered for Serviceability Limit State (SLS)

2. Overview of Design Rules

as well as for Ultimate Limit State (ULS). At SLS and at fatigue ULS the stress calculation is elastic, whereas at ULS the yield strength f_y could influence the stress distribution resulting in an elastoplastic shear lag.
- In longitudinally stiffened plates shear lag depends on the degree of stiffening of the flange through the following parameter:

$$\alpha_0 = \sqrt{1 + \frac{A_{sl}}{b_0 t}} \qquad (2.2)$$

where A_{sl} is the area of all longitudinal stiffeners welded to the flange within its gross width b_0 (see Fig. 2.5). It should be noted that A_{sl} does not include any adjacent parts of the plate.
- Shear lag effects depend on the shape of the global bending moment distribution over the girder. The steeper the gradient of the bending moment, the more important the shear force is, resulting in a larger reduction of the flange width. EN1993-1-5 consequently distinguishes the sagging bending region from the hogging bending region of the girder.

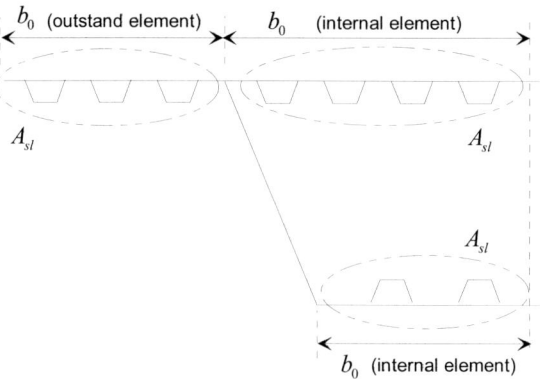

Fig. 2.5: Definition of notations (b_0, A_{sl})

2.3.2 Shear lag in global analysis (calculation of internal forces and moments)

EN1993-1-5, clause 2.2, defines a simple rule to take shear lag into account in the global analysis of a multi-span I- or box-girder. The effective[s] flange width (on each side of the main web) is assumed to be uniform over the length of each span. For each span of the girder, this effective[s] flange width b_{eff} should be taken as the lesser of the full width b_0 (on each side of the main web) and $L/8$, where L is the span of the girder. In case of a cantilever girder, L is equal to twice the distance from the support to the end of the cantilever.

$$b_{eff} = \min\left(b_0; \frac{L}{8}\right) \qquad (2.3)$$

The same effective[s] width applies for calculating the internal forces and moments at SLS and at ULS.

2.3.3 Elastic shear lag in section analysis (calculation of stresses at SLS and fatigue ULS)

First of all, EN1993-1-5, clause 3.1, indicates that shear lag in the flanges may be neglected if $b_0 < L_e / 50$. L_e is the effective length of a span, approximately corresponding to the distance between points of zero bending moments (see Fig. 2.6). With typical steel box-girder bridge dimensions the shear lag effect will almost always have to be considered for small or medium spans (up to around 70 m).

If shear lag should be considered, the full width b_0 is reduced to an effective[s] width b_{eff} by calculating the factor $\beta \leq 1.0$:

$$b_{eff} = \beta \cdot b_0 \qquad (2.4)$$

The definition of L_e (and consequently the different values of β) depends on the shape of the bending moment distribution. As already mentioned above, the reduction due to shear lag is more important in the hogging bending region surrounding internal supports than in the sagging bending region near mid-span. Between these two values, EN1993-1-5 adopts a linear distribution of the effective[s] width over quarter of spans, see Fig. 2.6.

The factor κ is directly related to the stiffening ratio α_0 of the flange:

2. OVERVIEW OF DESIGN RULES

$$\kappa = \alpha_0 \cdot \frac{b_0}{L_e} = \sqrt{1 + \frac{A_{sl}}{b_0 t} \cdot \frac{b_0}{L_e}} \quad (2.5)$$

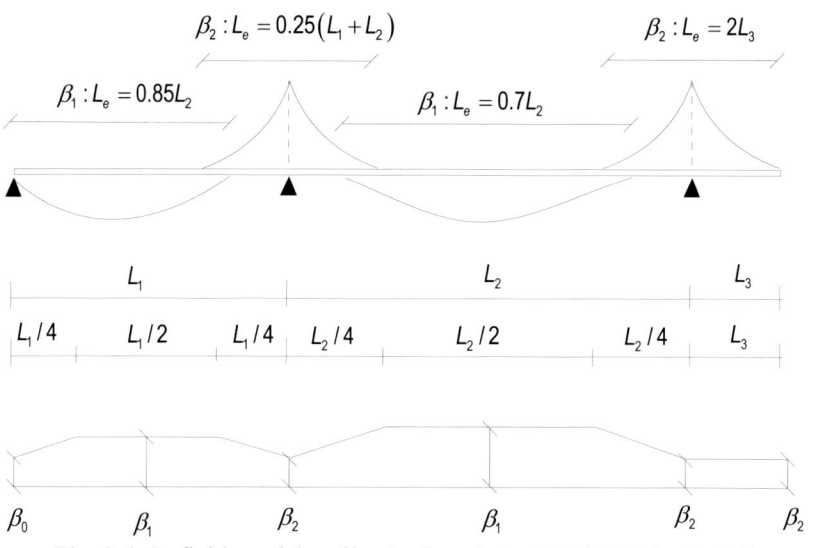

Fig. 2.6: Definition of the effective length L_e (EN1993-1-5, Fig 3.1)

κ	Verification	β – value
$\kappa \leq 0.02$		$\beta = 1.0$
$0.02 < \kappa \leq 0.7$	sagging bending	$\beta = \beta_1 = \dfrac{1}{1 + 6.4\kappa^2}$
	hogging bending	$\beta = \beta_2 = \dfrac{1}{1 + 6.0\left(\kappa - \dfrac{1}{2500\kappa}\right) + 1.6\kappa^2}$
$0.7 < \kappa$	sagging bending	$\beta = \beta_1 = \dfrac{1}{5.9\kappa}$
	hogging bending	$\beta = \beta_1 = \dfrac{1}{8.6\kappa}$
all κ	end support	$\beta_0 = \left(0.55 + \dfrac{0.025}{\kappa}\right)\beta_1$ but $\beta_0 < \beta_1$
all κ	Cantilever	$\beta = \beta_2$ at support and at the end

Fig. 2.7: Calculation of effective^s width factor (EN1993-1-5, Table 3.1)

2.3 SHEAR LAG IN MEMBER DESIGN

The following graph illustrates the influence of the stiffening ratio on the elastic shear lag at SLS (or at fatigue ULS). The more stiffened the flange is, the smaller its effective^s width is. However, it should be noticed that this influence is not so important (especially in hogging bending region).

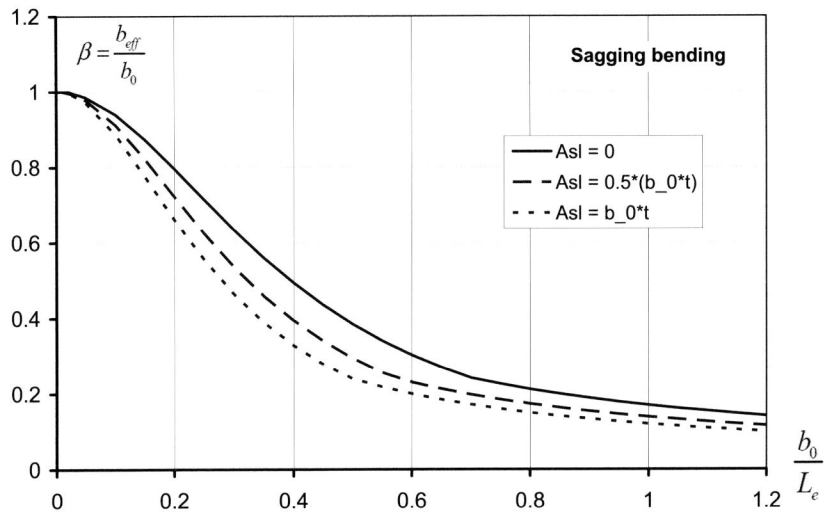

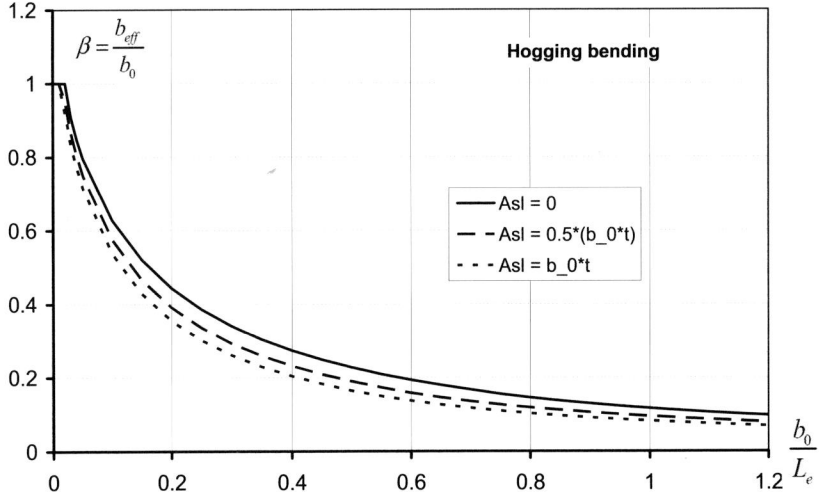

Fig. 2.8: Influence of the flange stiffening ratio on the elastic effective^s width

Having calculated the maximum elastic stress at the junction between the web and the flange (using the effective^s width from expressions 2.4), it

2. OVERVIEW OF DESIGN RULES

might be interesting to go back to the non-uniform transverse distribution of the longitudinal normal stress in the flange due to shear lag. EN1993-1-5, clause 3.2.2, gives analytical equations to draw this transverse distribution.

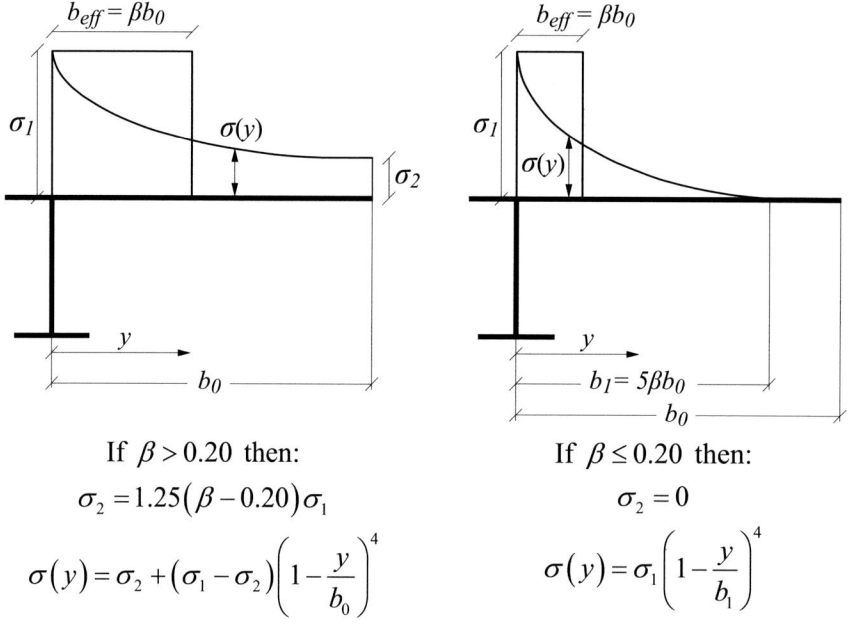

If $\beta > 0.20$ then:

$$\sigma_2 = 1.25(\beta - 0.20)\sigma_1$$

$$\sigma(y) = \sigma_2 + (\sigma_1 - \sigma_2)\left(1 - \frac{y}{b_0}\right)^4$$

If $\beta \leq 0.20$ then:

$$\sigma_2 = 0$$

$$\sigma(y) = \sigma_1\left(1 - \frac{y}{b_1}\right)^4$$

Fig. 2.9: Distribution of stresses due to shear lag (EN1993-1-5, Figure 3.3)

2.3.4 Elastoplastic shear lag in section analysis (calculation of stresses at ULS)

The distribution of stresses at ULS may be influenced by the yield strength f_y resulting in an elastoplastic zone in the flange (surrounding its junction with the web where the stress is maximum). This partial yielding occurs in a tension flange as well as in a compression flange. The consequence is a partial redistribution of the stresses across the flange width and an increased effective[s] width. Two options are allowed by EN1993-1-5 for taking the shear lag into account at ULS:

- Use the SLS elastic shear lag (conservative approach which does not consider the elastoplastic redistribution),

- Use the factor $\beta^\kappa \geq \beta$ allowing for limited plastic strains.

This latter option (dealt with in Note 3 of EN1993-1-5, clause 3.3) is the recommended one, but the final choice is taken at the national level in the National Annex.

Fig. 2.10 compares the shear lag reduction factor calculated by including the limited plastic strains (ULS) to the case where no plastic redistributions are allowed (SLS).

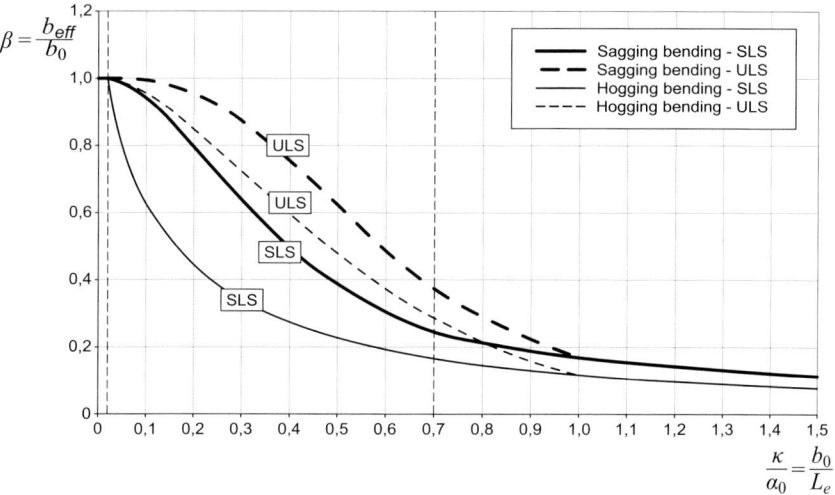

Fig. 2.10: Influence of the considered limit state and of the bending zone on the effective^s width (for the case $\alpha_0 = 1$)

2.3.5 Interaction between shear lag and plate buckling at ULS

For a flange in compression at ULS, the plate buckling effects may occur in addition to the shear lag effects. This plate buckling (due to local and global buckling) results in an effective^p area of the flange which should be combined with the effective^s area due to shear lag. Depending on the retained option for ULS shear lag (see previous section), two models are proposed in EN1993-1-5, the second one being recommended.

The first option consists of the following steps:

- Calculate the effective^p area according to plate buckling rules in EN1993-1-5, clauses 4.4 and 4.5,

2. OVERVIEW OF DESIGN RULES

- Define an effective^p stiffening ratio α_0^* to be used instead of the SLS stiffening ratio α_0 when calculating the reduction factor β (see Fig. 2.7 above):

$$\alpha_0^* = \sqrt{\frac{A_{c,eff}}{b_0 t}} \qquad (2.6)$$

where $A_{c,eff}$ is the effective^p area of the compression flange.
- Calculate the effective area A_{eff} for taking shear lag and plate buckling effect into account as follows:

$$A_{eff} = \beta A_{c,eff} \qquad (2.7)$$

The second option leads to an easier calculation. The elastoplastic reduction factor $\beta^\kappa \geq \beta$ is directly applied to the effective^p area of the compression flange (due to plate buckling) where κ is based on α_0:

$$A_{eff} = \beta^\kappa A_{c,eff} \qquad (2.8)$$

EN1993-1-5 does not specify how to apply the reduction to the area, but it is recommended here to apply it to the thickness (and not to the width) of the plate. See also the example of the box-girder bridge in chapter 4.

2.3.6 Design examples

Example 2.3-1: Effective^s widths due to shear lag effects.

A box cross section is selected in this numerical example to illustrate the determination of the shear lag effect. The gross cross section of the girder and the static system are given in Fig. 2.11.

Shear lag in the flanges has to be considered in the cross section design when $b_0 \geq L_e / 50$, where b_0 is taken as the flange outstand or half the width of an internal element and L_e is the length between points of zero bending moment.

2.3 SHEAR LAG IN MEMBER DESIGN

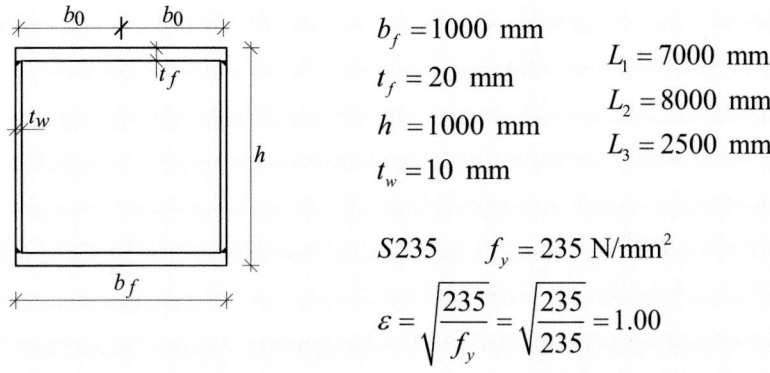

$b_f = 1000$ mm
$t_f = 20$ mm
$h = 1000$ mm
$t_w = 10$ mm

$L_1 = 7000$ mm
$L_2 = 8000$ mm
$L_3 = 2500$ mm

S235 $f_y = 235$ N/mm^2

$$\varepsilon = \sqrt{\frac{235}{f_y}} = \sqrt{\frac{235}{235}} = 1.00$$

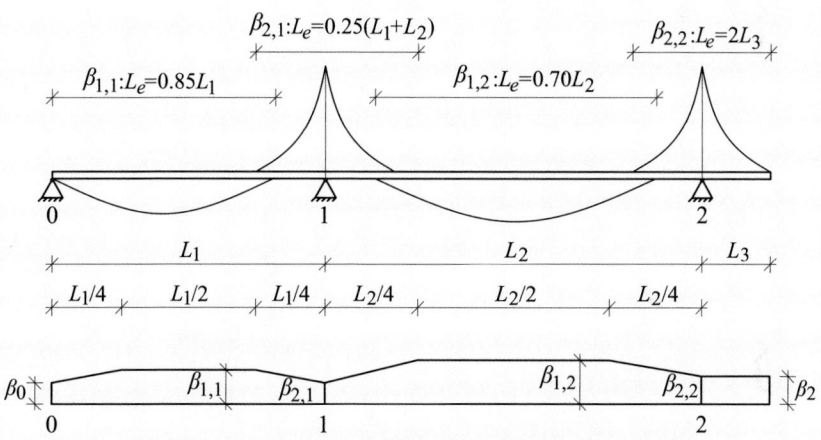

Fig. 2.11: Geometry of cross section and static system

a) Shear lag at serviceability limit state

Elastic shear lag at serviceability and fatigue limit state is usually considered by using an effective^s width and an elastic stress distribution.
The following parameters remain constant for all positions of shear lag evaluations:

$$b_0 = \frac{b_f - t_w}{2} = \frac{1000-10}{2} = 495 \text{ mm}, \quad A_{sl} = 0 \text{ mm}^2,$$

$$\alpha_0 = \sqrt{1 + \frac{A_{sl}}{b_0 \cdot t_f}} = \sqrt{1 + \frac{0}{495 \cdot 20}} = 1.$$

2. Overview of Design Rules

Cross section in span 1:

$$L_e = 0.85 \cdot L_1 = 0.85 \cdot 7000 = 5950 \text{ mm},$$

$$\kappa = \frac{\alpha_0 \cdot b_0}{L_e} = \frac{1 \cdot 495}{5950} = 0.083.$$

In the area of sagging bending moment the effective^s width factor for $0.02 < \kappa \leq 0.7$ is given with the following equation:

$$\beta_{1,1} = \frac{1}{1 + 6.4 \cdot \kappa^2} = \frac{1}{1 + 6.4 \cdot 0.083^2} = 0.958.$$

The effective^s width for shear lag under elastic conditions is determined from:

$$b_{eff} = \beta_{1,1} \cdot b_0 = 0.958 \cdot 495 = 474 \text{ mm}$$

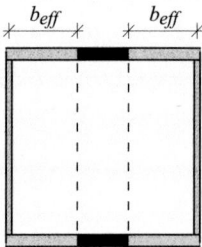

Cross section in span 2:

$$L_e = 0.70 \cdot L_2 = 0.70 \cdot 8000 = 5600 \text{ mm},$$

$$\kappa = \frac{\alpha_0 \cdot b_0}{L_e} = \frac{1 \cdot 495}{5600} = 0.088,$$

$$\beta_{1,2} = \frac{1}{1 + 6.4 \cdot \kappa^2} = \frac{1}{1 + 6.4 \cdot 0.088^2} = 0.952,$$

$$b_{eff} = \beta_{1,2} \cdot b_0 = 0.952 \cdot 495 = 471 \text{ mm}.$$

Cross section at the end support 0:

At the end support the effective width factor for $0.02 < \kappa \leq 0.7$ is given as ($\kappa = 0.083$, $\beta_{1,1} = 0.958$, see span 1):

2.3 Shear Lag in Member Design

$$\beta_0 = \min\left(\left(0.55 + \frac{0.025}{\kappa}\right) \cdot \beta_{1,1}, \ \beta_{1,1}\right) =$$

$$= \min\left(\left(0.55 + \frac{0.025}{0.083}\right) \cdot 0.958, \ 0.958\right) = 0.815,$$

$$b_{\mathit{eff}} = \beta_0 \cdot b_0 = 0.815 \cdot 495 = 403 \text{ mm}.$$

Cross section at the internal support 1:

$$L_e = 0.25 \cdot (L_1 + L_2) = 0.25 \cdot (7000 + 8000) = 3750 \text{ mm},$$

$$\kappa = \frac{\alpha_0 \cdot b_0}{L_e} = \frac{1 \cdot 495}{3750} = 0.132.$$

In the area of hogging bending moment the effective width factor for $0.02 < \kappa \leq 0.7$ is given with the following equation:

$$\beta_{2,1} = \frac{1}{1 + 6.0 \cdot \left(\kappa - \frac{1}{2500 \cdot \kappa}\right) + 1.6 \cdot \kappa^2} =$$

$$= \frac{1}{1 + 6.0 \cdot \left(0.132 - \frac{1}{2500 \cdot 0.132}\right) + 1.6 \cdot 0.132^2} = 0.555,$$

$$b_{\mathit{eff}} = \beta_{2,1} \cdot b_0 = 0.555 \cdot 495 = 275 \text{ mm}.$$

Cross section at support 2 and at cantilever:

$$L_e = 2 \cdot L_3 = 2 \cdot 2500 = 5000 \text{ mm},$$

$$\kappa = \frac{\alpha_0 \cdot b_0}{L_e} = \frac{1 \cdot 495}{5000} = 0.099,$$

$$\beta_{2,2} = \frac{1}{1 + 6.0 \cdot \left(\kappa - \frac{1}{2500 \cdot \kappa}\right) + 1.6 \cdot \kappa^2} =$$

2. Overview of Design Rules

$$= \frac{1}{1+6.0\cdot\left(0.099 - \dfrac{1}{2500\cdot 0.099}\right) + 1.6\cdot 0.104^2} = 0.631,$$

$$b_{eff} = \beta_{2,2}\cdot b_0 = 0.631\cdot 495 = 312 \text{ mm}.$$

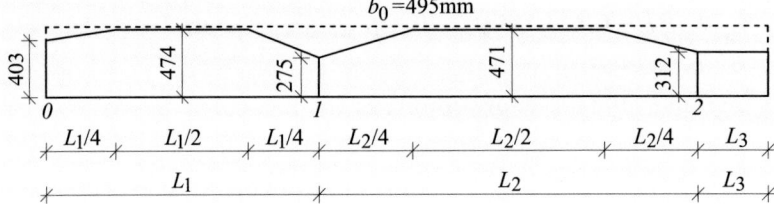

b)   Shear lag at ultimate limit state (intermediate support 1)

At the ultimate limit state shear lag effects may be conservatively determined as elastic shear lag or as elastoplastic shear lag effects with limited plastic strains. When plate buckling is also present, combined effects of shear lag and plate buckling should be considered in one of the following ways:

Combined effects of elastic shear lag and plate buckling

In the upper flange there is no interaction with plate buckling (tension stresses) and only shear lag is present ($\beta_{2,1} = 0.555$).

The lower flange in uniform compression is classified as Class 4:

$$\frac{b_f - 2\cdot t_w}{t_f} = \frac{1000 - 2\cdot 10}{20} = 49 \geq 42\cdot \varepsilon = 42\cdot 1 = 42.$$

The buckling coefficient at the stress ratio $\psi = 1$ is equal to $k_\sigma = 4$ and the plate slenderness can be obtained from:

$$\overline{\lambda}_p = \frac{\overline{b}}{t_f\cdot 28.4\cdot \varepsilon\cdot \sqrt{k_\sigma}} = \frac{b_f - 2\cdot t_w}{t_f\cdot 28.4\cdot \varepsilon\cdot \sqrt{k_\sigma}} = \frac{1000 - 2\cdot 10}{20\cdot 28.4\cdot 1\cdot \sqrt{4}} = 0.863.$$

The reduction factor ρ for internal compression elements is equal to:

2.3 SHEAR LAG IN MEMBER DESIGN

$$\rho = \frac{\overline{\lambda}_p - 0.055 \cdot (3+\psi)}{\overline{\lambda}_p^2} = \frac{0.863 - 0.055 \cdot (3+1)}{0.863^2} = 0.864.$$

Finally, the effective^p width considering plate buckling due to direct stresses may be obtained:

$$b_{eff} = \rho \cdot \overline{b} = 0.864 \cdot (1000 - 2 \cdot 10) = 846 \text{ mm, with}$$

$$b_{e1} = b_{e2} = 0.5 \cdot b_{eff} = 423 \text{ mm,}$$

where $b_{e,1}$ and $b_{e,2}$ denote effective^p width at both sides of the web.

The effective^s width factor for the effect of shear lag at the ultimate limit state may be determined as for elastic shear lag, with α_0 replaced by:

$$\alpha_0^* = \sqrt{\frac{A_{c,eff}}{(b_f - t_w) \cdot t_f}} = \sqrt{\frac{b_{eff} + t_w}{b_f - t_w}} = \sqrt{\frac{846 + 10}{1000 - 10}} = 0.930,$$

$$L_e = 3750 \text{ mm}, \quad \kappa = \frac{\alpha_0^* \cdot b_0}{L_e} = \frac{0.930 \cdot 495}{3750} = 0.123,$$

$$\beta_{ult} = \frac{1}{1 + 6.0 \cdot \left(\kappa - \dfrac{1}{2500 \cdot \kappa}\right) + 1.6 \cdot \kappa^2} =$$

$$= \frac{1}{1 + 6.0 \cdot \left(0.123 - \dfrac{1}{2500 \cdot 0.123}\right) + 1.6 \cdot 0.123^2} = 0.574.$$

The influence of the shear lag is taken into account by reducing the thickness of the flange:

$$t_{f,eff} = \beta_{ult} \cdot t_f = 0.574 \cdot 20 = 11.48 \text{ mm},$$

$$A_{eff,f} = A_{c,eff,f} \cdot \beta_{ult} =$$

$$= (b_{eff} + 2 \cdot t_w) \cdot t_f \cdot \beta_{ult} =$$

$$= (846 + 2 \cdot 10) \cdot 20 \cdot 0.574 =$$

$$= 9941.7 \text{ mm}^2.$$

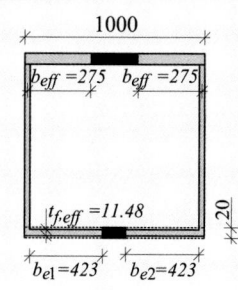

2. OVERVIEW OF DESIGN RULES

This approach leads to very conservative results. Eurocode EN 1993-1-5 recommends the use of elastoplastic shear lag.

Elastoplastic shear lag effects for limited plastic strains

In this case factors β and κ are calculated as for elastic shear lag. Shear lag – plate buckling interaction is accounted for by:

$$\beta = \beta_{2,1} = 0.555, \; \kappa = 0.132,$$

$$\beta_{e-p} = \max(\beta^\kappa, \beta) = \max(0.555^{0.132}, \; 0.555) = 0.925,$$

$$t_{f,eff} = \beta_{e-p} \cdot t_f = 0.925 \cdot 20 = 18.50 \text{ mm}.$$

$$A_{eff,f} = A_{c,eff,f} \cdot \beta_{e-p} = (b_{eff} + 2 \cdot t_w) \cdot t_f \cdot \beta_{e-p} =$$

$$= (846 + 2 \cdot 10) \cdot 20 \cdot 0.925 =$$

$$= 16021 \text{ mm}^2.$$

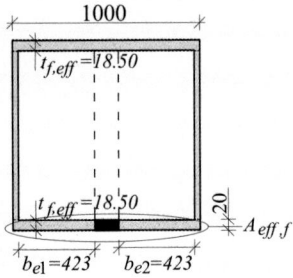

2.4 PLATE BUCKLING EFFECTS DUE TO DIRECT STRESSES (INCLUDING ANNEXES A AND E WHERE APPLICABLE)

2.4.1 Introduction

Slender plates in compression possess significant postcritical resistance that can be utilized in design procedures for plated structural elements. A typical response of slender plates in compression is shown in Fig. 2.12.

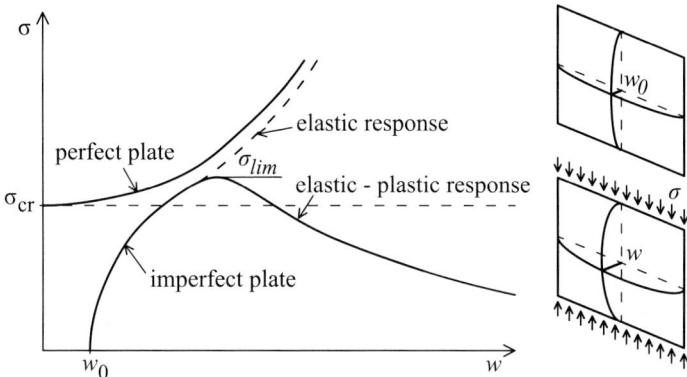

Fig. 2.12: Post-critical response of slender plates in compression

For geometrically perfect plates pre- and post-critical behaviour is very evident, while for imperfect plates the transition between pre- and post-critical behaviour is gradual and for larger imperfections nearly imperceptible. It is important that after reaching the elastic critical stress σ_{cr} the resistance is not exhausted, but it increases further until plastic collapse occurs. In the postcritical state the redistribution of compressive stresses takes place with the reduction of stresses in the middle buckled part, where axial stiffness is decreased, and with the increase of stresses near straight plate edges (see Fig. 2.13). The ultimate resistance is reached soon after the maximum edge stress has reached the plate yield strength, as in general slender plates do not have any ductility to redistribute stresses by developing zones of plastic strains. To deal with non-linear distribution of actual stresses, σ_{act} is not very practical and for this reason two simplified methods appropriate in practical design procedures were developed. The main idea of these methods is shown in Fig. 2.13.

The first method is based on the appropriate reduction of cross section in the central buckled part of the plate, assuming effective^p widths b_{eff} adjacent to edges as fully effective with stresses equal to f_y all over the effective^p width. This method is called effective width method or reduced cross section method.

The second method is based on the average stress σ_{lim} of the actual stress distribution σ_{act} in the ultimate state and is called reduced stress

2. Overview of Design Rules

method. Certainly, the reduction of a cross section or the reduction of stresses is such that the equilibrium with the actual distribution of stresses is maintained.

$$P_{ult} = \int_0^b \sigma_{act}\, dx = b_{eff} \cdot f_y = b \cdot \sigma_{lim} = \rho b \cdot f_y \qquad (2.9)$$

The plate buckling reduction factor

$$\rho = \frac{b_{eff}}{b} = \frac{\sigma_{lim}}{f_y} \qquad (2.10)$$

was determined by tests (Winter, 1947). Both methods give the same results for single plates and for cross sections built up of several plates loaded in pure compression. In other cases the effective width method gives higher resistance, because with the reduced stress method the weakest plate element governs the design (e.g. slender Class 4 web in the I profile with Class 3 flanges). The advantage of the reduced stress method is that it works on the level of stresses and therefore may be more appropriate for a more complex situation (e.g. non-uniform cross sections, complex stress state, different construction stages, etc). A disadvantage of this method is that it underestimates the maximum strain in the plate (disregard of stress redistribution across the cross section). The effective width method is given in section 4 of EN 1993-1-5 (CEN, 2006a) and will be described into detail in this chapter. The reduced stress method is given in section 10 of EN 1993-1-5 and will be described in sub-chapter 2.10.

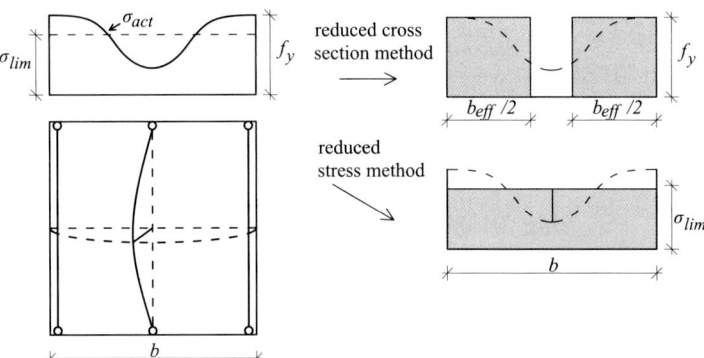

Fig. 2.13: Basic ideas of reduced cross section method and reduced stress method

2.4.2 Effective width method

2.4.2.1 General requirements

All the details on the determination of the resistance of Class 4 cross sections subjected to direct stresses are given in EN 1993-1-5. EN 1993-1-1 (CEN, 2005) gives only plate slenderness limits for Class 3 cross sections which are derived from the plate buckling curves for the case $\sigma = f_y$ (see Table 2.1).

The effective width method may be applied when the following requirements are fulfilled:

- The panels and the sub-panels are rectangular or nearly rectangular with flanges deviating from the horizontal line not more than 10°. For cases with the angle larger than 10° see section 2.2.3.
- The panels may be unstiffened or stiffened with longitudinal or transverse stiffeners or in both directions.
- Unstiffened openings and cut-outs should be small, with diameters not exceeding $0.05\,b$, where b is the width of the plate element. Properly stiffened holes may be larger, but EN 1993-1-5 does not provide any design rules (see http://lwo.steel-sci.org for documents on large web openings).
- Members are of uniform cross sections. When the thickness of the panel is not constant, then the equivalent thickness may be taken equal to the smallest one.
- Flange induced web buckling is prevented by selecting appropriate web slenderness, see sub-chapter 2.8.

2. OVERVIEW OF DESIGN RULES

Table 2.1: Slenderness limits between Class 3 and Class 4 cross sections

Internal compression parts				
Class	Part subject to bending	Part subject to compression	Part subject to bending and compression	Axis of bending
Stress distr. in parts (compression positive)	f_y / $-f_y$ (with $b/2$)	f_y (uniform +)	f_y / ψf_y	
3	$b/t \leq 124\varepsilon$	$b/t \leq 42\varepsilon$	when $\psi > -1$: $\dfrac{b}{t} \leq \dfrac{42\varepsilon}{0.67 + 0.33\psi}$ when $\psi \leq -1^{*)}$: $\dfrac{b}{t} \leq \left[62\varepsilon(1-\psi)\cdot\sqrt{(-\psi)}\right]$	

$\varepsilon = \sqrt{\dfrac{235}{f_y\,(\text{N/mm}^2)}}$	f_y	235	275	355	420	460
	ε	1.00	0.92	0.81	0.75	0.71

Outstand flanges

Rolled sections | Welded sections

Class	Part subject to compression	Part subject to bending and compression	
		Tip in compression	Tip in tension
Stress distr. in parts (compression positive)	(+) b	(+) b	(+) b
3	$b/t \leq 14\varepsilon$	$b/t \leq 21\varepsilon\sqrt{k_\sigma}$ For k_σ see EN 1993-1-5	

2.4 PLATE BUCKLING EFFECTS DUE TO DIRECT STRESSES

2.4.2.2 Principles of effective width calculation

To determine the resistance of Class 4 cross sections subject to direct stresses by using the effective width method, the effective^p widths of each plate element in compression are calculated independently. Based on these effective^p widths effective cross section area A_{eff}, effective second moment of inertia I_{eff} and effective section modulus W_{eff} are calculated (Fig. 2.14, Fig. 2.15, Fig. 2.16). If relevant, shear lag effects should be included. For compression elements the effective widths are determined by taking into account the combined effect of shear lag and plate buckling according to sub-chapter 2.3. For tension elements, effective^s widths come only from shear lag effects. Tension elements without shear lag effects are taken as fully effective. The effective cross section is then treated as an equivalent Class 3 cross section, assuming linear elastic strain and stress distribution over the reduced cross section. The ultimate resistance is reached with the onset of yielding in the center of the compressed plate located furthest from the centroid of the cross section.

The maximum stress may be calculated in the midplane of the critical plate – for I girders, for instance in the midplane of flanges (see Fig. 2.16).

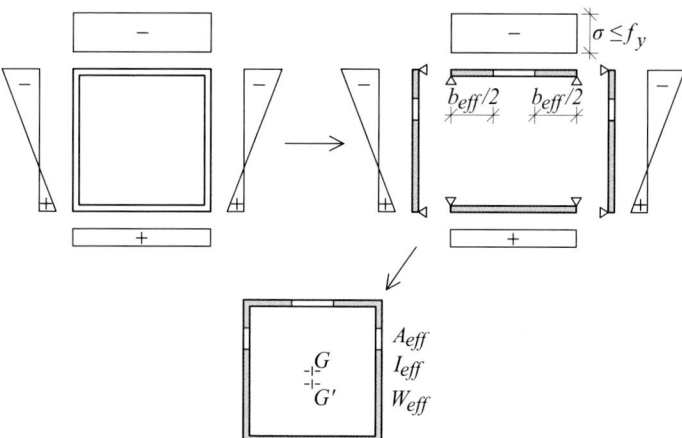

Fig. 2.14: Effective cross section

2. OVERVIEW OF DESIGN RULES

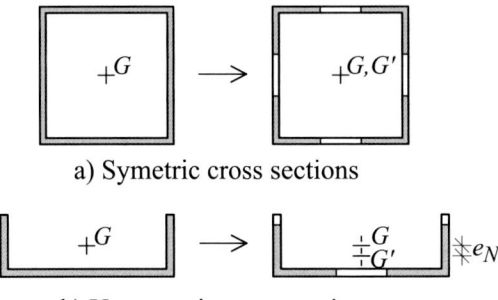

a) Symetric cross sections

b) Unsymetric cross sections

Fig. 2.15: Class 4 cross sections in pure compression

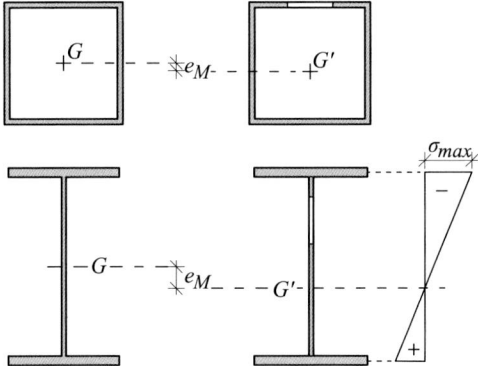

Fig. 2.16: Class 4 cross section in pure bending

If axial force and bending moment act simultaneously, the calculation of effective^p widths may be based on the resulting stress distribution. EN 1993-1-5 allows a simplified approach where A_{eff} is calculated only for stresses due to pure compression and W_{eff} only for stresses due to pure bending.

In non-symmetrical cross sections subject to an axial force N_{Ed}, a shift e_N occurs (of the centroid G′ of the effective area A_{eff} relative to the centre of gravity of the gross cross section G, see Fig. 2.15). This shift results in an additional bending moment $\Delta M = e_N N_{Ed}$ that should be taken into account in the cross section verification (see section 2.4.6). According to clause 4.3(3) of EN 1993-1-5 the shift e_M (see Fig. 2.16) of the centre of gravity due to pure bending can be disregarded in the calculation of ΔM, even if the cross section is subject to the combination of axial force and bending moment.

Generally the calculation of effective^p widths requires an iterative

2.4 Plate Buckling Effects Due to Direct Stresses

procedure shown in Fig. 2.17 that ends when the differences between two steps are sufficiently small.

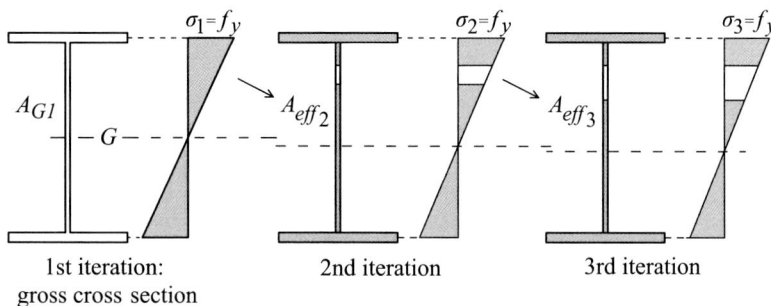

1st iteration:
gross cross section

2nd iteration

3rd iteration

Fig. 2.17: Determination of effective^p area by iterative procedure

The first iteration starts with the stress distribution on the gross cross section A_{GI}. The effective area for the second iteration A_{eff2} is calculated from this stress distribution and the effective area for the third iteration A_{eff3} from the stresses on A_{eff2}.

For I-section and box cross section in bending EN 1993-1-5 allows a simplified approach that ends in two steps. In the first step effective^p widths in flanges (if they are in Class 4) are determined from the stress distribution on the gross cross section. In the second step the stresses are determined on the cross section composed of the effective^p area of the compressed flanges and the gross areas of the web and the tension flanges. The effective^p width in the web is calculated based on these stresses and this is taken as the final result.

When different stages of construction have to be considered, which is a normal case in the design of composite bridges, the following simplified approach proposed in a Note to clause 4.4 (2) of EN 1993-1-5 may be used:

- In all relevant construction stages (e.g. concreting of the slab, normal use of a bridge) the stresses should be calculated on the gross cross section of the web and effective cross section of the flanges (plate buckling and/or shear lag), when relevant.
- The stresses from different construction stages are summed up and used to determine a single effective cross section of the web that is used for all construction stages.
- Finally, the stresses for individual construction stages are calculated

on corresponding effective cross sections and summed up to get the final cumulative stresses.

2.4.2.3 Hybrid girders

Hybrid girders where the steel grade of the flanges is higher than the steel grade of the web may represent an economic solution, because the stronger (and more expensive) material is put where it contributes the most. The following three requirements should be fulfilled:

- To utilize the full strength of the flanges, a partial plastic redistribution of stresses is allowed in the web (see Fig. 2.18).
- To assure some minimum ductility requirements in the web, the effective^p area of the web should be determined based on the flange yield strength f_{yf} and not on the web yield strength f_{yw}.
- To limit the partial plastic stress distribution in the web, for the flange to web yield strength ratio $\phi_h = f_{yf} / f_{yw}$ the following upper limit is recommended:

$$\phi_h \leq 2.0 \qquad (2.11)$$

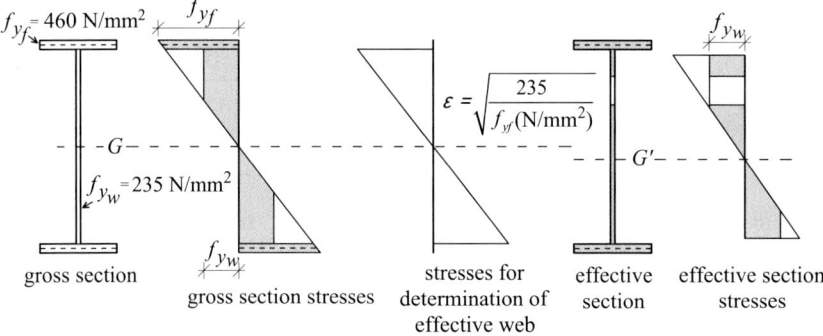

Fig. 2.18: Assumed stress distribution in a hybrid girder with $\phi_h = 460 \text{ N/mm}^2 / 235 \text{ N/mm}^2 = 1.96$

When calculating the location of the centre of gravity of the effective^p area G', a linear stress distribution in the web may be assumed, neglecting the limitation of the web stress $\sigma_w \leq f_{yw}$.

2.4.2.4 Plate-like and column-like buckling

As it was shown in section 2.4.1, slender plates possess a significant postcritical resistance. For shorter plates with low aspect ratios $\alpha = a/b$ this postcritical resistance gradually diminishes, because the "two-dimensional" plate-like behaviour changes into "one-dimensional" column-like behaviour that does not possess any postcritical resistance, see Fig. 2.19.

For unstiffened panels this occurs at aspect ratio $\alpha = a/b$ well below 1.0, but for longitudinally stiffened panels with pronounced orthotropic properties such behaviour may start at aspect ratios larger than $\alpha \geq 1.0$ (Fig. 2.19 c)).

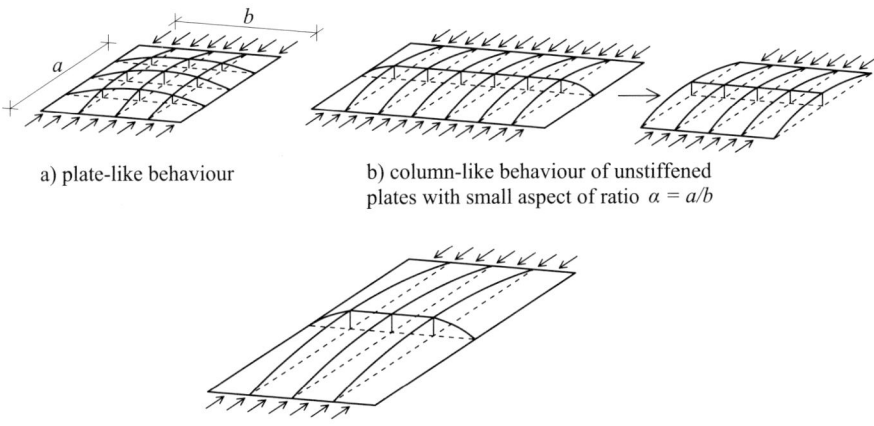

a) plate-like behaviour

b) column-like behaviour of unstiffened plates with small aspect of ratio $\alpha = a/b$

c) column-like behaviour of a longitudinally stiffened plate with aspect ratio $\alpha > 1.0$

Fig. 2.19: Plate-like and column-like behaviour of plates in compression

In EN 1993-1-5, plates in column-like buckling are treated as unsupported along the longitudinal edges. Therefore, critical stresses for plate-like buckling are always larger than critical stresses for column-like buckling.

The ultimate resistance of shorter plates depends on both types of buckling, plate-like as well as column-like, and a suitable interpolation between both types of behaviour was introduced in EN 1993-1-5 design procedures (see section 2.4.5 and numerical example 2.4-4).

2. OVERVIEW OF DESIGN RULES

2.4.3 Plate-like buckling

2.4.3.1 Unstiffened plates

The effective^p widths b_{eff} or effective areas $A_{c,eff}$ of the slender plate elements in compression are obtained with the help of the plate buckling reduction factor $\rho = \rho_{loc}$ (see Eq. (2.10) and Fig. 2.13):

$$b_{eff} = \rho_{loc} \cdot b \qquad (2.12)$$

$$A_{c,eff} = \rho_{loc} \cdot A \qquad (2.13)$$

The subscript label *loc* indicates that the reduction factor ρ_{loc} relates to a single panel or for stiffened plates to a single sub-panel. The reduction factor ρ_{loc} in EN 1993-1-5 comes from a slightly modified Winter formula (Winter, 1947) for effective^p widths of slender plates. EN 1993-1-5 gives two reduction coefficients – one for internal compression elements (like webs of I girders) and one for outstand compression elements (like flanges of I girders), see Fig. 2.20:

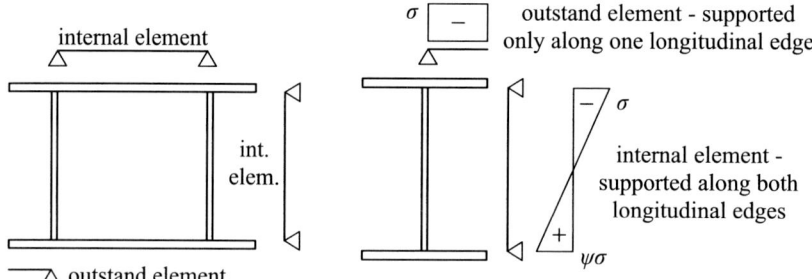

Fig. 2.20: Examples of internal and outstand plate elements of cross sections

- internal compression plate elements:

$$\rho_{loc} = 1.0 \qquad \text{for } \overline{\lambda}_p \leq 0.5 + \sqrt{0.085 - 0.055\psi}$$

$$\rho_{loc} = \frac{\overline{\lambda}_p - 0.055(3+\psi)}{\overline{\lambda}_p^2} \leq 1.0 \quad \text{for } \overline{\lambda}_p > 0.5 + \sqrt{0.085 - 0.055\psi} \qquad (2.14)$$

where ψ is the ratio of stresses at both edges of the plate with the maximum compression stress in the denominator;

- outstand compression plate elements:

$$\rho_{loc} = 1.0 \qquad \text{for } \bar{\lambda}_p \leq 0.748$$
$$\rho_{loc} = \frac{\bar{\lambda}_p - 0.188}{\bar{\lambda}_p^2} \leq 1.0 \quad \text{for } \bar{\lambda}_p > 0.748 \tag{2.15}$$

The plate slenderness $\bar{\lambda}_p$ is defined as:

$$\bar{\lambda}_p = \sqrt{\frac{f_y}{\sigma_{cr,p}}} \tag{2.16}$$

and the elastic critical plate buckling stress $\sigma_{cr,p}$ as:

$$\sigma_{cr,p} = k_\sigma \frac{\pi^2 E}{12(1-v^2)} \left(\frac{t}{b}\right)^2 \tag{2.17}$$

where
- b is the appropriate plate width (for definition see Table 2.1)
  $b = h - 3t$ for RHS
- t is the plate thickness
- E is elastic modulus of steel ($E = 210000$ N/mm^2)
- v is the Poisson coefficient of steel ($v = 0.3$)
- k_σ is the plate buckling coefficient, dependent on the stress ratio ψ and boundary conditions (for plates with $\alpha = a/b \geq 1.0$ k_σ is given in Table 2.2 and Table 2.3). For plates with $\alpha < 1.0$ and subject to uniform compression, k_σ is given as:

$$k_\sigma = \left(\alpha + \frac{1}{\alpha}\right)^2 \tag{2.18}$$

In all cases, plate elements are considered as simply supported along the edges.

By introducing Eq. (2.17) into Eq. (2.16) and by taking account of steel material properties, the plate slenderness may be rewritten as:

2. Overview of Design Rules

$$\bar{\lambda}_p = \frac{b}{t} \frac{1}{28.4\varepsilon\sqrt{k_\sigma}} \qquad (2.19)$$

where

$$\varepsilon = \sqrt{\frac{235}{f_y(\text{N/mm}^2)}} \qquad (2.20)$$

Table 2.2: Internal compression elements

Stress distribution (compression positive)	Effective^p width b_{eff}
σ_1 ▬▬ σ_2 ; b_{e1}, b_{e2}, b	$\psi = 1$ $b_{eff} = \rho b$ $b_{e1} = 0.5 b_{eff} \quad b_{e2} = 0.5 b_{eff}$
σ_1 ▬ σ_2 ; b_{e1}, b_{e2}, b	$1 > \psi \geq 0$ $b_{eff} = \rho b$ $b_{e1} = \dfrac{2}{5-\psi} b_{eff} \quad b_{e2} = b_{eff} - b_{e1}$
b_c, b_t; σ_1, σ_2; b_{e1}, b_{e2}, b	$\psi < 0$ $b_{eff} = \rho b_c = \rho b / (1-\psi)$ $b_{e1} = 0.4 b_{eff} \quad b_{e2} = 0.6 b_{eff}$

$\psi = \sigma_2/\sigma_1$	1	$1 > \psi > 0$	0	$0 > \psi > -1$	-1	$-1 > \psi > -3$
Buckling coefficient k_σ	4.0	$8.2/(1.05+\psi)$	7.8	$7.81 - 6.29\psi + 9.78\psi^2$	23.9	$5.98(1-\psi)^2$

Table 2.3: Outstand compression elements

Stress distribution (compression positive)	Effective^p width b_{eff}
Diagram: σ_2 (left) to σ_1 (right), b_{eff} at top of width b	$1 > \psi \geq 0$ $b_{eff} = \rho b$
Diagram: σ_2 (tension, left), σ_1 (compression, right), widths b_t and b_c, b_{eff} shown	$\psi < 0$ $b_{eff} = \rho b_c = \rho b / (1 - \psi)$

$\psi = \sigma_2 / \sigma_1$	1	0	-1	$-1 \geq \psi \geq -3$
Buckling coefficient k_σ	0.43	0.57	0.85	$0.57 - 0.21\psi + 0.07\psi^2$

Stress distribution (compression positive)	Effective^p width b_{eff}
Diagram: σ_1 (left) to σ_2 (right), b_{eff} at top, width b	$1 > \psi \geq 0$ $b_{eff} = \rho b$
Diagram: σ_1 (compression, left), σ_2 (tension, right), b_c and b_t, b_{eff} shown	$\psi < 0$ $b_{eff} = \rho b_c = \rho b / (1 - \psi)$

$\psi = \sigma_2 / \sigma_1$	1	$1 > \psi > 0$	0	$0 > \psi > -1$	1
Buckling coefficient k_σ	0.43	$1.578 / (\psi + 0.34)$	1.7	$1.7 - 5\psi + 17.1\psi^2$	23.8

For plates in pure compression ($\psi = 1.0$) effective^p widths are distributed symmetrically. For other stress distributions ($\psi \neq 1.0$) effective^p widths are determined according to Table 2.2 and Table 2.3. Note that if a part of the plate is in tension, the whole plate width is used in the calculation of the slenderness, Eq. (2.19), and only the compression part of the width b_c is used to calculate b_{eff}, Eq. (2.12).

The limit values of the ratios b/t between Class 3 and Class 4 cross sections from Table 2.1 generally do not correspond exactly to the b/t ratios

2. OVERVIEW OF DESIGN RULES

calculated from Eq. (2.14) when $\rho = 1.0$. The values in Table 2.1 were determined directly from tests and in some cases they are slightly more favourable (internal plate element in pure compression: $b/t = 41\varepsilon$ instead of 38.2ε, internal plate element in pure bending: $b/t = 124\varepsilon$ instead of 121.4ε).

The above procedure for the calculation of effective[p] widths is valid for fully utilized effective cross sections with the onset of yielding in the most stressed fibre. If the maximum compressive stress $\sigma_{com,Ed}$ is less than f_y, the effective cross section is larger and this beneficial effect may be accounted for by reducing the plate slenderness $\bar{\lambda}_p$ according to:

$$\bar{\lambda}_{p,red} = \bar{\lambda}_p \sqrt{\frac{\sigma_{com,Ed}}{f_y/\gamma_{M0}}} \qquad (2.21)$$

The above procedure is conservative and requires an iterative calculation. An alternative and more accurate procedure is given below (from Annex E, EN 1993-1-5):

- For internal compression elements

$$\rho = \frac{1-0.055(3+\psi)/\bar{\lambda}_{p,red}}{\bar{\lambda}_{p,red}} + 0.18\frac{\left(\bar{\lambda}_p - \bar{\lambda}_{p,red}\right)}{\left(\bar{\lambda}_p - 0.6\right)}, \text{ but } \rho \leq 1.0 \quad (2.22)$$

- For outstand compression elements:

$$\rho = \frac{1-0.188/\bar{\lambda}_{p,red}}{\bar{\lambda}_{p,red}} + 0.18\frac{\left(\bar{\lambda}_p - \bar{\lambda}_{p,red}\right)}{\left(\bar{\lambda}_p - 0.6\right)}, \text{ but } \rho \leq 1.0 \quad (2.23)$$

2.4.3.2 Longitudinally stiffened plates

Plate-like buckling of longitudinally stiffened plates means a global buckling of the whole panel composed of a plate and stiffeners (Fig. 2.21). When sub-panels of width b_i are slender and subject to local buckling, the interaction of local and global plate buckling should be considered (similar to the buckling check of columns with Class 4 cross sections, see EN 1993-1-1, clause 6.3.1).

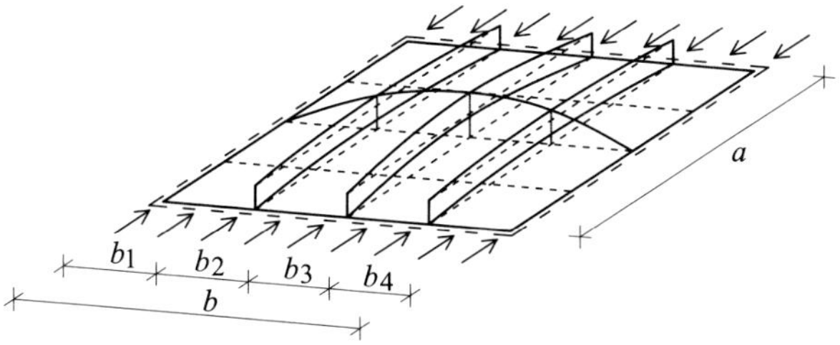

2.4 Plate Buckling Effects Due to Direct Stresses

Fig. 2.21: Plate-like buckling of a stiffened plate

This interaction is taken into account by a modified plate slenderness:

$$\bar{\lambda}_p = \sqrt{\frac{N_y}{N_{cr}}} = \sqrt{\frac{A_{c,eff,loc} f_y}{A_c \sigma_{cr,p}}} = \sqrt{\frac{\beta_{A,c} f_y}{\sigma_{cr,p}}} \quad (2.24)$$

where

$\sigma_{cr,p}$ is the elastic critical buckling stress of a stiffened plate,

$$\beta_{A,c} = \frac{A_{c,eff,loc}}{A_c} \quad (2.25)$$

$A_{c,eff,loc}$ is the sum of the effective^p areas of sub-panels and stiffeners according to sub-section 2.4.3.1, excluding edge parts along the longitudinal edges. Sub-panels are assumed to be fully supported by the stiffeners (no global buckling of stiffeners), see Fig. 2.22.

$$A_{c,eff,loc} = A_{sl,eff} + \sum_i \rho_{loc,i} \cdot b_{loc,i} \cdot t \quad (2.26)$$

$A_{sl,eff}$ is the sum of effective^p areas of longitudinal stiffeners according to sub-section 2.4.3.1 (without contributing plating)

$b_{loc,i}$ is the width of each individual sub-panel i

$\rho_{loc,i}$ is the reduction factor of each sub-panel i from sub-section 2.4.3.1

A_c is the gross cross section of the compression zone of the stiffened plate excluding edge parts along longitudinal edges (see Fig. 2.22).

2. Overview of Design Rules

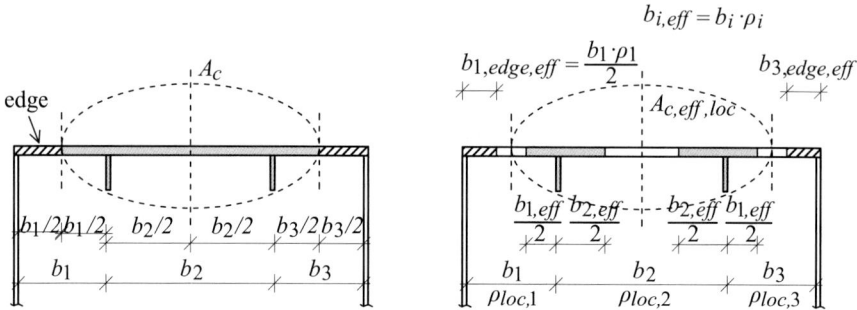

Fig. 2.22: Stiffened plate under uniform compression

When the plate is under a stress gradient, effective$^\text{p}$ widths and contributing widths of the gross area are determined according to Table 2.2 and Table 2.3. For the web of a plate girder, the principles for the determination of $A_{c,eff,loc}$ and A_c are shown in Fig. 2.23.

There are several possibilities to calculate the elastic critical stress $\sigma_{cr,p}$ of longitudinally stiffened plates. The basic expression for $\sigma_{cr,p}$ is the same as for unstiffened plates (Eq. (2.17)), but the calculation of the plate buckling coefficient $k_{\sigma,p}$ is more complex:

$$\sigma_{cr,p} = k_{\sigma,p} \frac{\pi^2 E}{12(1-v^2)} \left(\frac{t}{b}\right)^2 \qquad (2.27)$$

The plate buckling coefficient $k_{\sigma,p}$ may be determined by:

- Design charts for smeared or discretely spaced stiffeners;
- Simplified analytical expressions (two such procedures are given in EN 1993-1-5);
- Computer simulations.

The use of design charts is very simple but limited to the range of the charts. In charts for discretely spaced stiffeners usually the value of $k_{\sigma,p}$ is cut off at the onset of local buckling of sub-panels and therefore their use is somewhat limited. Well known are Klöppel charts (Klöppel and Scheer, 1960 and Klöppel and Möller, 1968) that contain $k_{\sigma,p}$ values for discretely spaced and smeared stiffeners.

2.4 PLATE BUCKLING EFFECTS DUE TO DIRECT STRESSES

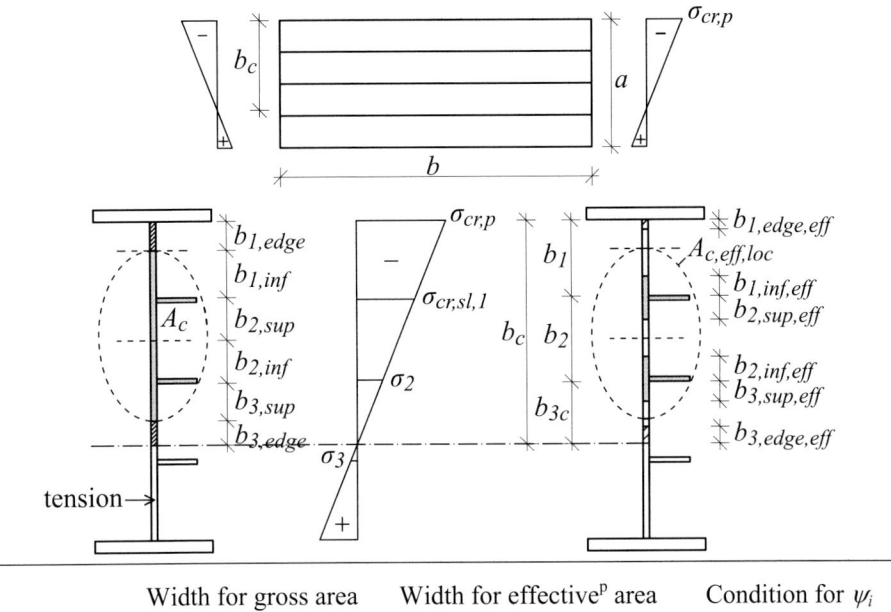

	Width for gross area	Width for effective^p area	Condition for ψ_i
$b_{1,edge}$	$\dfrac{2}{5-\psi_1}b_1$	$\dfrac{2}{5-\psi_1}b_{1,eff}$	$\psi_1 = \dfrac{\sigma_{cr,sl,1}}{\sigma_{cr,p}} > 0$
$b_{1,inf}$	$\dfrac{3-\psi_1}{5-\psi_1}b_1$	$\dfrac{3-\psi_1}{5-\psi_1}b_{1,eff}$	$\psi_1 > 0$
$b_{2,sup}$	$\dfrac{2}{5-\psi_2}b_2$	$\dfrac{2}{5-\psi_2}b_{2,eff}$	$\psi_2 = \dfrac{\sigma_2}{\sigma_{cr,sl,1}} > 0$
$b_{2,inf}$	$\dfrac{3-\psi_2}{5-\psi_2}b_2$	$\dfrac{3-\psi_2}{5-\psi_2}b_{2,eff}$	$\psi_2 > 0$
$b_{3,sup}$	$0.4 b_{3c}$	$0.4 b_{3c,eff}$	$\psi_3 = \dfrac{\sigma_3}{\sigma_2} < 0$
$b_{3,edge}$	$0.6 b_{3c}$	$0.6 b_{3c,eff}$	$\psi_3 < 0$

Fig. 2.23: Stiffened web plate in bending

There are two main possibilities for the determination of $k_{\sigma,p}$ using computer simulations. The first one is to use a general purpose FE software for structural applications (ABAQUS, ANSYS, etc.) and the second one is to use specialized software for plate buckling problems. A very good and freely available example is EBPlate (2007). To be on the safe side, simply supported edge boundary conditions should be used for plate elements.

EN 1993-1-5 brings two simple analytical methods to determine $\sigma_{cr,p}$:

2. Overview of Design Rules

Three or more equally spaced stiffeners with aspect ratio $\alpha = a/b \geq 0.5$.

The whole plate must be in compression with the edge stress ratio $\psi = \sigma_1/\sigma_2 \geq 0.5$.

$$k_{\sigma,p} = \frac{2\left((1+\alpha^2)^2 + \gamma - 1\right)}{\alpha^2(\psi+1)(1+\delta)} \quad \text{if } \alpha \leq \sqrt[4]{\gamma}$$

$$k_{\sigma,p} = \frac{4(1+\sqrt{\gamma})}{(\psi+1)(1+\delta)} \quad \text{if } \alpha > \sqrt[4]{\gamma}$$

(2.28)

where

$$\gamma = \frac{I_{sl}}{I_p}; \quad \delta = \frac{A_{sl}}{A_p}; \quad \alpha = \frac{a}{b} \geq 0.5$$

I_{sl} is the second moment of area of the whole stiffened plate
$I_p = bt^3/(12(1-v^2)) = bt^3/10.92$ is the second moment of area of the plate itself
A_{sl} is the sum of the gross areas of the individual longitudinal stiffeners
A_p is the gross area of the plate.

One or two stiffeners in the compression zone

In this method, stiffeners in the tension part of the plate are neglected and the stiffened plate is substituted by a fictive column on a continuous elastic support. The column represents a stiffener with the contributing part of the plate according to Fig. 2.23 and Fig. 2.24 (gross area) and the elastic support represents the flexural stiffness of the plate.

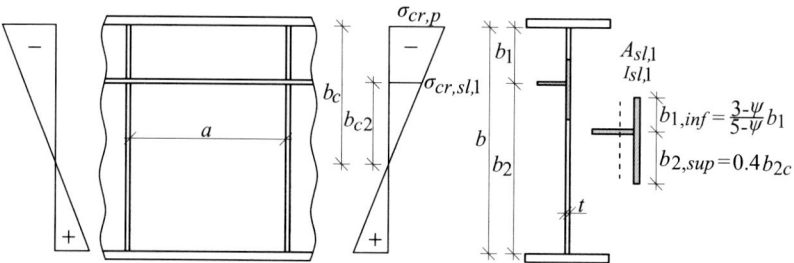

Fig. 2.24: Web plate with a single stiffener in compression

2.4 PLATE BUCKLING EFFECTS DUE TO DIRECT STRESSES

$$\sigma_{cr,sl} = \frac{1.05E}{A_{sl,1}} \frac{\sqrt{I_{sl,1} t^3 b}}{b_1 b_2} \qquad \text{if } \alpha \geq \alpha_c$$

$$\sigma_{cr,sl} = \frac{\pi^2 E I_{sl,1}}{A_{sl,1} a^2} + \frac{E t^3 b a^2}{4\pi^2 (1-v^2) A_{sl,1} b_1^2 b_2^2} \qquad \text{if } \alpha \leq \alpha_c \qquad (2.29)$$

$$a_c = 4.33 \sqrt[4]{\frac{I_{sl,1} b_1^2 b_2^2}{t^3 b}}$$

where

$A_{sl,1}$ and $I_{sl,1}$ are the gross area and the gross second moment area of the stiffener (see Fig. 2.24), respectively.

To determine the relevant elastic plate buckling stress $\sigma_{cr,p}$, defined at the most stressed compression part of the plate, $\sigma_{cr,sl}$ should be extrapolated to this edge (see Fig. 2.24).

$$\sigma_{cr,p} = \frac{b_c}{b_{c2}} \sigma_{cr,sl} \qquad (2.30)$$

One should be aware that when a stiffener is located in the neutral axis or very close to it, b_{c2} is zero or a very small value and $\sigma_{cr,p}$ tends to infinity. At first glance this result seems to be strange, but it simply tells that global plate buckling of a stiffened panel will not occur, because there is no compressive force in the stiffener. In this case the local buckling of the sub-panel b_1 prevails and the stiffener may even be neglected.

From Eq. (2.29) it is also clear that when a stiffener is very close to the compression flange, b_1 tends to a very small value and consequently $\sigma_{cr,sl}$ tends to infinity. This again means that the global plate buckling of the stiffened plate is not possible, as the stiffener is fully supported by the web plate.

In the case of two stiffeners the above procedure for one stiffener is repeated three times: for each of the stiffeners considering the other stiffener as a rigid support to a web and for a fictive lumped stiffener (see Fig. 2.25) defined as follows:

- The cross section properties are the sum of the properties of the individual stiffeners

2. Overview of Design Rules

- The lumped stiffener is located in the point of application of the stress resultants acting in individual stiffeners and may be calculated with Eq. (2.31), see also Fig. 2.25.

$$b_1^{I+II} = \frac{A_{sl,2}\, b_{c,2}}{A_{sl,1}\, b_{c,1} + A_{sl,2}\, b_{c,2}} b_2^{I} + b_1^{I} \qquad (2.31)$$

The smallest of the three results for $\sigma_{cr,p}$ is taken into account. This procedure may give quite conservative results, especially for the stiffeners located close to the compression flange or close to the neutral axis, and it is recommended to use for instance EBPlate instead.

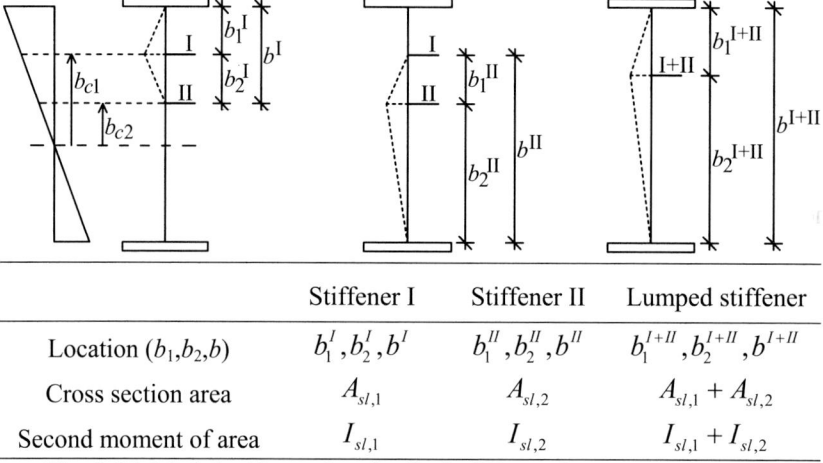

	Stiffener I	Stiffener II	Lumped stiffener
Location (b_1, b_2, b)	b_1^{I}, b_2^{I}, b^{I}	$b_1^{II}, b_2^{II}, b^{II}$	$b_1^{I+II}, b_2^{I+II}, b^{I+II}$
Cross section area	$A_{sl,1}$	$A_{sl,2}$	$A_{sl,1} + A_{sl,2}$
Second moment of area	$I_{sl,1}$	$I_{sl,2}$	$I_{sl,1} + I_{sl,2}$

Fig. 2.25: Model with two longitudinal stiffeners in compression zone

2.4.4 Column-like buckling

2.4.4.1 Unstiffened plates

For the calculation of the elastic critical column buckling stress $\sigma_{cr,c}$ the plate is considered completely unsupported along the longitudinal edges (Fig. 2.19 b):

$$\sigma_{cr,c} = \frac{\pi^2 E t^2}{12(1-v^2)a^2} \qquad (2.32)$$

2.4 PLATE BUCKLING EFFECTS DUE TO DIRECT STRESSES

The column slenderness $\bar{\lambda}_c$ is defined as

$$\bar{\lambda}_c = \sqrt{\frac{f_y}{\sigma_{cr,c}}} \tag{2.33}$$

The corresponding column reduction factor χ_c is obtained from clause 6.3.1.2 of EN 1993-1-1 by selecting buckling curve a ($\alpha = 0.21$).

2.4.4.2 Longitudinally stiffened plates

The elastic critical column buckling stress $\sigma_{cr,c}$ is determined as the buckling stress $\sigma_{cr,sl}$ of a single stiffener closest to the panel edge having the highest compression stress:

$$\sigma_{cr,sl} = \frac{\pi^2 E I_{sl,1}}{A_{sl,1} a^2} \tag{2.34}$$

where

$I_{sl,1}$ is the second moment of area of the gross cross section of the stiffener and the adjacent parts of the plate (out-of-plane bending of the plate). For the details of the calculation of gross cross section see Fig. 2.22, Fig. 2.23 and Fig. 2.24.

$A_{sl,1}$ is the gross cross section of the stiffener and adjacent parts of the plate (Fig. 2.22, Fig. 2.23 and Fig. 2.24).

a is the buckling length of a stiffener normally equal to the distance between rigid transverse stiffeners (a panel length). Note that for large distances between transverse stiffeners this leads to small $\sigma_{cr,c}$ and plate-like buckling completely prevails (plate buckling in several half waves).

For uniform compression, the elastic critical column buckling stress is $\sigma_{cr,c} = \sigma_{cr,sl}$. For other stress ratios ψ, $\sigma_{cr,c}$ is calculated by extrapolating $\sigma_{cr,sl}$ to the edge of the stiffened plate using Eq. (2.30).

2. Overview of Design Rules

The column slenderness for stiffened plates is defined as:

$$\bar{\lambda}_c = \sqrt{\frac{\beta_{A,c} f_y}{\sigma_{cr,c}}} \tag{2.35}$$

$$\beta_{A,c} = \frac{A_{sl,1,eff}}{A_{sl,1}}$$

where

$A_{sl,1}$ is the gross cross sectional area of the stiffener and adjacent parts of the plate (Fig. 2.22, Fig. 2.23, Fig. 2.24)

$A_{sl,1,eff}$ is the effective^p cross sectional area of the stiffener and adjacent parts of the plate with due allowance for plate buckling of sub-panels (Fig. 2.22, Fig. 2.23).

The corresponding column reduction factor χ_c is obtained from clause 6.3.1.2 of EN 1993-1-1. For stiffened plates, increased values of the imperfection parameter α should be used:

$$\alpha_e = \alpha + \frac{0.09}{i/e} \tag{2.36}$$

where

$$i = \sqrt{\frac{I_{sl,1}}{A_{sl,1}}}$$

$\alpha = 0.34$ (buckling curve b) for closed stiffeners
$ = 0.49$ (buckling curve c) for open stiffeners
$e = max\ (e_1, e_2)$

e_1 for single-sided stiffeners is the distance between the centres of gravity of the stiffener alone G_{st} and the stiffener with the contributing plating G_{sl} (see Fig. 2.26a)

e_2 is the distance between the centres of gravity of the contributing plating alone G_p and the stiffener with the contributing plating G_{sl}. For double-sided symmetrical stiffeners $e_1 = e_2$ (see Fig. 2.26b).

2.4 PLATE BUCKLING EFFECTS DUE TO DIRECT STRESSES

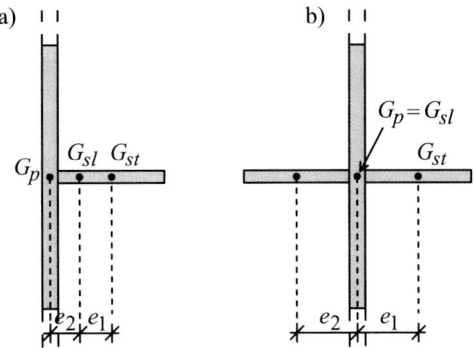

Fig. 2.26: Definition of distances e_1 and e_2

2.4.5 Interpolation between plate-like and column-like buckling

As it was discussed in sub-section 2.4.2.4, for shorter plates column-like buckling becomes important and the interaction of the plate-like and column-like buckling has to be considered. EN 1993-1-5 gives the following interpolation formula in order to obtain the final reduction factor ρ_c:

$$\rho_c = (\rho - \chi_c)\xi(2-\xi) + \chi_c \qquad (2.37)$$

$$\xi = \frac{\sigma_{cr,p}}{\sigma_{cr,c}} - 1, \text{ but } 0 \leq \xi \leq 1 \qquad (2.38)$$

where

ρ and χ_c are plate buckling reduction factor (based on $\overline{\lambda}_p$, see section 2.4.3) and column buckling reduction factor (based on $\overline{\lambda}_p$ and α_e, see section 2.4.4) of unstiffened or stiffened plates

$\sigma_{cr,p}$ and $\sigma_{cr,c}$ are elastic critical stresses for plate-like (see section 2.4.3) and column-like buckling (see section 2.4.4) of unstiffened or stiffened plates

By definition $\sigma_{cr,p}$ is always larger than $\sigma_{cr,c}$, because $\sigma_{cr,c}$ is calculated with the assumption of unsupported longitudinal edges. For shorter plates, where column-like buckling prevails, the ratio $\sigma_{cr,p}/\sigma_{cr,c}$ is close to 1.0 and $\xi \approx 0$. For longer plates the ratio $\sigma_{cr,p}/\sigma_{cr,c}$ increases over 2 ($\xi = 1$) and plate-

2. Overview of Design Rules

like buckling prevails. Comparison of slendernesses, Eq. (2.24) and Eq. (2.35), shows that because β_{AC} is equal in both cases, plate slenderness is always smaller than column slenderness.

$$\overline{\lambda}_p < \overline{\lambda}_c \qquad (2.39)$$

Consequently, for the same plate the reduction parameter ρ will always be larger than χ_c, because the most favourable buckling curve a (unstiffened plate) always lies below the most unfavourable curve for ρ (plate in uniform compression), see Fig. 2.27. A typical relation ρ - ξ is shown in Fig. 2.28.

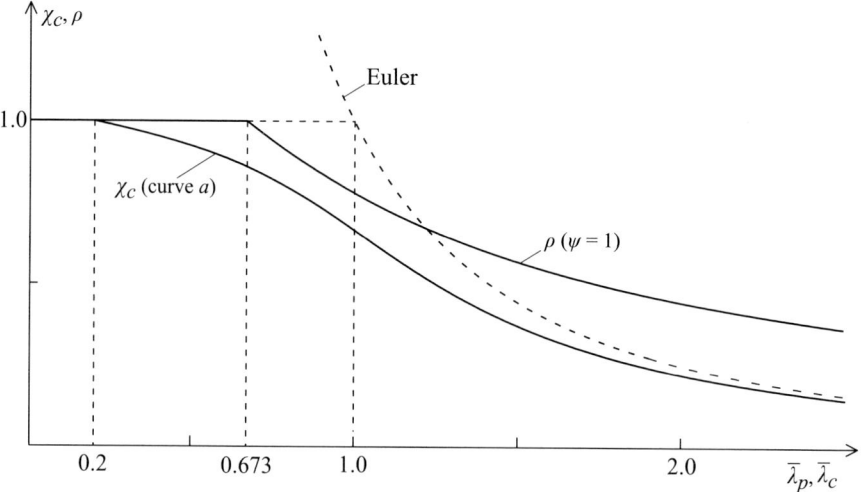

Fig. 2.27: Comparison of χ_c and ρ curves

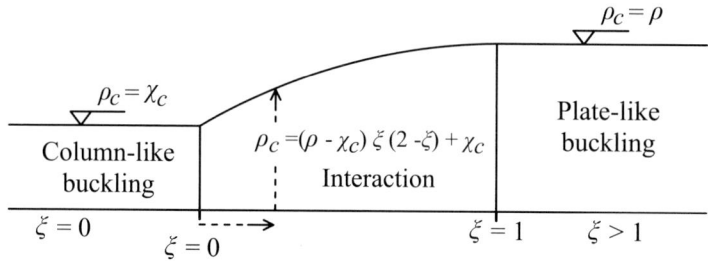

Fig. 2.28: Interpolation between plate-like and column-like behaviour

In practical calculations by using simplified methods for $\sigma_{cr,p}$ it may happen that $\sigma_{cr,p}$ is found to be smaller than $\sigma_{cr,c}$. Such situation is physically not possible but it does not affect much the design procedure, because the smaller column-like buckling resistance prevails anyhow.

A simplified and conservative approach for the design of stiffened plates is possible by taking ρ_c equal to χ_c. In this way the postcritical resistance of the stiffened plate in global buckling is completely neglected, but the postcritical resistance of sub-panels remains active. For longer plates such approach may be too conservative, as in some cases the ratio ρ/χ_c may exceed the value 2. On the other hand, for shorter plates such approach does not make much difference in the final resistance and the calculation of $\sigma_{cr,p}$ may be skipped.

The final effective^p area of the compression zone $A_{c,eff}$ of the unstiffened plate is simply:

$$A_{c,eff} = \rho_c b_{eff} \qquad (2.40)$$

For longitudinally stiffened plates $A_{c,eff}$ is:

$$A_{c,eff} = \rho_c A_{c,eff,loc} + \sum_i b_{i,edge,eff} \, t \qquad (2.41)$$

where

$A_{c,eff,loc}$ is given by Eq. (2.26)
$b_{i,edge,eff}$ is defined in Fig. 2.22.

$\rho_c = 1.0$ means that the stiffeners are fully effective and that the overall buckling with stiffeners involved does not take place. At values $\rho_c <$ 1.0 stiffeners are not fully effective and they get involved in the overall buckling of the plate. This is taken into account by reducing their effective^p area proportionally to ρ_c. When calculating the geometrical properties A_{eff}, I_{eff}, W_{eff} of the final effective^p area of the plate, or more often of the cross section composed of more plates, the easiest way to do this is to replace the thickness of the stiffeners t_{st} and the contributing plating t by the reduced thickness $t_{st} \cdot \rho_c$ and $t \cdot \rho_c$ (see Fig. 2.29).

For wider flanges, shear lag - plate buckling interaction effects should be included in compression flanges and shear lag effects in tension flanges (see sub-chapter 2.3).

2. Overview of Design Rules

When a simplified method for one or two longitudinal stiffeners in the compression zone is applied to calculate the elastic critical plate buckling stress (clause 2.4.3.2 or Annex A.2 of EN 1993-1-5) the reduction due to ρ_c needs to be accounted for only if $\rho_c f_y / \gamma_{M1}$ is smaller than the average stress $\sigma_{com,Ed}$ in the column (stiffener). The effective^p area of that column should then be reduced according to:

$$A_{c,eff,loc} = \frac{\rho_c f_y A_{sl,1}}{\sigma_{com,Ed} \gamma_{M1}} \qquad (2.42)$$

The average stress $\sigma_{com,Ed}$ should be calculated based on the effective^p area of the stiffened plate. This approach is beneficial for web panels in bending where due to the stress gradient the average stress in the stiffener is smaller than f_y. For longitudinally stiffened flanges of box-girders in pure compression both approaches lead to the same result.

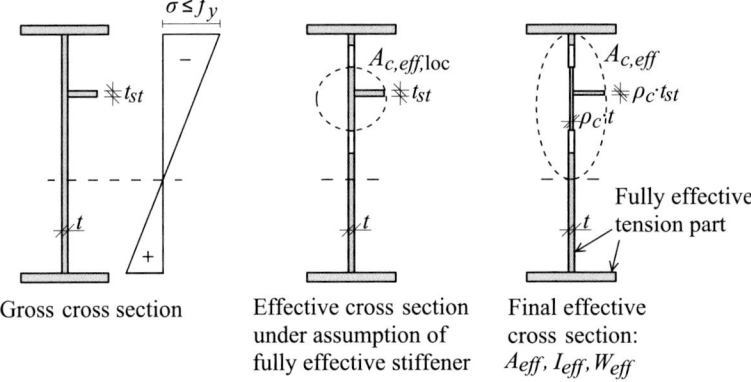

Fig. 2.29: Evolution of effective^p cross section

2.4.6 Verification of the cross section resistance in ultimate limit states

Members with cross sections composed of unstiffened or stiffened plates are checked for the cross section resistance as follows:

- uniaxial bending with axial force

$$\eta_1 = \frac{N_{Ed}}{\frac{f_y A_{eff}}{\gamma_{M0}}} + \frac{M_{Ed} + N_{Ed} e_N}{\frac{f_y W_{eff}}{\gamma_{M0}}} \leq 0 \qquad (2.43)$$

- biaxial bending with axial force

$$\eta_1 = \frac{N_{Ed}}{\frac{f_y A_{eff}}{\gamma_{M0}}} + \frac{M_{y,Ed} + N_{Ed} e_{y,N}}{\frac{f_y W_{y,eff}}{\gamma_{M0}}} + \frac{M_{z,Ed} + N_{Ed} e_{z,N}}{\frac{f_y W_{z,eff}}{\gamma_{M0}}} \leq 0 \qquad (2.44)$$

where

A_{eff} is the effective cross section due to pure compression

$W_{y,eff}, W_{z,eff}$ are the effective elastic section modules due to pure bending for the corresponding bending axes

e_{yN}, e_{zN} are the shifts in the position of the neutral axis calculated in pure compression, see sub-section 2.4.2.2

N_{Ed} is the design axial force

M_{yEd}, M_{zEd} are design bending moments

γ_{M0} is the partial factor given in the application parts of Eurocode 3 (EN 1993-1-1 and EN 1993-2 to EN 1993-6). In all these standards the recommended value is $\gamma_{M0} = 1.0$.

In the calculation of internal forces N_{Ed} and M_{Ed} second order effects should be included when relevant.

The design checks in Eq. (2.43) and Eq. (2.44) look like ordinary cross section checks, but actually they relate to the whole panel length a between adjacent rigid transverse stiffeners (buckling verification on the panel length). For this reason the plate buckling verification may be performed for N_{Ed} and M_{Ed} calculated at a distance of $0.4a$ or $0.5b$, whichever is smaller, from the panel end with larger stresses. When large moment gradients are present, this may be very favourable. In this case an additional gross cross section check has to be performed at the end of the panel (see Fig. 2.30). Conservatively, the buckling check may be performed at the most stressed end of the panel.

2. OVERVIEW OF DESIGN RULES

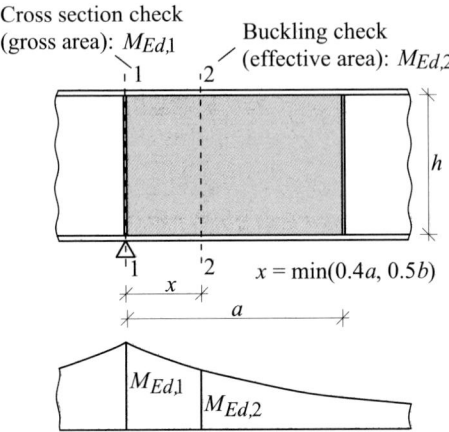

Fig. 2.30: Location of the buckling and cross section check

Note that, in case of a longitudinally stiffened web or flange panel, even if all sub-panels are classified as Class 1 or 2 elements (leading to a stiffened plate in Class 1 or 2), a plastic cross section analysis should not be used automatically without global buckling verification of a stiffened panel according to sections 2.4.3 – 2.4.5.

2.4.7 Verification of plated structural elements in the serviceability limit states

When necessary, the verification at the serviceability limit state may be performed according to the design rules given in sections 2.4.1 to 2.4.6 by calculating ρ_{loc} and ρ with Eq. (2.22) or Eq. (2.23). The reduced plate slenderness $\overline{\lambda}_{p,red}$ (Eq. (2.21)) should be replaced by $\overline{\lambda}_{p,ser}$:

$$\overline{\lambda}_{p,ser} = \overline{\lambda}_p \sqrt{\frac{\sigma_{com.Ed.ser}}{f_y}} \qquad (2.45)$$

where

$\sigma_{com,Ed,ser}$ is defined as the maximum compressive stress of the effective cross section under action effects at the serviceability limit state.

To calculate deflections at the serviceability limit state, the second moment of area I_{eff} may be calculated by an interpolation between the second moment of area of the gross cross section I_{gr} and the second moment of area of the effective cross section I_{eff} ($\sigma_{com,Ed,ser}$) determined according to the previous paragraph:

$$I_{eff} = I_{gr} - \frac{\sigma_{gr}}{\sigma_{com,Ed,ser}}\left(I_{gr} - I_{eff}\left(\sigma_{com,Ed,ser}\right)\right) \qquad (2.46)$$

In principle, the procedure to determine I_{eff} is iterative, but by assessing an upper bound for $\sigma_{com,Ed,ser}$, the calculation changes to a one-step procedure (for instance $\sigma_{com,Ed,ser} = f_y/\gamma$ leads to a conservative upper bound with γ taken as $\gamma = 1.40$ for buildings and $\gamma = 1.35$ for bridges)

The effective second moment of area I_{eff} may be taken as variable along the span following the stress intensity or may be conservatively taken as a constant value determined at the maximum value of $\sigma_{com,Ed,ser}$ within the span.

2.4.8 Design examples

Example 2.4-1: Class 4 cross section under uniform compression.

$h = 600$ mm
$b = 600$ mm
$t_w = 10$ mm
$t_{f1} = 10$ mm
$t_{f2} = 20$ mm
$A = 29400$ mm^2
$I_y = 1.748 \cdot 10^9$ mm^4

$f_y = 275$ N/mm^2 $\qquad N_{Ed} = 5.5 \cdot 10^6$ N $\qquad \gamma_{M0} = 1.0$

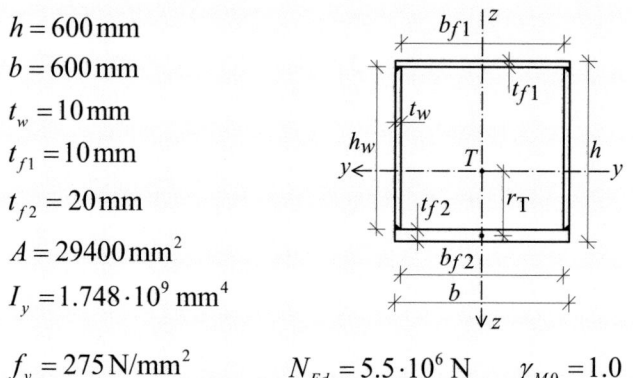

Fig. 2.31: Geometry of box cross section

The box cross section shown in Fig. 2.31 shall be verified against uniform compression by the following criterion:

2. Overview of Design Rules

$$\frac{N_{Ed}}{A_{eff} \cdot f_y / \gamma_{M0}} + \frac{N_{Ed} \cdot e_{N,y}}{W_{eff,y} \cdot f_y / \gamma_{M0}} \leq 1.0,$$

where

- A_{eff} — is the effective area of the cross section when subject to uniform compression,
- $W_{eff,y}$ — is the effective section modulus determined assuming the cross section is subject only to bending,
- $e_{N,y}$ — is the shift of the centroid of the effective area relative to the centre of gravity of the gross cross section determined assuming uniform axial compression.
- f_y — is the yield stress according to Table 3.1 of EN 1993-1-1

a) Uniform compression

Cross section class check

$$b_{f1} = b_{f2} = b - 2 \cdot t_w = 600 - 2 \cdot 10 = 580 \, \text{mm}$$

$$h_w = h - t_{f1} - t_{f2} = 600 - 10 - 20 = 570 \, \text{mm}$$

Upper flange (compression):

$$\varepsilon = \sqrt{\frac{235}{f_y}} = \sqrt{\frac{235}{275}} = 0.924$$

$$\frac{b_{f1}}{t_{f1}} = \frac{580}{10} = 58.0 > 42 \cdot \varepsilon = 42 \cdot 0.924 = 38.8 \; (\text{Class 4})$$

Lower flange (compression):

$$\frac{b_{f2}}{t_{f2}} = \frac{580}{20} = 29.0 < 42 \cdot \varepsilon = 38.8 \quad (\text{Class 3 — but it also fulfils}$$
requirements for Class 1 (33ε))

2.4 PLATE BUCKLING EFFECTS DUE TO DIRECT STRESSES

Web (compression):

$$\frac{h_w}{t_w} = \frac{570}{10} = 57.0 > 42 \cdot \varepsilon = 38.8 \quad \text{(Class 4)}$$

The cross section is classified as Class 4.

Determination of the characteristics of the gross cross section

$$S_y = b \cdot t_{f1} \cdot \left(h - \frac{t_{f1} + t_{f2}}{2}\right) + 2 \cdot h_w \cdot t_w \cdot \left(\frac{h_w + t_{f2}}{2}\right) =$$

$$= \frac{1}{29400} \cdot \begin{pmatrix} 600 \cdot 10 \cdot \left(600 - \dfrac{10+20}{2}\right) \\ + 2 \cdot 570 \cdot 10 \cdot \left(600 - \dfrac{570+20}{2}\right) \end{pmatrix} = 6.873 \cdot 10^6 \text{ mm}^3$$

$$r_T = \frac{S_y}{A} = \frac{6.873 \cdot 10^6}{29400.0} = 233.8 \text{ mm}$$

where

S_y — is the first moment of area of the gross cross section with respect to the centroid of the lower flange (y-y axis),

r_T — is the distance from the centroid of the lower flange to the centroid of the gross cross section.

Calculation of effective^p width of the upper flange

$$\psi = 1.0 \quad \Rightarrow \quad k_\sigma = 4.0$$

$$\bar{\lambda}_p = \frac{b_{f1}}{t_{f1} \cdot 28.4 \cdot \varepsilon \cdot \sqrt{k_\sigma}} = \frac{580}{10 \cdot 28.4 \cdot 0.924 \cdot \sqrt{4.0}} = 1.105$$

$$\bar{\lambda}_p = 1.105 > 0.5 + \sqrt{0.085 - 0.055 \cdot \psi} = 0.5 + \sqrt{0.085 - 0.055 \cdot 1} = 0.673$$

$$\rho = \frac{\bar{\lambda}_p - 0.055 \cdot (3+\psi)}{\bar{\lambda}_p^2} = \frac{1.105 - 0.055 \cdot (3+1)}{1.105^2} = 0.725$$

2. Overview of Design Rules

$$b_{eff,f} = \rho \cdot b_{f1} = 0.725 \cdot 580 = 420.5 \, \text{mm}$$

$$b_{e1,f} = b_{e2,f} = 0.5 \cdot b_{eff,f} = 0.5 \cdot 420.5 = 210.2 \, \text{mm}$$

Calculation of effective^p width of the web

$$\psi = 1.0 \implies k_\sigma = 4.0$$

$$\overline{\lambda}_p = \frac{h_w}{t_w \cdot 28.4 \cdot \varepsilon \cdot \sqrt{k_\sigma}} = \frac{570}{10 \cdot 28.4 \cdot 0.924 \cdot \sqrt{4.0}} = 1.086$$

$$\overline{\lambda}_p = 1.086 > 0.5 + \sqrt{0.085 - 0.055 \cdot \psi} = 0.5 + \sqrt{0.085 - 0.055 \cdot 1} = 0.673$$

$$\rho = \frac{\overline{\lambda}_p - 0.055 \cdot (3+\psi)}{\overline{\lambda}_p^2} = \frac{1.086 - 0.055 \cdot (3+1)}{1.086^2} = 0.734$$

$$b_{eff,w} = \rho \cdot h_w = 0.734 \cdot 570 = 418.7 \, \text{mm}$$

$$b_{e1,w} = b_{e2,w} = 0.5 \cdot b_{eff,w} = 0.5 \cdot 418.7 = 209.3 \, \text{mm}$$

Determination of characteristics of effective cross section considering effective widths of the upper flange and webs in uniform compression

$$x_f = b_{f1} - b_{eff,f} = 580.0 - 420.5 = 159.5 \, \text{mm}$$

$$x_w = h_w - b_{eff,w} = 570.0 - 418.7 = 151.3 \, \text{mm}$$

$$A_{eff} = \begin{bmatrix} A - (x_f \cdot t_{f1} + 2 \cdot x_w \cdot t_w) = \\ = 29400 - (159.5 \cdot 10 + 2 \cdot 151.3 \cdot 10) \end{bmatrix} = 24778.1 \, \text{mm}^2$$

$$r_f = h - \frac{t_{f1} + t_{f2}}{2} - r_T = 600 - \frac{10+20}{2} - 233.8 = 351.2 \, \text{mm}$$

2.4 PLATE BUCKLING EFFECTS DUE TO DIRECT STRESSES

$$r_w = h_w + \frac{t_{f2}}{2} - r_T - b_{e1,w} - \frac{x_w}{2} =$$

$$= 570 + \frac{10}{2} - 233.8 - 209.3 - \frac{151.3}{2} = 61.2 \text{ mm}$$

$$e_{N,y} = \frac{2 \cdot r_w \cdot x_w \cdot t_w + r_f \cdot x_f \cdot t_{f1}}{A_{eff}} =$$

$$= \frac{2 \cdot 61.2 \cdot 151.3 \cdot 10 + 351.2 \cdot 159.5 \cdot 10}{24778.1} = 30.1 \text{ mm}$$

$$r_{Teff,N} = r_T - e_{N,y} = 233.8 - 30.1 = 203.7 \text{ mm},$$

where

$e_{N,y}$ — is the shift of the centroid of the effective area relative to the centre of gravity of the gross cross section determined assuming uniform axial compression.

$r_{Teff,N}$ — is the distance from the centroid of the bottom flange to the centroid of the effective cross section under uniform compression.

b) Bending

The effective section modulus $W_{eff,y}$ is determined on the cross section subject only to bending moment.

Cross section class check

Upper flange (compression – the same as in 1): Class 4.

Determination of characteristics of effective cross section considering effective widths of the upper flange (calculation of effective width of the upper flange is already done in section 1) and gross cross section of the web:

2. Overview of Design Rules

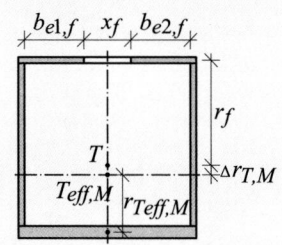

$$A_{eff} = A - x_f \cdot t_{f1}$$
$$= 29400 - 159.5 \cdot 10 = 27804.9 \text{ mm}$$

$$\Delta r_{T,M} = \frac{r_f \cdot x_f \cdot t_{f1}}{A_{eff}} = \frac{351.2 \cdot 159.5 \cdot 10}{24778.1} = 20.1 \text{ mm}$$

$$r_{Teff,M} = r_T - \Delta r_{T,M} = 233.8 - 20.1 = 213.6 \text{ mm}$$

$$I^I_{eff,y} = I_y + A_{eff} \cdot \Delta r^2_{T,M} - \left(\frac{x_f \cdot t_f^3}{12} + x_f \cdot t_f \cdot (r_f + \Delta r_{T,M})^2 \right) =$$

$$= \left[\begin{array}{c} 1.748 \cdot 10^9 + 27804.9 \cdot 20.1^2 - \\ \left(\dfrac{159.5 \cdot 10^3}{12} + \right. \\ \left. +159.5 \cdot 10 \cdot (351.2 + 20.1)^2 \right) \end{array} \right] = 1.539 \cdot 10^9 \text{ mm}^4$$

where

$I^I_{eff,y}$ – is the effective second moment of area (cross section under pure bending) with respect to y-y considering the effective width of the upper flange.

The effective section moduli at the upper and lower edge of the girder's web, $W^I_{eff,y,1}$ and $W^I_{eff,y,2}$ are, respectively:

$$W^I_{eff,y,1} = \frac{I^I_{eff,y}}{h_w + \dfrac{t_{f2}}{2} - r_{Teff,M}} = \frac{1.540 \cdot 10^9}{570 - \dfrac{20}{2} - 213.6} = 4.200 \cdot 10^6 \text{ mm}^3$$

$$W^I_{eff,y,2} = \frac{I^I_{eff,y}}{r_{Teff,M} - \dfrac{t_{f2}}{2}} = \frac{1.540 \cdot 10^9}{213.6 - \dfrac{20}{2}} = 7.558 \cdot 10^6 \text{ mm}^3$$

2.4 PLATE BUCKLING EFFECTS DUE TO DIRECT STRESSES

Web (bending):

$$\psi^I = \frac{\sigma_2^I}{\sigma_1^I} = \frac{M_{y,Ed}/W_{eff,y,2}^I}{M_{y,Ed}/W_{eff,y,1}^I} = \frac{W_{eff,y,1}^I}{W_{eff,y,2}^I} = \frac{4.200 \cdot 10^6}{7.558 \cdot 10^6} = -0.56 > -1$$

$$\frac{h_w}{t_w} = \frac{570}{10} = 57.0 > \frac{42 \cdot \varepsilon}{0.67 + 0.33 \cdot \psi^I} = \frac{42 \cdot 0.924}{0.67 - 0.33 \cdot 0.56} = 79.8 \text{ Class 3}$$

The web is at least of Class 3.

In case of a slender web, the effective^p width should be determined on the basis of stress ratio ψ^I.

The effective section modulus $W_{eff,y}$ for the design resistance to uniform bending is defined as the smallest value of the effective section moduli at the centroid of the upper and the lower flange, $W_{eff,y,1}$ and $W_{eff,y,2}$, respectively:

$$W_{eff,y,1} = \frac{I_{eff,y}^I}{h_w + \frac{t_{f1}+t_{f2}}{2} - r_{Teff,M}} = \frac{1.540 \cdot 10^9}{570 - \frac{10+20}{2} - 213.6} =$$

$$= 4.144 \cdot 10^6 \text{ mm}^3$$

$$W_{eff,y,2} = \frac{I_{eff,y}^I}{z_{Teff}} = \frac{1.540 \cdot 10^9}{213.6} = 7.205 \cdot 10^6 \text{ mm}^3$$

Here, $W_{eff,y,1}$ governs.

c) Cross section resistance check

Additional bending moment $N_{Ed} \cdot e_{N,y}$ causes compression at the upper flange (+ compression).

$$\frac{N_{Ed}}{A_{eff} \cdot f_y / \gamma_{M0}} + \frac{N_{Ed} \cdot e_{N,y}}{W_{eff,y,1} \cdot f_y / \gamma_{M0}} =$$

$$= \frac{5.5 \cdot 10^6}{24778.1 \cdot 275/1.0} + \frac{5.5 \cdot 10^6 \cdot 30.1}{4.144 \cdot 10^6 \cdot 275/1.0} = 0.807 + 0.145 =$$

2. OVERVIEW OF DESIGN RULES

$= 0.95 < 1.0$

Example 2.4-2: Bending resistance of unstiffened plated girder at the intermediate support.

The geometry and the basic parameters of the cross section of the unstiffened plated girder are shown in Fig. 2.32.

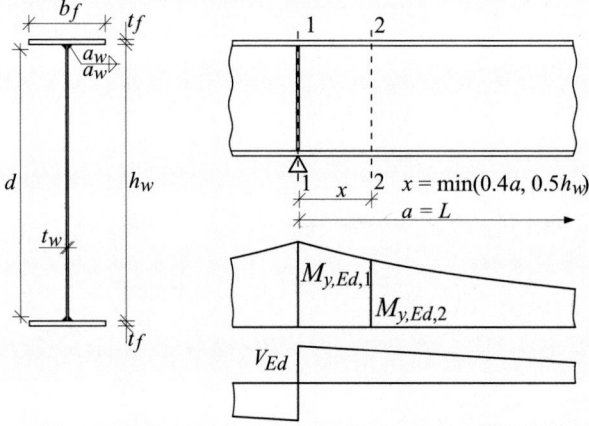

Fig. 2.32: Geometry of cross section and distribution of internal forces in the plated girder at the intermediate support

$h_w = 1400$ mm $d = h_w - 2a_w\sqrt{2} = 1388.7$ mm $x = 700$ mm

$t_w = 10$ mm $A = 34000$ mm^2 $M_{y,Ed,1} = 6.1 \cdot 10^9$ Nmm

$b_f = 400$ mm $I_y = 1.244 \cdot 10^{10}$ mm^4 $M_{y,Ed,2} = 5.6 \cdot 10^9$ Nmm

$t_f = 25$ mm $M_{pl,y,Rd} = 6.798 \cdot 10^9$ Nmm $\eta = 1.2$

$a_w = 4$ mm $f_y = 355$ N/mm^2 $\gamma_{M0} = 1.0$

The plate buckling verification of the panel may be performed for $M_{y,Ed,2}$ calculated at a distance of 0.4a or 0.5h_w, whichever is smaller, from the panel end with larger stresses. In this case of an unstiffened plated girder, the value 0.5h_w governs ($a \geq 1.25\ h_w$). An additional gross cross section check has to be performed at the end of the panel (see Fig. 2.32).

Distance from the centroid of the bottom flange to the centroid of the gross cross section r_T:

$$r_T = \frac{h_w + t_f}{2} = \frac{1400 + 25}{2} \text{ mm} = 712.5 \text{ mm}$$

The elastic section moduli of the gross cross section with respect to y-y axis $W_{y,1}$, $W_{y,2}$, at the centroid of the upper and lower flange are, respectively:

$$W_{y,1} = W_{y,2} = \frac{I_y}{r_T} = \frac{1.244 \cdot 10^{10}}{712.5} = 1.746 \cdot 10^7 \text{ mm}^3$$

The design elastic moment resistance of the gross cross section $M_{el,y,Rd}$ is:

$$M_{el,y,Rd} = W_{y,1} \cdot f_y / \gamma_{M0} = 1.746 \cdot 10^7 \cdot 355 / 1.0 = 6.199 \cdot 10^9 \text{ Nmm}$$

Cross section class check

Upper flange (compression):

$$\varepsilon = \sqrt{\frac{235}{f_y}} = \sqrt{\frac{235}{355}} = 0.814$$

$$\frac{\frac{b_f - t_w}{2} - a_w\sqrt{2}}{t_f} = \frac{\frac{400 - 10}{2} - 4 \cdot \sqrt{2}}{25} = 7.6 < 10 \cdot \varepsilon = 10 \cdot 0.814 = 8.14$$

Class 2

Web (bending):

$$\frac{d}{t_w} = \frac{1388.7}{10} = 138.9 > 124 \cdot \varepsilon = 100.9 \text{ Class 4}$$

The cross section is of Class 4.

Calculation of the effective^p width of the web

$$\psi = -1 \Rightarrow k_\sigma = 23.9$$

$$\bar{\lambda}_p = \frac{d/t_w}{28.4 \cdot \varepsilon \cdot \sqrt{k_\sigma}} = \frac{1388.7/10}{28.4 \cdot 0.814 \cdot \sqrt{23.9}} = 1.229$$

$$\bar{\lambda}_p = 1.229 > 0.5 + \sqrt{0.085 - 0.055 \cdot \psi} = 0.5 + \sqrt{0.085 + 0.055 \cdot 1} = 0.874$$

$$\rho = \frac{\bar{\lambda}_p - 0.055 \cdot (3+\psi)}{\bar{\lambda}_p^2} = \frac{1.229 - 0.055 \cdot (3-1)}{1.229^2} = 0.741$$

$$b_{eff} = \rho \cdot b_c = 0.741 \cdot 694.3 = 514.3 \, mm$$

$$b_c = \frac{d}{(1-\psi)} = \frac{1388.7}{(1+1)} = 694.3 \, mm$$

$$b_{e1} = 0.4 \cdot b_{eff} + a_w\sqrt{2} = 0.4 \cdot 514.3 + 4 \cdot \sqrt{2} = 211.4 \, mm$$

$$b_{e2} = 0.6 \cdot b_{eff} = 0.6 \cdot 514.2 = 308.6 \, mm$$

$$x_w = b_c - b_{eff} = 694.3 - 514.3 = 180.1 \, mm$$

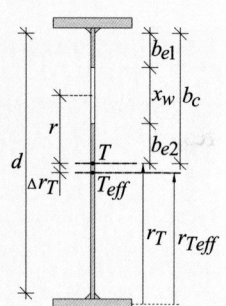

Calculation of effective cross section characteristics

Effective cross section area A_{eff}:

$$\Delta A = t_w \cdot x_w = 10 \cdot 180.1 = 1800.7 \, mm^2$$

$$A_{eff} = A - \Delta A = 34000 - 1800.7 = 32199.3 \, mm^2$$

$$r = \frac{d - x_w}{2} - (b_{e1} - a_w\sqrt{2}) = \frac{1388.7 - 180.1}{2} - (211.4 - 4 \cdot \sqrt{2})$$

$$= 398.6 \, mm$$

$$\Delta r_T = \frac{r \cdot \Delta A}{A_{eff}} = \frac{398.6 \cdot 1800.7}{32199.3} = 22.3 \, mm$$

where

Δr_T — is the shift in the position of neutral axis

2.4 PLATE BUCKLING EFFECTS DUE TO DIRECT STRESSES

The distance between the centroid of the bottom flange and the centroid of effective cross section $r_{T,eff}$ can be expressed as:

$$r_{T,eff} = r_T - \Delta r_T = 712.5 - 22.3 = 690.2 \text{ mm}$$

The second moment of area of the effective cross section with respect to y-y axis becomes:

$$I_{eff,y} = I_y + A \cdot \Delta r_T^2 - \left(\frac{x_w^3 \cdot t_w}{12} + \Delta A \cdot (r + \Delta r_T)^2 \right) =$$

$$= \begin{bmatrix} 1.244 \cdot 10^{10} + 34000 \cdot 22.3^2 - \\ -\left(\dfrac{180.1^3 \cdot 10}{12} + 1800.7 \cdot (398.6 + 22.3)^2 \right) \end{bmatrix} =$$

$$= 1.213 \cdot 10^{10} \text{ mm}^4$$

The elastic section moduli of effective cross section $W_{eff,y,1}$, $W_{eff,y,2}$ with respect to the centroid of the upper flange and lower flange are, respectively:

$$W_{eff,y,1} = \frac{I_{eff,y}}{h_w + t_f - r_{T,eff}} = \frac{1.213 \cdot 10^{10}}{1400 + 25 - 690.2} = 1.651 \cdot 10^7 \text{ mm}^3$$

$$W_{eff,y,2} = \frac{I_{eff,y}}{r_{T,eff}} = \frac{1.214 \cdot 10^{10}}{690.2} = 1.758 \cdot 10^7 \text{ mm}^3$$

The design elastic moment resistance of the effective cross section $M_{c,y,Rd}$ is:

$$M_{c,y,Rd} = \min(W_{eff,y,1}, W_{eff,y,2}) \cdot f_y / \gamma_{M0}$$

$$= \min(1.651, 1.758) \cdot 10^7 \cdot 355 / 1.0 = 5.862 \cdot 10^9 \text{ Nmm}$$

The plate buckling verification of the panel performed for $M_{y,Ed,2}$ calculated at a distance of $0.5 h_w$ is:

$$\eta_1 = \frac{M_{y,Ed,2}}{M_{c,y,Rd}} = \frac{5.600 \cdot 10^9}{5.862 \cdot 10^9} = 0.95 < 1.0$$

Additional gross cross section bending check at the end of the panel

2. OVERVIEW OF DESIGN RULES

becomes:

$$M_{y,Ed,1} = 6.100 \cdot 10^9 \text{ Nmm} < M_{el,y,Rd} = 6.199 \cdot 10^9 \text{ Nmm}$$

Example 2.4-3: Calculation of elastic critical plate buckling stress.

Elastic critical plate buckling stress can be computed in different ways. In this example the critical plate buckling stress is determined by using:

- Klöppel diagrams (Klöppel and Scheer, 1960)
- EBPlate (2007)
- FEM software
- EN 1993-1-5 rules

The outline of stiffened plate, its dimensions and boundary conditions are given in Fig. 2.33.

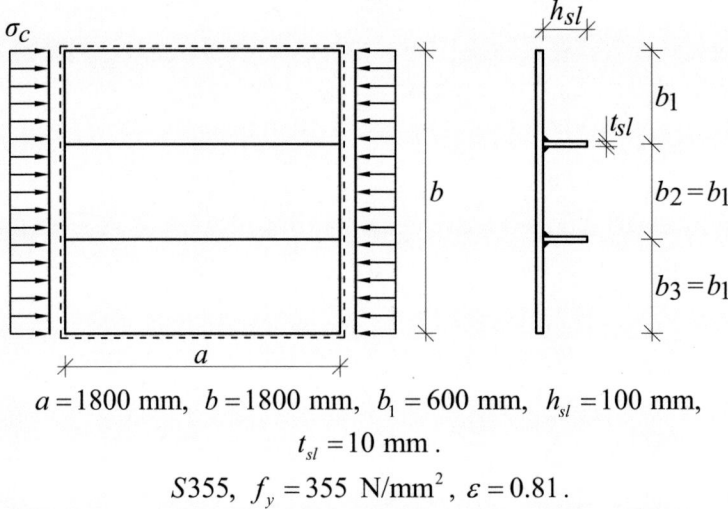

$a = 1800$ mm, $b = 1800$ mm, $b_1 = 600$ mm, $h_{sl} = 100$ mm, $t_{sl} = 10$ mm.

S355, $f_y = 355$ N/mm², $\varepsilon = 0.81$.

Fig. 2.33: The layout of stiffened plate

2.4 PLATE BUCKLING EFFECTS DUE TO DIRECT STRESSES

a) $\sigma_{cr,p}$ – KLÖPPEL

$\sigma_{cr,p}$ is given with the following equation:

$$\sigma_{cr,p} = k_{\sigma,p} \cdot \sigma_E,$$

Where $\sigma_E = \dfrac{\pi^2 \cdot E \cdot t^2}{12 \cdot (1-v^2) \cdot b^2} = \dfrac{\pi^2 \cdot 210000 \cdot 12^2}{12 \cdot (1-0.3^2) \cdot 1800^2} = 8.436$ N/mm^2,

$k_{\sigma,p}$ is the elastic critical plate buckling coefficient according to Klöppel.

The parameters needed for the evaluation of $k_{\sigma,p}$ are:

$$\alpha = \frac{a}{b} = \frac{1800}{1800} = 1, \; \delta = \frac{A_{sl}}{b \cdot t} = \frac{b_{sl} \cdot t_{sl}}{b \cdot t} = \frac{100 \cdot 10}{1800 \cdot 12} = 0.05,$$

$$\gamma = \frac{(I_{sl} + A_{sl} \cdot e^2) \cdot 12 \cdot (1-v^2)}{b \cdot t^3} =$$

$$= \frac{(b_{sl}^3 \cdot t_{sl}/12 + b_{sl} \cdot t_{sl} \cdot e^2) \cdot 12 \cdot (1-v^2)}{b \cdot t^3} =$$

$$= \frac{(100^3 \cdot 10/12 + 100 \cdot 10 \cdot 50^2) \cdot 12 \cdot (1-0.3^2)}{1800 \cdot 12^3} = 11.70$$

Note that parameters α and δ above are not the same as in EN 1993-1-5, Annex A1, where the procedure for plates stiffened with more than two stiffeners is given.

The plate buckling coefficient is obtained from the diagram (according to Klöppel) in Fig. 2.34:

2. OVERVIEW OF DESIGN RULES

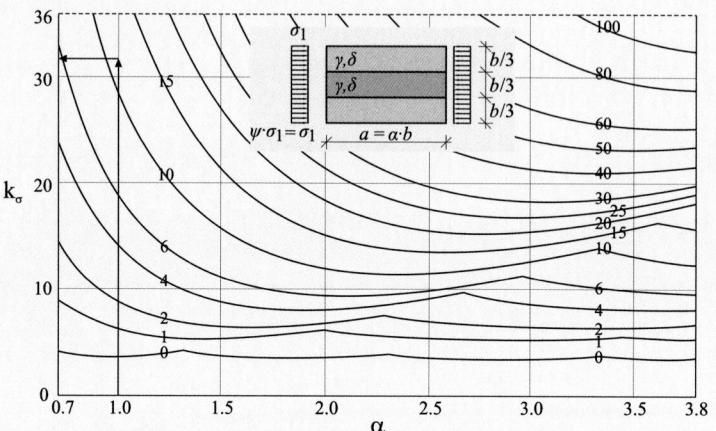

Fig. 2.34: Buckling coefficient according to Klöppel

$k_\sigma = 32.5$

Finally, the critical buckling stress is equal to:

$$\sigma_{cr,p} = k_\sigma \cdot \sigma_E = 32.5 \cdot 8.436 = 274.17 \text{ N/mm}^2.$$

b) $\sigma_{cr,p}$ – **EBPlate**

In this case the critical stress will be calculated in two ways. In the first case the usual procedure (calculation of buckling modes) for the calculation of critical stresses is presented by using EBPlate. Usually for plates with stronger stiffeners the appropriate buckling mode is difficult to obtain because local buckling of the sub-panels governs. For this reason a method in EBPlate was proposed to assess $\sigma_{cr,p}$, which will be used and presented in the second case.

$\sigma_{cr,p}$ – **General method to assess buckling modes**

The data needed for the evaluation of the buckling modes are:

plate: $a = 1800$ mm, $b = 1800$ mm, $t = 12$ mm,

stiffener: $h = b_{sl} = 100$ mm, $t = t_{sl} = 10$ mm,

stiffener position: $b_1 = 600$ mm.

2.4 PLATE BUCKLING EFFECTS DUE TO DIRECT STRESSES

Fig. 2.35 shows the buckling modes and the corresponding critical stresses.

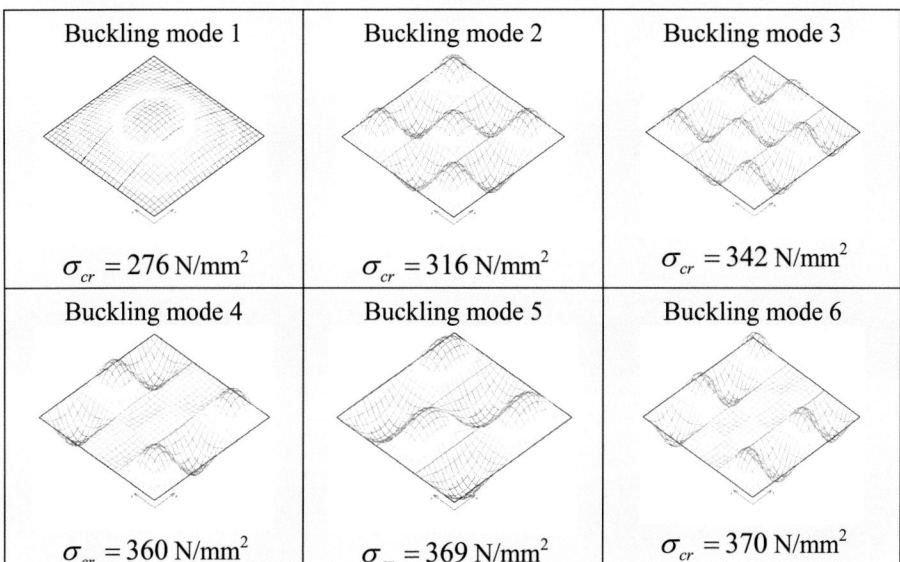

Fig. 2.35: Buckling modes with their critical stresses

The first buckling mode corresponds to the global plate type behaviour with critical plate buckling stress:

$$\sigma_{cr,p} = 276 \, \text{N/mm}^2.$$

$\sigma_{cr,p}$ – Proposed method in EBPlate

In this method the stresses are "transferred" from the plate to the stiffeners (see the figure below) by modifying the relative axial rigidity of each longitudinal stiffener in the compression zone in the following way:

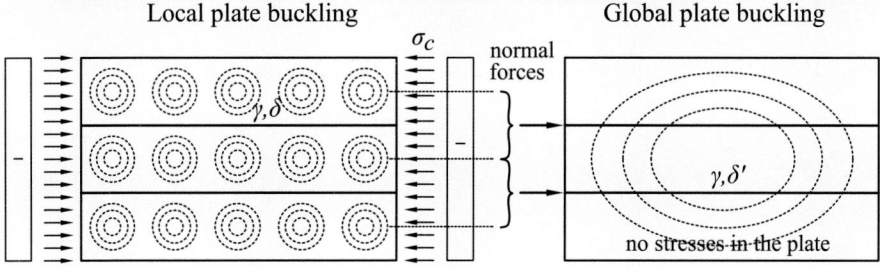

2. Overview of Design Rules

$$\delta' = \delta + \left(\frac{3-\psi_1}{5-\psi_1}\cdot\frac{b_1}{b} + \frac{2}{5-\psi_2}\cdot\frac{b_2}{b}\right) = \frac{b_{st}\cdot t_{st}}{b\cdot t} + \left(\frac{3-1}{5-1}\cdot\frac{b_1}{b} + \frac{2}{5-1}\cdot\frac{b_2}{b}\right) =$$

$$= \frac{100\cdot 10}{1800\cdot 12} + \left(\frac{3-1}{5-1}\cdot\frac{600}{1800} + \frac{2}{5-1}\cdot\frac{600}{1800}\right) = 0.38,$$

where $\psi_1 = \psi_2 = 1$ and $b_1 = b_2 = 600$ mm.

For the calculation of the critical buckling shape the relative bending rigidity of the stiffener has to be determined:

$$\gamma = \frac{I_{sl}}{I_p} = \frac{I_{sl}\cdot 12\cdot(1-v^2)}{b\cdot t^3} = \frac{3.33\cdot 10^6\cdot 12\cdot(1-0.3^2)}{1800\cdot 12^3} = 11.69,$$

where I_{sl} is the second moment of area of the gross cross section of the stiffener and its adjacent parts of the plate:

$$I_{sl} = \frac{(2\cdot 15\cdot\varepsilon\cdot t + t_{sl})\cdot t^3}{12} + \frac{b_{sl}^3\cdot t_{sl}}{12} + (2\cdot 15\cdot\varepsilon\cdot t + t_{sl})\cdot t\cdot e_2^2 + b_{sl}\cdot t_{sl}\cdot e_1^2 =$$

$$= \frac{(2\cdot 15\cdot 0.81\cdot 12 + 10)\cdot 12^3}{12} + \frac{100^3\cdot 10}{12} + (2\cdot 15\cdot 0.81\cdot 12 + 10)\cdot$$
$$\cdot 12\cdot 12.12^2 + 100\cdot 10\cdot 43.88^2 = 3.3\cdot 10^6 \text{ mm}^4$$

$$e_2 = \frac{b_{sl}\cdot t_{sl}\cdot(b_{sl}+t)/2}{b_{sl}\cdot t_{sl} + (2\cdot 15\cdot\varepsilon\cdot t + t_{sl})\cdot t} =$$

$$= \frac{100\cdot 10\cdot(100+12)/2}{100\cdot 10 + (2\cdot 15\cdot 0.81\cdot 12 + 10)\cdot 12} =$$

$$= 12.12 \text{ mm},$$

$$e_1 = \frac{b_{sl}+t}{2} - e_2 = \frac{100+12}{2} - 12.12 = 43.88 \text{ mm}.$$

The critical stress is then equal to $\sigma_{cr.p} = 289$ N/mm^2 with the buckling shape plotted in the Fig. 2.36.

2.4 PLATE BUCKLING EFFECTS DUE TO DIRECT STRESSES

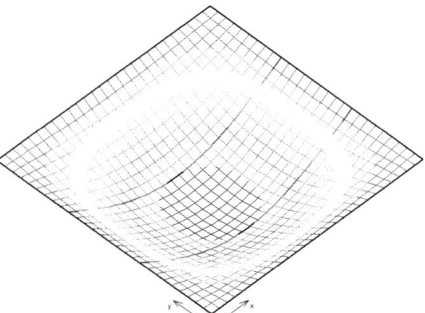

Fig. 2.36: Critical plate buckling shape

c) $\sigma_{cr,p}$ – **general purpose FEM software**

The critical plate stress is determined by using general purpose FEM software. Here ABAQUS ("Abaqus FEA", 2007) was chosen. For this particular case, where the flexural rigidity of the stiffeners is small, the appropriate buckling mode is easy to find, while on the other hand for plates with a large stiffness of the stiffeners the appropriate buckling mode is difficult to determine because most of the buckling modes show local buckling of sub-panels.

The mathematical model used in the FEM analysis with its boundary conditions and the results of buckling analysis are shown in Fig. 2.37 and Fig. 2.38.

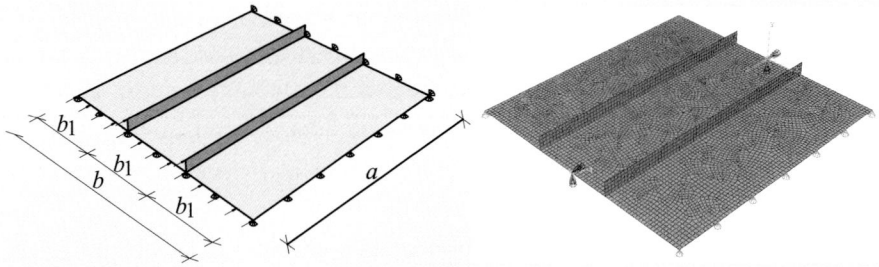

Fig. 2.37: Mathematical model

2. OVERVIEW OF DESIGN RULES

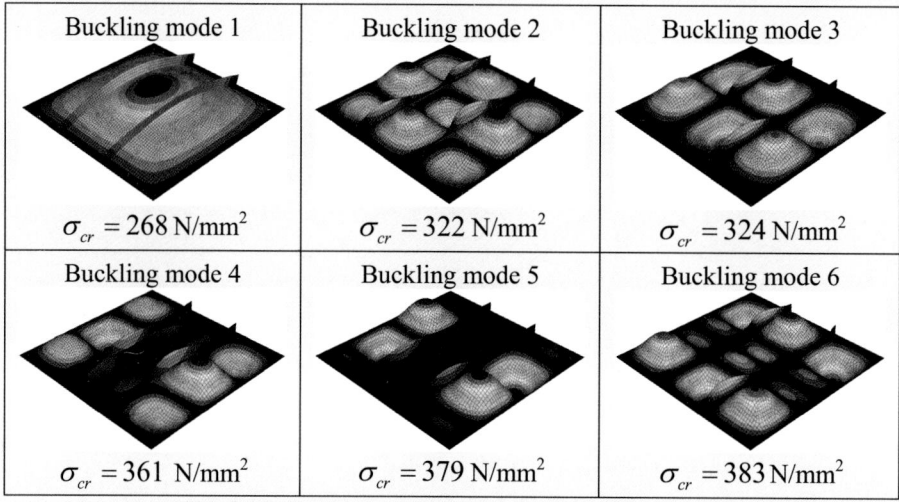

Fig. 2.38: Buckling modes and their critical stresses

The first buckling mode corresponds to the global plate type behaviour with critical plate buckling stress:

$$\sigma_{cr,p} = 268 \text{ N/mm}^2.$$

d) $\sigma_{cr,p}$ – **EN1993-1-5 A.2**

Finally, the critical plate buckling stress is calculated according to EN 1993-1-5, Annex A.2. The plate can be treated as an equivalent orthotropic plate if it is stiffened with at least three stiffeners. In this case the plate is stiffened only with two stiffeners. The plate-like behaviour is modelled by the buckling of each stiffener as a column on continuous elastic support provided by plate, while the other stiffener acts as a rigid support. Buckling of both stiffeners simultaneously is accounted for by considering a single lumped stiffener, which substitutes both stiffeners in such a way that its cross sectional area and its second moment of area are the sum of the individual stiffeners. It is positioned at the location of the resultant of the respective forces in the individual stiffeners.

2.4 PLATE BUCKLING EFFECTS DUE TO DIRECT STRESSES

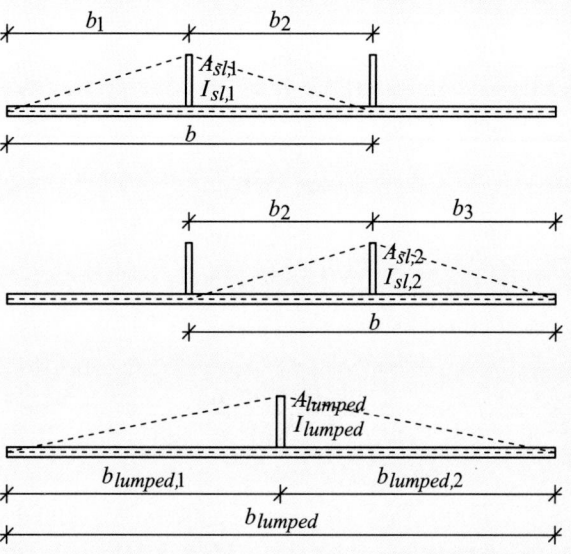

Stiffener I, II

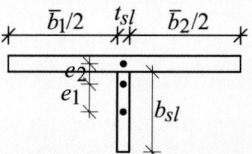

$e_1 = 49.20$ mm, $e_2 = 6.80$ mm, $\bar{b}_1 = 595$ mm, $\bar{b}_2 = 590$ mm,

$b_1 = b_2 = 600$ mm, $b = b_1 + b_2 = 600 + 600 = 1200$ mm,

$$A_{sl,1} = \left(\frac{\bar{b}_1 + \bar{b}_2}{2} + t_{sl}\right) \cdot t + b_{sl} \cdot t_{sl} = \left(\frac{595 + 590}{2} + 10\right) \cdot 12 + 100 \cdot 10 =$$

$$= 8230 \text{ mm}^2,$$

$$I_{sl,1} = \frac{b_{sl}^3 \cdot t_{sl}}{12} + \frac{\left(\left(\bar{b}_1 + \bar{b}_2\right)/2 + t_{sl,1}\right) \cdot t^3}{12} + b_{sl} \cdot t_{sl} \cdot e_1^2 +$$

$$+ \left(\left(\bar{b}_1 + \bar{b}_2\right)/2 + t_{sl,1}\right) \cdot t \cdot e_2^2 = \frac{100^3 \cdot 10}{12} +$$

2. Overview of Design Rules

$$+\frac{((595+590)/2+10)\cdot 12^3}{12}+100\cdot 10\cdot 49.2^2+$$

$$+((595+590)/2+10)\cdot 12\cdot 6.80^2 = 3.68\cdot 10^6 \text{ mm}^4,$$

$$a_c = 4.334\sqrt[4]{\frac{I_{sl,1}\cdot b_1^2\cdot b_2^2}{t^3\cdot b}} = 4.334\sqrt[4]{\frac{3.68\cdot 10^6\cdot 600^2\cdot 600^2}{12^3\cdot 1200}} = 2998 \text{ mm}.$$

As $a \leq a_c$ ($a = 1800$ mm), the column buckles in a 1-wave mode and the buckling stress is obtained as follows:

$$\sigma_{cr,sl} = \frac{\pi^2\cdot E\cdot I_{sl,1}}{A_{sl,1}\cdot a^2} + \frac{E\cdot t^3\cdot b\cdot a^2}{4\cdot \pi^2\cdot (1-v^2)\cdot A_{sl,1}\cdot b_1^2\cdot b_2^2} =$$

$$= \frac{\pi^2\cdot 210000\cdot 3.68\cdot 10^6}{8230\cdot 1800^2} + \frac{210000\cdot 12^3\cdot 1200\cdot 1800^2}{4\cdot \pi^2\cdot (1-v^2)\cdot 8230\cdot 600^2\cdot 600^2} =$$

$$= 322 \text{ N/mm}^2.$$

In case of a stress gradient over the plate width, the critical plate buckling stress should be properly interpolated from the position of the stiffener to the most stressed edge of the plate. In this case no stress gradient over the depth of the plate is present. Therefore, the critical plate buckling stress is equal to the critical stress calculated for the buckling of the stiffener on the elastic support:

$$\sigma_{cr,p}^I = \sigma_{cr,p}^{II} = \sigma_{cr,sl} = 322 \text{ N/mm}^2.$$

Lumped stiffener

$$b_{lumped,1} = b_{lumped,2} = 900 \text{ mm}, \quad b_{lumped} = 1800 \text{ mm},$$

$$A_{lumped} = A_{sl}^I + A_{sl}^{II} = 8230 + 8230 = 16460 \text{ mm}^4,$$

$$I_{lumped} = I_{sl}^I + I_{sl}^{II} = 3.675\cdot 10^6 + 3.675\cdot 10^6 = 7.35\cdot 10^6 \text{ mm}^4,$$

$$a_c = 4.334\sqrt[4]{\frac{I_{lumped}\cdot b_{lumped,1}^2\cdot b_{lumped,2}^2}{t^3\cdot b_{lumped}}} = 4.334\sqrt[4]{\frac{7.35\cdot 10^6\cdot 900^2\cdot 900^2}{12^3\cdot 1800}} =$$

= 4832 mm.

As $a \leq a_c$ ($a = 1800$ mm), the column buckles in a 1-wave mode and the buckling stress is obtained with equation:

$$\sigma_{cr,lumped} = \frac{\pi^2 \cdot E \cdot I_{lumped}}{A_{lumped} \cdot a^2} + \frac{E \cdot t^3 \cdot b_{lumped} \cdot a^2}{4 \cdot \pi^2 \cdot (1-v^2) \cdot A_{lumped} \cdot b_{lumped,1}^2 \cdot b_{lumped,2}^2} =$$

$$= \frac{\pi^2 \cdot 210000 \cdot 7.35 \cdot 10^6}{16460 \cdot 1800^2} + \frac{210000 \cdot 12^3 \cdot 1800 \cdot 1800^2}{4 \cdot \pi^2 \cdot (1-v^2) \cdot 16460 \cdot 900^2 \cdot 900^2} =$$

$$= 290 \text{ N/mm}^2.$$

$$\sigma_{cr,p}^{lumped} = \sigma_{cr,lumped} = 290 \text{ N/mm}^2.$$

$$\sigma_{cr,p} = \min\left[\sigma_{cr,p}^I, \sigma_{cr,p}^{lumped}\right] = \min[322, 290] = 290 \text{ N/mm}^2.$$

5 SUMMARY

The critical plate buckling stress was calculated by using: Klöppel diagrams, EBPlate software, FEM software and EN1993-1-5 rules. The results are summarised in Table 2.4.

A special case was chosen to demonstrate different calculation methods of critical plate buckling stress. All methods used in these calculations give very similar results. The maximum deviation compared to the lowest critical stress is 8.21%

Table 2.4: Results for elastic critical plate buckling stress

METHOD	[N/mm^2]	$\dfrac{\sigma_{cr,p} - \sigma_{cr,p,ABAQUS}}{\sigma_{cr,p,ABAQUS}} \cdot 100\,[\%]$
Klöppel	274	2.23
EBPlate- a)	276	2.99
EBPlate – b)	289	7.84
ABAQUS	268	/
EN1993-1-5 A.2	290	8.21

2. OVERVIEW OF DESIGN RULES

The stiffness of the stiffener was small in order to determine plate buckling stress according to Klöppel and also to find an appropriate buckling mode by using numerical tools. The calculation of the plate buckling stress using eigenvalue analysis leads to an unsolvable problem when the stiffeners are stronger. In these cases global modes are very difficult to detect due to a large number of local modes. By using the proposed method in EBPlate the global plate buckling mode can be easily obtained.

Example 2.4-4: Interpolation between plate-like and column-like buckling.

To interpolate between plate-like and column-like behaviour (see section 2.4.5) a parameter ξ (Eq.(2.38)) should be calculated:

$$\xi = \frac{\sigma_{cr.p}}{\sigma_{cr.c}} - 1, \text{ but } 0 \leq \xi \leq 1$$

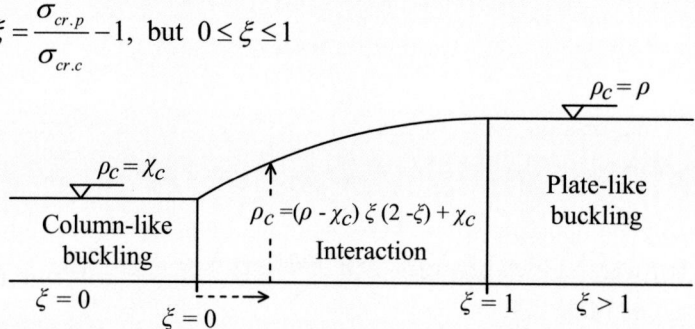

Fig. 2.39: Interpolation between plate-like and column-like behaviour

For unstiffened plates, Eqs. (2.17) and (2.32) may be used and ξ is then given as:

$$\xi = k_\sigma \alpha^2 - 1.0.$$

For longitudinally stiffened plates, Eqs. (2.27) and (2.34) give:

$$\xi = \frac{k_{\sigma,p} \alpha^2 (1+\delta)}{\gamma} - 1.0$$

where $I_{sl,1}$ and $A_{sl,1}$ in Eq. (2.34) were expressed in terms of parameters δ and γ that are defined below Eq. (2.28).

2.4 PLATE BUCKLING EFFECTS DUE TO DIRECT STRESSES

A typical behaviour of unstiffened and stiffened plates regarding the plate-like and column-like buckling interaction is demonstrated by two simple examples (Fig. 2.40):

- Unstiffened rectangular plate in pure compression
- Plate in pure compression stiffened with more than two longitudinal stiffeners

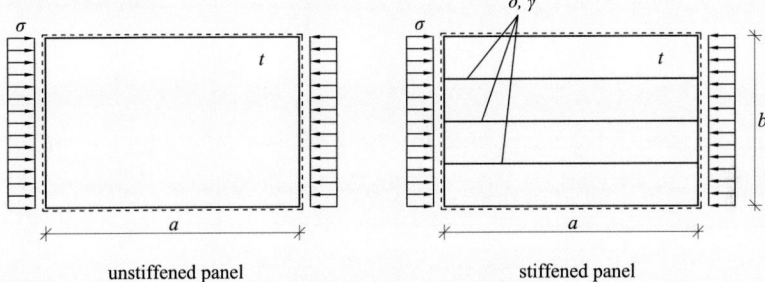

unstiffened panel   stiffened panel

Fig. 2.40: Unstiffened and stiffened plate

For pure compression, plate buckling coefficients and parameter ξ are defined as follows:

- Unstiffened plate:

$$k_\sigma = \left(\frac{m}{\alpha} + \frac{\alpha}{m}\right)^2$$

where m is the number of half buckles in the longitudinal direction

$m = 2$ for $\sqrt{2} < \alpha \le \sqrt{6}$

$m = 1$ for $\alpha \le \sqrt{2}$

$$\xi = \left(m + \frac{\alpha^2}{m}\right)^2 - 1.0$$

- Stiffened plate (Eq. (2.28)):

$$k_{\sigma.p} = \frac{\left(1+\alpha^2\right)^2 + \gamma - 1}{\alpha^2 (1+\delta)} \quad \text{if } \alpha \le \sqrt[4]{\gamma}$$

2. OVERVIEW OF DESIGN RULES

$$k_{\sigma.p} = \frac{2(1+\sqrt{\gamma})}{(1+\delta)} \quad \text{if } \alpha > \sqrt[4]{\gamma}$$

and

$$\xi = \frac{(1+\alpha^2)^2 + \gamma - 1}{\gamma} - 1.0 \quad \text{if } \alpha \leq \sqrt[4]{\gamma}$$

$$\xi = \frac{2(1+\sqrt{\gamma})\alpha^2}{\gamma} - 1.0 \quad \text{if } \alpha > \sqrt[4]{\gamma}$$

Values of parameter ξ are plotted in Fig. 2.41 as a function of α and γ. Note that ξ does not depend on δ or on the plate slenderness. When $\gamma = 1.0$, the plate is unstiffened, while $\gamma = 5$ or 10 means lightly stiffened plate, $30 \leq \gamma \leq 100$ normally stiffened plate and larger values of γ represent heavily stiffened plates.

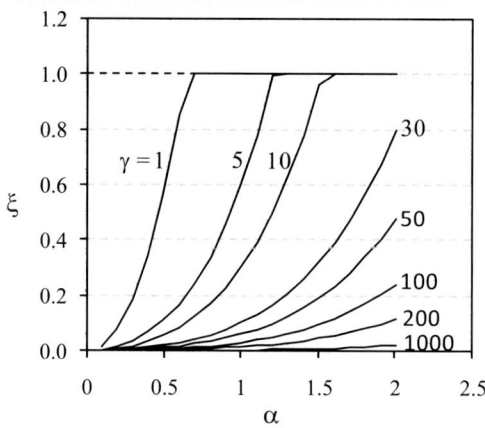

Fig. 2.41: Diagrams ξ - α at different level of stiffening (γ)

For very small aspect ratios α, parameter ξ is close to 0 for all cases and column-like buckling prevails. For an unstiffened plate ξ quickly rises and reaches the limiting value 1.0 at α around 0.7. This means that for $\alpha > 0.7$ an unstiffened plate behaves completely in a plate-like mode. For lightly stiffened plates plate-like behaviour prevails when α is somewhere between 1.0 and 1.5. Normally stiffened plates reach plate-like behaviour at much larger values of α, while heavily stiffened plates remain in the domain of column-like behaviour. Consequently, at realistic aspect ratios α, plate-like behaviour may be easily ignored for heavily stiffened and even for normally stiffened plates and column-like behaviour for unstiffened plates.

Example 2.4-5: Determination of deflection at serviceability limit state.

This numerical example shows the procedure for the determination of the effective characteristics of a cross section in order to check the serviceability limit state of unstiffened homogeneous plated girder.

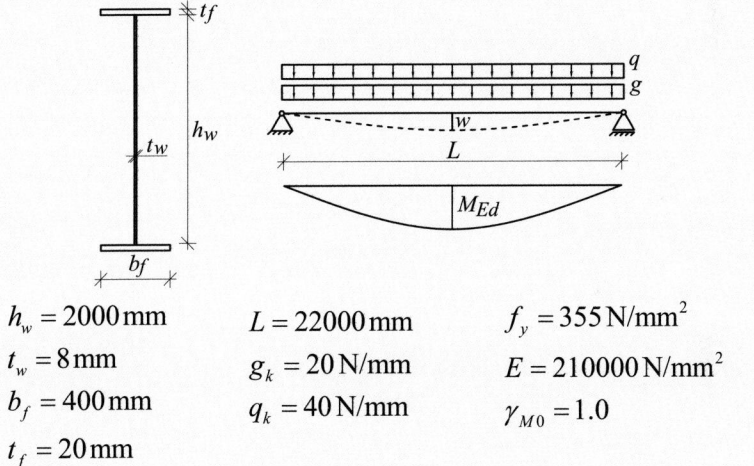

$h_w = 2000 \, \text{mm}$ $\qquad L = 22000 \, \text{mm} \qquad f_y = 355 \, \text{N/mm}^2$
$t_w = 8 \, \text{mm} \qquad\qquad g_k = 20 \, \text{N/mm} \qquad E = 210000 \, \text{N/mm}^2$
$b_f = 400 \, \text{mm} \qquad\;\, q_k = 40 \, \text{N/mm} \qquad \gamma_{M0} = 1.0$
$t_f = 20 \, \text{mm}$

Fig. 2.42: The outline of the plate girder, load and geometry of cross section

In order to determine the effective characteristics of the cross section as well as deformations of the plate girder the frequent combination of loads is used:

$$q_{Ed,ser} = g_k + \psi_1 \cdot q_k = 20 + 0.50 \cdot 40 = 40 \, \text{N/mm}$$

The bending moment for the determination of the maximum design compressive stress in the cross section is:

$$M_{Ed,y,ser} = \frac{q_{Ed,ser} \cdot L^2}{8} = \frac{40 \cdot 22000^2}{8} = 2.420 \cdot 10^9 \, \text{Nmm}$$

The geometrical characteristics of the gross cross section are:

2. Overview of Design Rules

$$A = 2 \cdot b_f \cdot t_f + h_w \cdot t_w = 2 \cdot 400 \cdot 20 + 2000 \cdot 8 = 32000.0 \, \text{mm}^2$$

$$r_T = \frac{h_w + t_f}{2} = \frac{2000 + 20}{2} = 1010.0 \, \text{mm}$$

$$I_y = 2 \cdot \left(\frac{b_f \cdot t_f^3}{12} + b_f \cdot t_f \cdot r_T^2 \right) + \frac{h_w^3 \cdot t_w}{12} =$$

$$= \left[2 \cdot \left(\frac{400 \cdot 20^3}{12} + 400 \cdot 20 \cdot 1010.0^2 \right) + \frac{2000^3 \cdot 8}{12} \right] = 2.166 \cdot 10^{10} \, \text{mm}^4$$

Section moduli $W_{y,1}$ and $W_{y,2}$ at the upper and lower edge of the web of cross section, respectively, are defined as:

$$W_{y,1} = W_{y,2} = \frac{I_y}{h_w / 2} = \frac{2.166 \cdot 10^{10}}{2000 / 2} = 2.166 \cdot 10^7 \, \text{mm}^3$$

Cross section class check

Upper flange (compression):

$$\frac{b_f / 2 - t_w / 2}{t_f} = \frac{400 / 2 - 8 / 2}{t_f} = 9.8 < 14 \cdot \varepsilon = 14 \cdot 0.814 = 11.4 \; (\text{Class 3})$$

Web (bending):

$$\frac{h_w}{t_w} = \frac{2000}{8} = 250 > 124 \cdot \varepsilon = 124 \cdot 0.814 = 100.9 \; (\text{Class 4})$$

The cross section is Class 4. As in Example 2.4-2 the weld throat size could be taken into accout in the cross section classification.

Calculation of the effective^p width of the girder's web is iterative:

1st iteration: gross cross section

The stress ratio determined on the gross cross section is $\psi_1 = -1.0$. Therefore, the buckling coefficient for the web of the girder is $k_{\sigma,1} = 23.9$.

$$\bar{\lambda}_{p,1} = \frac{h_w}{t_w \cdot 28.4 \cdot \varepsilon \cdot \sqrt{k_{\sigma,1}}} = \frac{2000}{8 \cdot 28.4 \cdot 0.814 \cdot \sqrt{23.9}} = 2.213$$

$$\bar{\lambda}_{p,1} = 2.213 > 0.5 + \sqrt{0.085 - 0.055 \cdot \psi_1} = 0.5 + \sqrt{0.085 + 0.055 \cdot 1} =$$

$$= 0.87$$

$$\rho_1 = \frac{\bar{\lambda}_{p,1} - 0.055 \cdot (3+\psi_1)}{\bar{\lambda}_{p,1}^2} = \frac{2.213 - 0.055 \cdot (3-1)}{2.213^2} = 0.429 < 1.0$$

$$b_{c,1} = \frac{h_w}{1-\psi_1} = \frac{2000}{1+1} = 1000 \text{ mm}$$

$$b_{eff,1} = \rho_1 \cdot b_{c,1} = 0.429 \cdot 1000 = 429.4 \text{ mm}$$

$$b_{e1,1} = 0.4 \cdot b_{eff,1} = 0.4 \cdot 429.4 = 171.8 \text{ mm}$$

$$b_{e2,1} = 0.6 \cdot b_{eff,1} = 0.6 \cdot 429.4 = 257.6 \text{ mm}$$

$$x_{w,1} = b_{c,1} - b_{eff,1} = 1000 - 429.4 = 570.6 \text{ mm}$$

The calculation of the geometrical characteristics of the effective cross section should be determined as follows:

$$\Delta A_1 = x_w \cdot t_w = 570.6 \cdot 8 = 4564.9 \text{ mm}^2$$

$$A_{eff,1} = A - \Delta A_1 = 32000 - 4564.9 = 27435.2 \text{ mm}^2$$

$$r_1 = \frac{h_w}{2} - b_{e1} - \frac{x_w}{2} = \frac{2000}{2} - 171.8 - \frac{570.6}{2} = 542.9 \text{ mm}$$

$$\Delta r_{T,1} = \frac{r_1 \cdot \Delta A_1}{A_{eff,1}} = \frac{542.9 \cdot 4564.9}{27435.2} = 90.3 \text{ mm}$$

The distance between the centroid of the lower flange to the centroid of the effective cross section $r_{Teff,1}$ can be expressed as:

$$r_{Teff,1} = r_{T,1} - \Delta r_{T,1} = 1010.0 - 90.3 = 919.7 \text{ mm}$$

2. OVERVIEW OF DESIGN RULES

The second moment of area of the effective cross section becomes:

$$I_{eff,y,1} = I_y + A \cdot \Delta r_{T,1}^2 - \left(\frac{x_w^3 \cdot t_w}{12} + \Delta A_1 \cdot (r_1 + \Delta r_{T,1})^2 \right) =$$

$$= \left[\begin{array}{l} 2.166 \cdot 10^{10} + 32000 \cdot 90.3^2 - \\ - \left(\dfrac{570.6^3 \cdot 8}{12} + 4564.9 \cdot (542.9 + 90.3)^2 \right) \end{array} \right]$$

$$= 1.996 \cdot 10^{10} \text{ mm}^4$$

Effective section moduli $W^{(1)}_{eff,y,1}$ and $W^{(1)}_{eff,y,2}$ at the upper and lower edge of the web of effective cross section, respectively, are defined as:

$$W^{(1)}_{eff,y,1} = \frac{I_{eff,y,1}}{h_w + \dfrac{t_f}{2} - r_{Teff,1}} = \frac{1.996 \cdot 10^{10}}{2000 + \dfrac{20}{2} - 919.7} = 1.831 \cdot 10^7 \text{ mm}^3$$

$$W^{(1)}_{eff,y,2} = \frac{I_{eff,y,1}}{r_{Teff,1} - \dfrac{t_f}{2}} = \frac{1.996 \cdot 10^{10}}{919.7 - \dfrac{20}{2}} = 2.194 \cdot 10^7 \text{ mm}^3$$

Effective section modulus $W^{(1)}_{eff,y}$ is defined as the lower value of $W^{(1)}_{eff,y,1}$ and $W^{(1)}_{eff,y,2}$:

$$W^{(1)}_{eff,y} = \min\left[W_{eff,y,1}, W_{eff,y,2} \right] =$$

$$= \min[1.831, 2.194] \cdot 10^7 = 1.830 \cdot 10^7 \text{ mm}^3$$

2nd iteration:

$$\psi_2 = \frac{W^{(1)}_{eff,y,1}}{W^{(1)}_{eff,y,2}} = -\frac{1.831 \cdot 10^7}{2.194 \cdot 10^7} = -0.834$$

$$k_{\sigma,2} = 7.81 - 6.29 \cdot \psi_2 + 9.78 \cdot \psi_2^2 =$$

$$= 7.81 + 6.29 \cdot 0.834 + 9.78 \cdot 0.834^2 = 19.928$$

$$\bar{\lambda}_{p,2} = \frac{h_w}{t_w \cdot 28.4 \cdot \varepsilon \cdot \sqrt{k_{\sigma,2}}} = \frac{2000}{8 \cdot 28.4 \cdot 0.814 \cdot \sqrt{19.928}} = 2.424$$

$$\sigma_{com,Ed,ser,2} = \frac{M_{y,Ed,ser}}{W_{eff,y}^{(1)}} = \frac{2.420 \cdot 10^9}{1.830 \cdot 10^7} = 132.2 \, \text{N/mm}^2,$$

where

$\sigma_{com,Ed,ser,2}$ — is the largest compressive stress, calculated on the basis of the effective cross section after the first iteration, under service load calculated on the upper edge of the web.

$$\bar{\lambda}_{p,ser,2} = \bar{\lambda}_{p,2} \cdot \sqrt{\frac{\sigma_{com,Ed,ser,2}}{f_y}} = 2.424 \cdot \sqrt{\frac{132.2}{355}} = 1.479$$

$$\rho_{ser,2} = \frac{1 - 0.055 \cdot (3 + \psi_2)/\bar{\lambda}_{p,ser,2}}{\bar{\lambda}_{p,ser,2}} + 0.18 \cdot \frac{\bar{\lambda}_{p,2} - \bar{\lambda}_{p,ser,2}}{\bar{\lambda}_{p,2} - 0.6} =$$

$$= \frac{1 - 0.055 \cdot (3 - 0.834)/1.479}{1.479} + 0.18 \cdot \frac{2.424 - 1.479}{2.424 - 0.6} = 0.715 < 1.0$$

$$b_{c,ser,2} = \frac{h_w}{1 - \psi_2} = \frac{2000}{1 + 0.834} = 1090.3 \, \text{mm}$$

$$b_{eff,ser,2} = \rho_{ser,2} \cdot b_{c,ser,2} = 0.715 \cdot 1090.3 = 779.5 \, \text{mm}$$

$$b_{e1,ser,2} = 0.4 \cdot b_{eff,ser,2} = 0.4 \cdot 779.5 = 311.8 \, \text{mm}$$

$$b_{e2,ser,2} = 0.6 \cdot b_{eff,ser,2} = 0.6 \cdot 779.5 = 467.7 \, \text{mm}$$

$$x_{w,ser,2} = b_{c,ser,2} - b_{eff,ser,2} = 1090.3 - 779.5 = 310.8 \, \text{mm}$$

Calculation of the geometrical characteristics of the effective cross section is done in the same way as in the first iteration. The results are summarised below:

$$W_{eff,y,1}^{(2)} = 1.997 \cdot 10^7 \, \text{mm}^3, \, W_{eff,y,2}^{(2)} = 2.185 \cdot 10^7 \, \text{mm}^3$$

$$W_{eff,y}^{(2)} = 1.997 \cdot 10^7 \text{ mm}^3, \quad I_{eff,y,2} = 2.087 \cdot 10^{10} \text{ mm}^4$$

3rd iteration:

$$\sigma_{com,Ed,ser,3} = \frac{M_{y,Ed,ser}}{W_{eff,y}^{(2)}} = \frac{2.420 \cdot 10^9}{1.997 \cdot 10^7} = 121.2 \text{ N/mm}^2$$

$$W_{eff,y}^{(3)} = 2.033 \cdot 10^7 \text{ mm}^3, \quad I_{eff,y,3} = 2.103 \cdot 10^{10} \text{ mm}^4$$

4th iteration:

$$\sigma_{com,Ed,ser,4} = \frac{M_{y,Ed,ser}}{W_{eff,y}^{(3)}} = \frac{2.420 \cdot 10^9}{2.033 \cdot 10^7} = 119.1 \text{ N/mm}^2$$

$$W_{eff,y}^{(4)} = 2.041 \cdot 10^7 \text{ mm}^3, \quad I_{eff,y,4} = 2.107 \cdot 10^{10} \text{ mm}^4$$

5th iteration:

$$\sigma_{com,Ed,ser,5} = \frac{M_{y,Ed,ser}}{W_{eff,y}^{(4)}} = \frac{2.420 \cdot 10^9}{2.041 \cdot 10^7} = 118.6 \text{ N/mm}^2$$

$$W_{eff,y}^{(5)} = 2.043 \cdot 10^7 \text{ mm}^3, \quad I_{eff,y,5} = 2.108 \cdot 10^{10} \text{ mm}^4$$

6th iteration:

Results for $\sigma_{com,Ed,ser}$ and $I_{eff,y,6}$ are shown below:

$$\sigma_{com,Ed,ser,6} = \frac{M_{y,Ed,ser}}{W_{eff,y}^{(5)}} = \frac{2.420 \cdot 10^9}{2.043 \cdot 10^7} = 118.5 \text{ N/mm}^2$$

$$I_{eff,y,6} = 2.108 \cdot 10^{10} \text{ mm}^4$$

By comparing the results of performed iterations, $\sigma_{com,Ed,ser}$ and $I_{eff,y}$ coverge to the required tolerance after the 6th iteration.

Finally, the second moment of area $I_{eff,y,ser}$ is calculated by an interpolation between the gross cross section and the effective cross section (computed after the 6th iteration) for the frequent combination of the serviceability limit state:

$$I_{eff,y,ser} = I_{gr,y} - \frac{\sigma_{gr}}{\sigma_{com,Ed,ser}} \cdot \left(I_{gr,y} - I_{eff,y}\left(\sigma_{com,Ed,ser}\right)\right)$$

$$\sigma_{com,Ed,ser} = \sigma_{com,Ed,6} = 118.5 \text{ N/mm}^2$$

$$I_{gr,y} = I_y = 2.166 \cdot 10^{10} \text{ mm}^4$$

$$\sigma_{gr} = \frac{M_{Ed,y,ser}}{W_y} = \frac{2.420 \cdot 10^9}{2.166 \cdot 10^7} = 111.8 \text{ N/mm}^2,$$

where

$I_{gr,y}$ – is the second moment of area of the gross cross section with respect to y-y axis,

σ_{gr} – is the maximum bending stress at serviceability limit state based on the gross cross section,

$I_{eff,y}(\sigma_{com,Ed,ser})$ – is the second moment of area of the effective cross section with allowance for local buckling according to EC 1993-1-5, Annex E, calculated for the maximum stress $\sigma_{com,Ed,ser} \geq \sigma_{gr}$ within the span.

$$I_{eff,y,ser} = 2.166 \cdot 10^{10} - \frac{111.8}{118.5} \cdot (2.166 - 2.108) \cdot 10^{10} = 2.111 \cdot 10^{10} \text{ mm}^4$$

The vertical deflection of the simply supported plated girder is defined as follows:

$$w = \frac{5 \cdot q_{Ed,ser} \cdot L^4}{384 \cdot E \cdot I_{eff,y,ser}} = \frac{5 \cdot 40 \cdot 22000^4}{384 \cdot 210000 \cdot 2.111 \cdot 10^{10}} = 27.5 \text{ mm}$$

As an alternative, a more practical one-step procedure may be used, where a conservative value of $\sigma_{com,Ed,ser}$ (for frequent load combination of SLS) is assumed:

$$\sigma_{com,Ed,ser} \geq f_y \cdot \frac{g + \psi_1 \cdot q}{1.35 \cdot g + 1.5 \cdot q} = f_y \cdot \frac{20 + 0.5 \cdot 40}{1.35 \cdot 20 + 1.5 \cdot 40} =$$

2. Overview of Design Rules

$$\geq 0.460 \cdot f_y = 163.3 \text{ N/mm}^2$$

In the case of a full utilisation at the ultimate limit state the proposed assumption for the stress $\sigma_{com,Ed,ser}$ leads to a fairly good guess, otherwise the result is somewhat conservative.

The stress ratio determined on the gross cross section is $\psi = -1.0$. Therefore, the buckling coefficient for the web of the girder is $k_\sigma = 23.9$.

$$\overline{\lambda} = \overline{\lambda}_{p,1} = 2.213$$

$$\overline{\lambda}_{p,ser} = \overline{\lambda}_p \cdot \sqrt{\frac{\sigma_{com,Ed,ser}}{f_y}} = 2.213 \cdot \sqrt{\frac{163.3}{355}} = 1.501$$

$$\rho_{ser} = \frac{1 - 0.055 \cdot (3+\psi)/\overline{\lambda}_{p,ser}}{\overline{\lambda}_{p,ser}} + 0.18 \cdot \frac{\overline{\lambda}_p - \overline{\lambda}_{p,ser}}{\overline{\lambda}_p - 0.6} =$$

$$= \frac{1 - 0.055 \cdot (3-1)/1.501}{1.501} + 0.18 \cdot \frac{2.213 - 1.501}{2.213 - 0.6} = 0.697 < 1.0$$

$$b_{c,ser} = \frac{h_w}{1-\psi} = \frac{2000}{1+1} = 1000.0 \text{ mm}$$

$$b_{eff,ser} = \rho_{ser} \cdot b_{c,ser} = 0.697 \cdot 1000.0 = 696.9 \text{ mm}$$

$$b_{e1,ser} = 0.4 \cdot b_{eff,ser} = 0.4 \cdot 696.9 = 278.7 \text{ mm}$$

$$b_{e2,ser} = 0.6 \cdot b_{eff,ser} = 0.6 \cdot 696.9 = 418.1 \text{ mm}$$

$I_{eff,y,ser}$ of the effective cross section:

$$I_{eff,y,ser} = 2.079 \cdot 10^{10} \text{ mm}^4$$

Vertical deflection of the girder:

$$w = \frac{5 \cdot q_{Ed,ser} \cdot L^4}{384 \cdot E \cdot I_{eff,y,ser}} = \frac{5 \cdot 40 \cdot 22000^4}{384 \cdot 210000 \cdot 2.079 \cdot 10^{10}} = 28.0 \text{ mm}$$

The result obtained by the simplified one-step procedure is in this particular numerical example very close to that of the more elaborated iterative procedure. With a good guess for $\sigma_{com,Ed,ser}$ the results generally do not differ much.

2.5 RESISTANCE TO SHEAR (INCLUDING ANNEX A WHERE APPLICABLE)

2.5.1 Collapse behaviour

The behaviour of plates under shear comprises two phenomena: the state of pure shear stress and the tension field. Prior to buckling, pure shear stresses occur in the plate. If these shear stresses τ are transformed into principal stresses, they correspond to principal tensile stresses σ_1 and principal compressive stresses σ_2 with equal magnitude and inclined by 45° with regard to the longitudinal axis of the girder. Only constant shear stresses occur at the edges, see Fig. 2.43a).

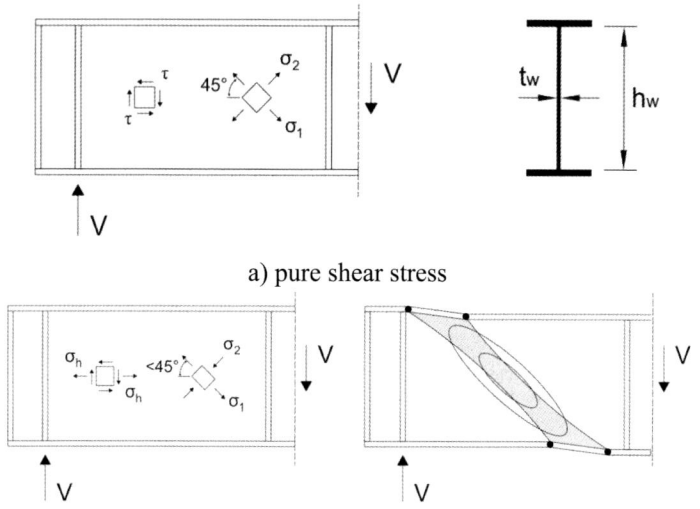

a) pure shear stress

b) tension field action   c) plastic hinge flange mechanism
Fig. 2.43: Stress states and collapse behaviour of a plate girder subjected to shear

2. OVERVIEW OF DESIGN RULES

As for plates subjected to direct compressive stress, slender plates under shear possess a post-critical reserve. After buckling, the plate reaches the post-critical stress state, while a shear buckle forms in the direction of the principal tensile stresses σ_1. Due to buckling, no significant increase of the stresses in the direction of the principal compressive stresses σ_2 is possible, whereas the principal tensile stresses can still increase. As a result, stress values of different magnitude occur (tension > compression), which lead to a rotation of the stress field for equilibrium reasons and which is denoted tension field action, see Fig. 2.43b). The development of such a tensile force is only possible if the boundary elements provide a sufficient anchorage for the axial forces. However, it can be shown that intermediate transverse stiffeners are not needed for the development of the tension field but they are practically always needed at the supports. The maximum amount of axial force which can be carried depends on the extensional stiffness and flexural rigidity of the boundary elements. Since the flanges restrain the relative deformation of the transverse stiffener to each other, the tension field can be anchored. When reaching ultimate load, a plastic hinge mechanism forms in the flange, see Fig. 2.43c).

2.5.2 Design according to section 5, EN 1993-1-5

There are many tension field theories which aim to describe the ultimate resistance of plates under shear, see Johansson et al (2007) for further details. In EN 1993-1-5 the rotated stress field theory proposed by Höglund (1981) was adopted. It was initially developed for unstiffened plates with large panel aspect ratios ($\alpha > 3$) because other existing models led to very conservative results in this case. In EN 1993-1-5 the rotated stress field theory was generally accepted, since it provides adequate results regardless of the panel aspect ratio. In this method, the shear resistance $V_{b,Rd}$ comprises contributions from the web $V_{bw,Rd}$ and from the flanges $V_{bf,Rd}$, see Eq. (2.47). However, the full shear resistance $V_{b,Rd}$ can never be larger than the plastic shear resistance of the web alone.

$$V_{b,Rd} = V_{bw,Rd} + V_{bf,Rd} \leq h_w \cdot t_w \cdot \frac{\eta \cdot f_{yw}}{\sqrt{3} \cdot \gamma_{M1}} \tag{2.47}$$

where

$V_{bw,Rd}$	resistance from the web according to Eq. (2.51)
$V_{bf,Rd}$	resistance from flanges according to Eq. (2.61)
h_w	web depth
t_w	web thickness
η	factor depending on the steel grade according to Eq. (2.54)
f_{yw}	web yield strength
γ_{M1}	partial safety factor

The verification of a girder subjected to shear reads as follows:

$$\eta_3 = \frac{V_{Ed}}{V_{b,Rd}} \leq 1.0 \qquad (2.48)$$

where

V_{Ed}	design shear force
$V_{b,Rd}$	design resistance to shear according to Eq. (2.47)

The resistance to shear buckling has to be verified whenever the ratio of web depth h_w and web thickness t_w is larger than the following values:

- For unstiffened webs

$$\frac{h_w}{t_w} > 72 \cdot \frac{\varepsilon}{\eta} \qquad (2.49)$$

- For stiffened webs

$$\frac{h_w}{t_w} > 31 \cdot \frac{\varepsilon}{\eta} \cdot \sqrt{k_\tau} \qquad (2.50)$$

where k_τ is the shear buckling coefficient and $\varepsilon = \sqrt{\dfrac{235}{f_y \, [\text{N/mm}^2]}}$

If these limits are exceeded, the girder should be provided with transverse stiffeners at the supports.

2. Overview of Design Rules

Contribution from the web

The contribution of the web is determined according to Eq. (2.51).

$$V_{bw,Rd} = \chi_w \cdot h_w \cdot t_w \cdot \frac{f_{yw}}{\sqrt{3} \cdot \gamma_{M1}} \qquad (2.51)$$

where χ_w is the reduction factor for shear buckling.

The reduction factor χ_w considers components of pure shear and anchorage of membrane forces by transverse stiffeners due to tension field action. Since the axial and flexural stiffness of the transverse end stiffeners influence the post-critical reserve, Eqs. (2.52) and (2.53) distinguish between non-rigid and rigid end posts in the determination of the reduction factor χ_w, see Fig. 2.44. Requirements for rigid end posts are given in sub-section 2.9.2.2.

- Non-rigid end post

$$\chi_w = \eta \quad \text{for} \quad \overline{\lambda}_w < \frac{0.83}{\eta}$$
$$\chi_w = \frac{0.83}{\overline{\lambda}_w} \quad \text{for} \quad \overline{\lambda}_w \geq \frac{0.83}{\eta} \qquad (2.52)$$

- Rigid end post

$$\chi_w = \eta \quad \text{for} \quad \overline{\lambda}_w < \frac{0.83}{\eta}$$
$$\chi_w = \frac{0.83}{\overline{\lambda}_w} \quad \text{for} \quad \frac{0.83}{\eta} \leq \overline{\lambda}_w < 1.08 \qquad (2.53)$$
$$\chi_w = \frac{1.37}{0.7 + \overline{\lambda}_w} \quad \text{for} \quad \overline{\lambda}_w \geq 1.08$$

As shown in Fig. 2.44, $\chi_w = \eta$ is defined for a small slenderness with a η-value larger than 1 according to Eq. (2.54). Tests on stocky beams showed that the shear capacity can reach 70 % to 80 % of the tensile yield strength, which corresponds approximately to the increase of 20 % of the shear yield strength. It is attributed to strain hardening which can be tolerated in this case since it does not lead to excessive deformations. Evidence is available for steel grades up to S460. Note that National Annexes can give different η-values, also depending on the field of application. The recommended values for η according to EN 1993-1-5 are:

for $f_y \leq 460$ N/mm²: $\eta = 1.2$ (2.54)

for $f_y > 460$ N/mm²: $\eta = 1.0$

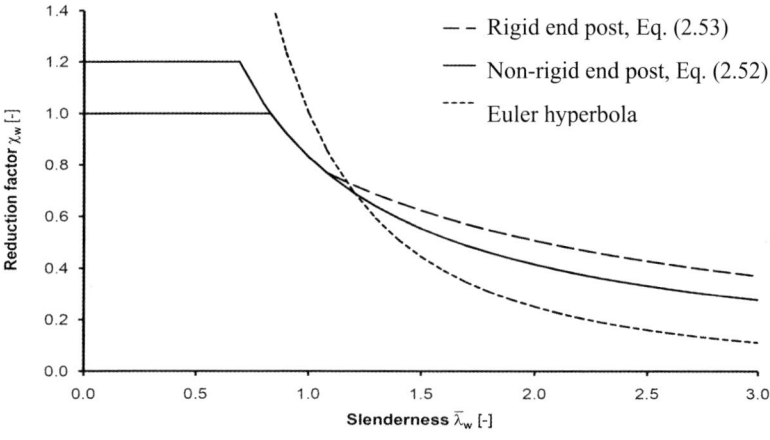

Fig. 2.44: Reduction curves for shear buckling

The reduction curves according to Eqs. (2.52) and (2.53) apply for the verification of both unstiffened and stiffened webs. They are based on the plate slenderness $\overline{\lambda}_w$. In case of a stiffened panel, the largest value of the slenderness $\overline{\lambda}_w$ of all sub-panels and the stiffened panel governs. $\overline{\lambda}_w$ is determined according to Eq. (2.55).

$$\overline{\lambda}_w = \sqrt{\frac{f_{yw}/\sqrt{3}}{\tau_{cr}}} = 0.76 \cdot \sqrt{\frac{f_{yw}}{\tau_{cr}}} \quad \text{with } \tau_{cr} = k_\tau \cdot \sigma_E \quad (2.55)$$

For the calculation of $\overline{\lambda}_w$, Eq. (2.55) can be further simplified to Eqs. (2.56) and (2.57).

2. OVERVIEW OF DESIGN RULES

- For transverse stiffeners at supports only

$$\overline{\lambda}_w = \frac{h_w}{86.4 \cdot t_w \cdot \varepsilon} \qquad (2.56)$$

- For transverse stiffeners at supports, intermediate stiffeners or longitudinal stiffeners or both

$$\overline{\lambda}_w = \max\left(\frac{h_w}{37.4 \cdot t_w \cdot \varepsilon \cdot \sqrt{k_\tau}}; \frac{h_{wi}}{37.4 \cdot t_w \cdot \varepsilon \cdot \sqrt{k_{\tau i}}}\right) \qquad (2.57)$$

where
- k_τ shear buckling coefficient of the web between flanges
- $k_{\tau,i}$ shear buckling coefficient of sub-panels i
- h_w clear web depth between flanges
- h_{wi} clear depth of sub-panels i

In Annex A.3, EN 1993-1-5, formulas for the hand calculation of the shear buckling coefficient k_τ for plates are given as shown below. Alternatively, buckling charts and advanced software may be used.

- For panels without longitudinal stiffeners such as sub-panels of stiffened panels or
- For panels with rigid transverse stiffeners only

$$k_\tau = 4.00 + 5.34 \cdot \left(\frac{h_w}{a}\right)^2 \quad \text{for} \quad \frac{a}{h_w} < 1.0$$

$$k_\tau = 5.34 + 4.00 \cdot \left(\frac{h_w}{a}\right)^2 \quad \text{for} \quad \frac{a}{h_w} \geq 1.0 \qquad (2.58)$$

- For stiffened panels with one or two longitudinal stiffeners and $\alpha = a/h_w < 3.0$

$$k_\tau = 4.1 + \frac{6.3 + 0.18 \cdot \frac{I_{s\ell}}{t^3 \cdot h_w}}{\alpha^2} + 2.2 \cdot \sqrt[3]{\frac{I_{s\ell}}{t^3 \cdot h_w}} \qquad (2.59)$$

2.5 Resistance to Shear

- For stiffened panels with one or two longitudinal stiffeners and $\alpha = a/h_w \geq 3.0$

or

for stiffened panels with more than two longitudinal stiffeners

$$k_\tau = 4.00 + 5.34 \cdot \left(\frac{h_w}{a}\right)^2 + k_{ts\ell} \quad \text{for} \quad \frac{a}{h_w} < 1.0$$

$$k_\tau = 5.34 + 4.00 \cdot \left(\frac{h_w}{a}\right)^2 + k_{ts\ell} \quad \text{for} \quad \frac{a}{h_w} \geq 1.0$$

(2.60)

with

$$k_{ts\ell} = 9 \cdot \left(\frac{h_w}{a}\right)^2 \cdot \sqrt[4]{\left(\frac{I_{s\ell}}{t^3 \cdot h_w}\right)^3} > \frac{2.1}{t} \cdot \sqrt[3]{\frac{I_{s\ell}}{h_w}}$$

The second moment of area $I_{s\ell}$ is determined with an effective plate width of $15 \cdot \varepsilon \cdot t$ on each side of the stiffener, see Fig. 2.45, up to the maximum existing geometrical width without overlapping parts. $I_{s\ell}$ is determined for buckling perpendicular to the plane of the plate. For stiffened panels with two or more longitudinal stiffeners, $I_{s\ell}$ is the sum of all individual stiffeners regardless of whether they have an equidistant spacing or not.

In order to apply the buckling curves according to Eqs. (2.52) and (2.53) for a stiffened panel, a reduction of the moment of inertia of the longitudinal stiffener $I_{s\ell,1}$ to 1/3 of its actual value is required when calculating k_τ. This accounts for the reduced post-critical reserve of stiffened panels in comparison to unstiffened plates. Eqs. (2.59) and (2.60) already consider the 1/3-reduction of the moment of inertia of the longitudinal stiffener. However, current research results (Pavlovčič et al, 2007; Kuhlmann et al, 2007) show that such a reduction is only necessary for stiffeners with a small torsional rigidity, e.g. flat bar stiffeners. Regarding longitudinal stiffeners with a large torsional rigidity, e.g. trapezoidally shaped stiffeners, the actual value of the moment of inertia can be taken into account.

Where intermediate non-rigid transverse stiffeners are used, EN 1993-

2. OVERVIEW OF DESIGN RULES

1-5 provides verification schemes, but no formulas are given to determine the shear buckling coefficients for girders with non-rigid transverse stiffener other than at supports. In this case e. g. adequate software could be used. In modern steel structures intermediate non-rigid transverse stiffeners are not applied in practice at all, since the increase of shear resistance may be very low. Even intermediate rigid transverse stiffeners usually do not pay off if shear resistance and reduction of web thickness are traded against additional cost of welding.

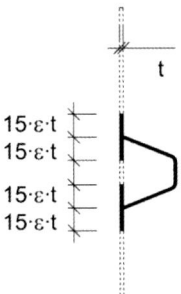

Fig. 2.45: Effective cross section of stiffener (trapezoidal shape)

Contribution from the flanges

The contribution from the flanges can be accounted for according to Eq. (2.61) which assumes the formation of four plastic hinges in the flanges at a distance c, see Fig. 2.46.

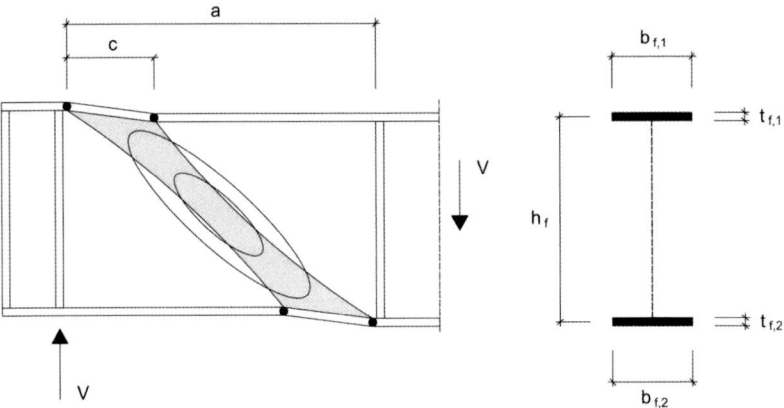

Fig. 2.46: Anchorage of the tension field in the flanges

2.5 Resistance to Shear

$$V_{bf,Rd} = \frac{b_f \cdot t_f^2}{c} \cdot \frac{f_{yf}}{\gamma_{M1}} \left[1 - \left(\frac{M_{Ed}}{M_{f,Rd}}\right)^2\right] \quad (2.61)$$

where

$$c = a \cdot \left(0.25 + \frac{1.6 \cdot b_f \cdot t_f^2 \cdot f_{yf}}{t_w \cdot h_w^2 \cdot f_{yw}}\right) \quad (2.62)$$

In Eqs. (2.61) to (2.64) b_f and t_f are the dimensions of the flange with the least axial resistance where b_f should not exceed $15 \cdot \varepsilon \cdot t$ on each side of the web. The contribution from the flanges is reduced if they resist longitudinal stresses due to normal force N_{Ed} or bending moment M_{Ed}, see the last term of Eq. (2.61). The design bending moment resistance $M_{f,Rd}$ consists of a cross section with the effective area of the flanges only, see Fig. 2.46. $M_{f,Rd}$ is reduced according to Eq. (2.64) in case a normal force N_{Ed} is also acting. The required $M_{f,k}$ is determined according to Eq. (2.63) and Fig. 2.46.

$$M_{f,k} = \min\left(A_{f,1} \cdot f_{yf,1} \cdot h_f ; A_{f,2} \cdot f_{yf,2} \cdot h_f\right) \quad (2.63)$$

where

$A_{f,1}$ = $b_{f,1} \cdot t_{f,1}$ cross sectional area of flange 1
$A_{f,2}$ = $b_{f,2} \cdot t_{f,2}$ cross sectional area of flange 2
$f_{yf,1}$ yield strength of flange 1
$f_{yf,2}$ yield strength of flange 2
h_f distance between mid-plane of flanges

Thus, Eq. (2.61) considers an interaction between shear force, bending moment and normal force for $M_{Ed} < M_{f,Rd}$. For $M_{Ed} > M_{f,Rd}$, see sub-chapter 2.7.

$$M_{f,Rd} = \frac{M_{f,k}}{\gamma_{M0}} \cdot \left[1 - \frac{N_{Ed}}{\left(A_{f1} + A_{f2}\right) \cdot \dfrac{f_{yf}}{\gamma_{M0}}}\right] \quad (2.64)$$

2. Overview of Design Rules

For areas with a high utilisation level due to normal force and bending moment, the determination of $V_{bf,Rd}$ can be neglected in practical application because the main resistance to shear comes from the web contribution $V_{bw,Rd}$.

2.5.3 Design example

Example 2.5-1: Shear resistance of unstiffened plated girder.

The geometry and the basic parameters of the gross cross section of the longitudinally unstiffened plated girder as well as support conditions are shown in Fig. 2.32.

$$V_{Ed} = 761 \cdot 10^3 \text{ N}$$

The unstiffened web of the cross section has a ratio $d/t_w = 138.9$, which is larger than $72 \cdot \varepsilon/\eta = 48.8$. Therefore, it should be checked for resistance to shear buckling and should be provided with transverse stiffener at the supports.

For the unstiffened web, the design resistance for shear should be taken as:

$$V_{b,Rd} = V_{bw,Rd} + V_{bf,Rd} \leq \frac{\eta \cdot f_{yw} \cdot d \cdot t_w}{\sqrt{3} \cdot \gamma_{M1}}$$

Calculation of the contribution from the web considering a non-rigid end post:

$$\bar{\lambda}_w = \frac{d}{86.4 \cdot t_w \cdot \varepsilon} = \frac{1388.7}{86.4 \cdot 10 \cdot 0.814} = 1.975$$

$$\bar{\lambda}_w = 1.975 > 1.08 \quad \Rightarrow \quad \chi_w = \frac{0.83}{\bar{\lambda}_w} = \frac{0.83}{1.975} = 0.420$$

$$V_{bw,Rd} = \frac{\chi_w \cdot f_{yw} \cdot d \cdot t_w}{\sqrt{3} \cdot \gamma_{M1}} = \frac{0.420 \cdot 355 \cdot 1388.7 \cdot 10}{\sqrt{3} \cdot 1.1} = 1.087 \cdot 10^6 \text{ N}$$

Calculation of the contribution from the flanges:

Since the web is transversely stiffened only at supports, the contribution from the flanges is assumed to be negligible:

$$V_{bf,Rd} = 0$$

Total resistance and verification check:

Therefore, the design shear resistance is:

$$V_{b,Rd} = V_{bw,Rd} + V_{bf,Rd} = 1.087 \cdot 10^6 + 0 = 1.087 \cdot 10^6 \text{ N}$$

$$V_{b,Rd} = 1.087 \cdot 10^6 \text{ N} \leq \frac{\eta \cdot f_{yw} dt_w}{\sqrt{3} \cdot \gamma_{M1}} \leq \frac{1.2 \cdot 355 \cdot 1388.7 \cdot 10}{\sqrt{3} \cdot 1.1} = 3.105 \cdot 10^6 \text{ N}$$

Because the web slenderness is large, the last check is not relevant and may be omitted.

The verification of the shear resistance should be performed as follows:

$$\eta_3 = \frac{V_{Ed}}{V_{b,Rd}} = \frac{761000}{1.087 \cdot 10^6} = 0.7 < 1.0$$

2.6 RESISTANCE TO TRANSVERSE LOADING

2.6.1 Collapse behaviour

Transverse loading denotes a load which is applied perpendicular to the flange in the plane of the web. The loading is usually free and transient, as for crane runway girders or bridge girders during launching, so that in this case transverse stiffeners are not appropriate. A concentrated transverse loading is often referred to as patch loading.

The collapse behaviour of girders subjected to transverse loading is characterised by three failure modes: yielding, buckling or crippling of the web, see Fig. 2.47. In reality, however, no accurate separation of these phenomena is possible so that an individual treatment of each of them is not reasonable. There are many parameters which influence the ultimate load capacity, such as geometry and material strength ratio of flange and web.

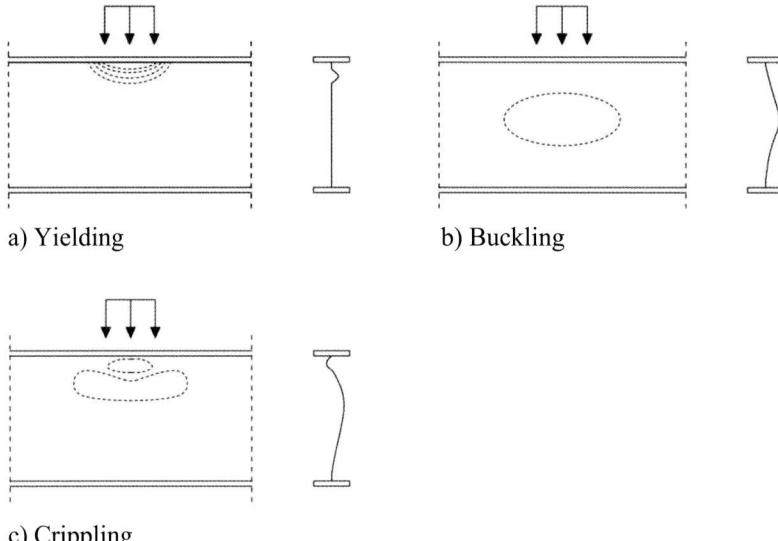

a) Yielding

b) Buckling

c) Crippling

Fig. 2.47: Schematic failure modes of girders subjected to transverse loading

2.6.2 Design according to section 6, EN 1993-1-5

While in ENV 1993-1-1 (CEN, 1993) separate verifications had to be performed for yielding, buckling or crippling of the web and the lowest resistance governs, in EN 1993-1-5 these verifications were merged into a single verification based on Lagerqvist (1994) and Lagerqvist and Johansson (Lagerqvist and Johansson, 1996). Their approach presumes that the load is introduced into the plate via the flanges, thus it should not be applied to single plates under patch load. The rules of section 6, EN 1993-1-5 (CEN, 2006a), cover both rolled and welded girders, with and without longitudinal stiffeners, up to steel grades of S690. It is assumed that the compression flange has an adequate lateral and torsional restraint, which needs to be taken into account when designing e.g. the launching shoes for bridge launching. EN 1993-1-5 covers three different types of transverse load application:

- Load application through one flange, see Fig. 2.48a)

- Load application through both flanges, see Fig. 2.48b)
- Load application through one flange adjacent to an unstiffened end, see Fig. 2.48c)

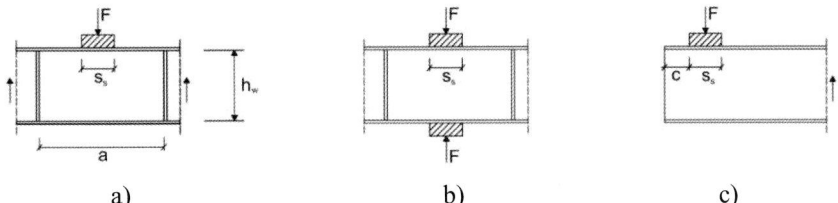

Fig. 2.48: Types of transverse load application

The verification of a girder subject to transverse forces is:

$$\eta_2 = \frac{F_{Ed}}{F_{Rd}} \leq 1 \qquad (2.65)$$

where

F_{Ed} design transverse loading over the length s_s

F_{Rd} design resistance to transverse loading according to Eq. (2.66)

The length of stiff bearing s_s corresponds to the loaded length on top of the flange. In Fig. 2.49a) to c) the determination of s_s is shown for different cases which assume a load distribution with a slope of 45° (1:1) in the load introducing element. For a load introduced via rollers, each roller should be verified with $s_s = 0$ and with s_s according to the layout in Fig. 2.49d). If the load introducing element is not able to follow the deformation of the girder, s_s should be set to zero, see Fig. 2.49e). Additional load spreading through the flange is considered in the formula for the effective loaded length.

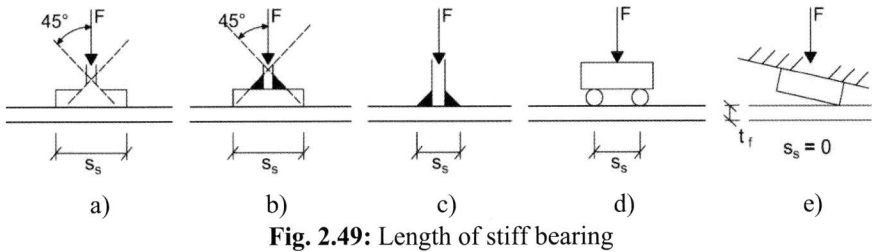

Fig. 2.49: Length of stiff bearing

2. Overview of Design Rules

The verification format follows the general method in terms of forces to assess the resistance when instability phenomena are present, i.e. here the yield resistance F_y is reduced depending on the plate slenderness $\bar{\lambda}_F$ and a corresponding reduction factor χ_F. Thus, the design resistance to transverse loading F_{Rd} is determined as follows:

$$F_{Rd} = \chi_F \cdot \frac{F_y}{\gamma_{M1}} = \chi_F \cdot \frac{\ell_y \cdot t_w \cdot f_{yw}}{\gamma_{M1}} \qquad (2.66)$$

where

- χ_F reduction factor for transverse loading
- ℓ_y effective loaded length
- t_w web thickness
- f_{yw} web yield strength
- γ_{M1} partial safety factor

The reduction factor χ_F is based on a reduction curve according to Eq. (2.67).

$$\chi_F = \frac{0.5}{\bar{\lambda}_F} \leq 1 \qquad (2.67)$$

where

- $\bar{\lambda}_F = \sqrt{F_y / F_{cr}}$ slenderness of the web panel
- F_y yield load
- F_{cr} elastic critical load

The slenderness of the web panel is calculated with the elastic critical load F_{cr} according to Eq. (2.68) and the yield load F_y according to Eq. (2.75). Firstly, the elastic critical load F_{cr} is determined as follows:

$$F_{cr} = 0.9 \cdot k_F \cdot E \cdot \frac{t_w^3}{h_w} \qquad (2.68)$$

where

- k_F buckling value for transverse loading according to Eqs. (2.69) to (2.72)

2.6 RESISTANCE TO TRANSVERSE LOADING

E Young's modulus (for steel $E = 210000$ N/mm^2)
t_w web thickness
h_w web depth

For girders without longitudinal stiffeners, the buckling value k_F is determined depending on the type of transverse load application as follows:

- Load application through one flange, see Fig. 2.48a)

$$k_F = 6 + 2 \cdot \left(\frac{h_w}{a}\right)^2 \tag{2.69}$$

- Load application through both flanges, see Fig. 2.48b)

$$k_F = 3.5 + 2 \cdot \left(\frac{h_w}{a}\right)^2 \tag{2.70}$$

- Load application through one flange adjacent to an unstiffened end, see Fig. 2.48c)

$$k_F = 2 + 6 \cdot \left(\frac{s_s + c}{h_w}\right) \leq 6 \tag{2.71}$$

For girders with longitudinal stiffeners and load application through one flange, see Fig. 2.48a), a second term is added to Eq. (2.69) and the buckling value k_F is determined according to Eq. (2.72).

$$k_F = 6 + 2 \cdot \left(\frac{h_w}{a}\right)^2 + \left[5.44 \cdot \frac{b_1}{a} - 0.21\right] \cdot \sqrt{\gamma_s} \tag{2.72}$$

$$\text{for } \frac{b_1}{h_w} \leq 0.3 \text{ and } 0.05 \leq \frac{b_1}{a} \leq 0.3 \tag{2.73}$$

where

$$\gamma_s = 10.9 \cdot \frac{I_{s\ell,1}}{h_w \cdot t_w^3} \leq 13 \cdot \left(\frac{a}{h_w}\right)^3 + 210 \cdot \left(0.3 - \frac{b_1}{a}\right) \tag{2.74}$$

2. OVERVIEW OF DESIGN RULES

b_1 height of the loaded sub-panel taken as the clear distance between the loaded flange and the longitudinal stiffener

$I_{s\ell,1}$ second moment of inertia of the longitudinal stiffener closest to the loaded flange including contributing parts of the web with $15 \cdot \varepsilon \cdot t$ on each side of the stiffener web, see Fig. 2.45

Eq. (2.72) and (2.74) consider only the longitudinal stiffener which is closest to the loaded flange. Further longitudinal stiffeners are neglected since they usually have a minor influence on the resistance to transverse forces. The longitudinal stiffener can only be accounted for within the limits given in Eq. (2.73). These limits respect the approach to use the smallest eigenvalue as proposed in Graciano (2002) and Graciano and Johansson (2003), for which an increasing distance of the longitudinal stiffener from the loaded flange leads to an increased eigenvalue as well as an increased resistance. However, this is in contradiction to experimental and numerical research results which show a smaller resistance for an increasing distance of the longitudinal stiffener from the loaded flange, see Fig. 2.50, so that an upper bound for the position of the longitudinal stiffener has to be defined according to Eq. (2.73).

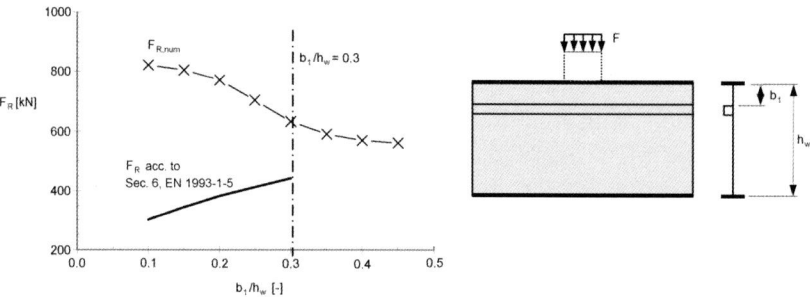

Fig. 2.50: Comparison of resistances according to EN 1993-1-5 and simulations

Although current EN 1993-1-5 rules lead to safe results, they are not satisfying, which is the reason why a national choice is allowed in clause 6.4(2), EN 1993-1-5. A proposal developed by Davaine (2005) and Davaine et al (2004) improves the current EN 1993-1-5 rules. Their suggestion is given at the end of this section.

The calibration of the reduction factor χ_F according to Eq. (2.67) requires the determination of the buckling value k_F according to Eqs. (2.69)

2.6 RESISTANCE TO TRANSVERSE LOADING

to (2.72). Note that these equations take into account simplified assumptions so that a more refined determination of k_F by means of FE eigenvalue analysis or from literature is not allowed.

Secondly, the plate slenderness of the web panel is calculated with the yield load F_y according to Eq. (2.75) for which an effective loaded length ℓ_y is introduced.

$$F_y = \ell_y \cdot t_w \cdot f_{yw} \tag{2.75}$$

where

ℓ_y effective loaded length
t_w web thickness
f_{yw} web yield strength

The effective loaded length ℓ_y corresponds to the effective loaded length of the web taking into account the influence of the flange. For load application through one flange or both flanges, the four-hinge mechanical model originally proposed by Roberts and Rockey (1979) is used, see Fig. 2.51. This model assumes two inner and two outer plastic hinges M_i and M_o, the resistance of which depends on several flange and web parameters covered by the dimensionless parameters m_1 and m_2. Fig. 2.51 shows that for the outer plastic hinges an effective web depth of $0.14 \cdot h_w$ is taken into account. For load application near an unstiffened end, other failure modes are possible, see Johansson et al (2007) for further details, which are governed by the minimum of Eqs. (2.76) to (2.79). In all cases, the contributing width of the flange should be limited to $15 \cdot \varepsilon \cdot t$ on each side of the web.

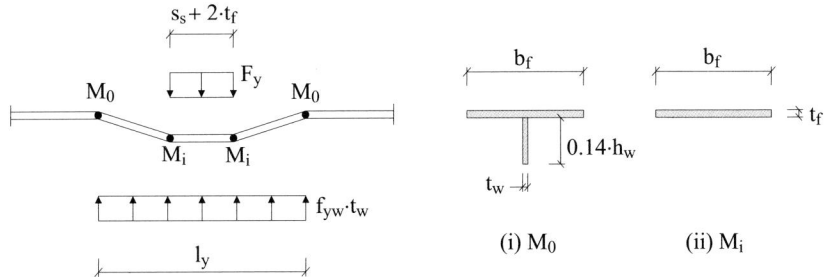

Fig. 2.51: Four-hinge mechanical model

2. Overview of Design Rules

The effective loaded length ℓ_y is determined depending on the type of transverse load application as follows:

- Load application through one flange, see Fig. 2.48a), or both flanges, see Fig. 2.48b)

$$\ell_y = s_s + 2 \cdot t_f \cdot \left(1 + \sqrt{m_1 + m_2}\right) \leq a \qquad (2.76)$$

where
  a is the distance between adjacent transverse stiffeners

- Load application through one flange adjacent to an unstiffened end, see Fig. 2.48c)

$$\ell_y = \min(\ell_y, \ell_{y1}, \ell_{y2}); \; (\ell_y, \text{ see Eq. (2.76)}) \qquad (2.77)$$

and

$$\ell_{y1} = \ell_e + t_f \cdot \sqrt{\frac{m_1}{2} + \left(\frac{\ell_e}{t_f}\right)^2 + m_2} \qquad (2.78)$$

$$\ell_{y2} = \ell_e + t_f \cdot \sqrt{m_1 + m_2} \qquad (2.79)$$

where

$$\ell_e = \frac{k_F \cdot E \cdot t_w^2}{2 \cdot f_{yw} \cdot h_w} \leq s_s + c$$

Note that in EN 1993-1-5 (CEN, 2006a) and in the Corrigendum to EN 1993-1-5 (CEN, 2009) by mistake l_y according to (2.76) is not considered in (2.77).

The dimensionless parameters m_1 and m_2 are determined according to Eqs. (2.80) and (2.81).

$$m_1 = \frac{f_{yf} \cdot b_f}{f_{yw} \cdot t_w} \qquad (2.80)$$

2.6 RESISTANCE TO TRANSVERSE LOADING

$$m_2 = 0 \quad \text{for} \quad \overline{\lambda}_F \leq 0.5$$
$$m_2 = 0.02 \cdot \left(\frac{h_w}{t_f}\right)^2 \quad \text{for} \quad \overline{\lambda}_F > 0.5 \quad (2.81)$$

For cross sections with inclined webs it has to be taken into account that transverse stresses are not only induced in the web but also in the bottom plate so that the corresponding in-plane components of the transverse loading have to be considered, see Fig. 2.52.

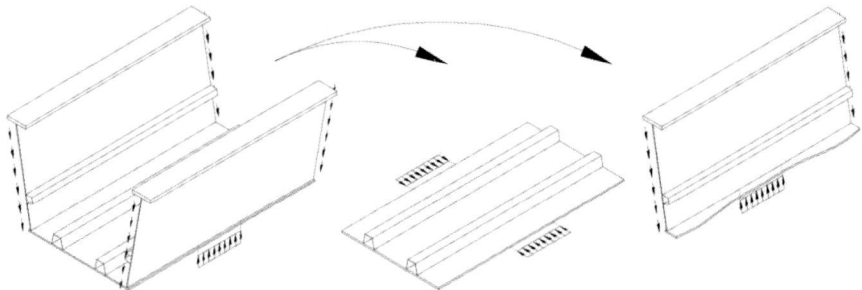

Fig. 2.52: Patch loading of girders with inclined webs

For webs with longitudinal stiffeners, the proposal developed by Davaine, (2005) and Davaine et al (2004) improves current EN 1993-1-5 rules. It is suggested to determine the critical load F_{cr} by using the following procedure:

$$k_{F,2} = \left(0{,}8\frac{s_s + 2t_f}{a} + 0{,}6\right)\left(\frac{a}{b_1}\right)^{0{,}6\frac{s_s+2t_f}{a}+0{,}5} \quad (2.82)$$

$$F_{cr,2} = k_{F,2}\frac{\pi^2 E}{12(1-v^2)}\frac{t_w^3}{b_1} \quad (2.83)$$

$$F_{cr} = \frac{F_{cr,1}F_{cr,2}}{F_{cr,1}+F_{cr,2}} \quad (2.84)$$

where $F_{cr,1}$ is given by Equation (2.68) using the buckling coefficient k_F according to Eq. (2.72). The reduction function χ_F should be determined from the following equation:

$$\chi_F = \frac{1}{\varphi_F + \sqrt{\varphi_F^2 - \overline{\lambda}_F}} \leq 1,0 \qquad (2.85)$$

with

$$\varphi_F = 0,5\left(1 + 0,21(\overline{\lambda}_F - 0,8) + \overline{\lambda}_F\right). \qquad (2.86)$$

For the determination of the yield load F_y according to Eq. (2.75), the effective loaded length ℓ_y should be determined according to Eq. (2.76) with $m_2 = 0$.

Note that this proposal is not completely in accordance with EN 1993-1-5 where the elastic critical force F_{cr} may be defined in the National Annex, while the reduction χ_F is not a Nationally Determined Parameter.

2.6.3 Design examples

Example 2.6-1: Longitudinally stiffened girder subjected to transverse forces.

A plate girder with transverse stiffeners and one longitudinal stiffener is checked for resistance against transverse forces. Two methods are employed: the first one from EN 1993-1-5 and the second one by Davaine (2005). The girder layout and the cross section geometry are shown in the figure below. At the end, the calculated resistance of the same girder, but without longitudinal stiffener, is shown for comparison.

2.6 RESISTANCE TO TRANSVERSE LOADING

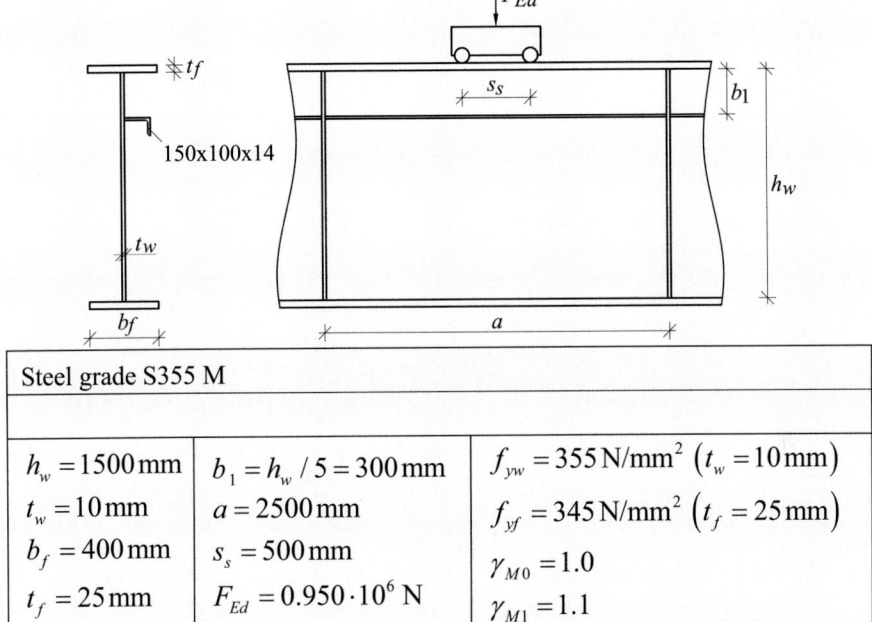

$h_w = 1500\,\text{mm}$	$b_1 = h_w/5 = 300\,\text{mm}$	$f_{yw} = 355\,\text{N/mm}^2\ (t_w = 10\,\text{mm})$
$t_w = 10\,\text{mm}$	$a = 2500\,\text{mm}$	$f_{yf} = 345\,\text{N/mm}^2\ (t_f = 25\,\text{mm})$
$b_f = 400\,\text{mm}$	$s_s = 500\,\text{mm}$	$\gamma_{M0} = 1.0$
$t_f = 25\,\text{mm}$	$F_{Ed} = 0.950 \cdot 10^6\,\text{N}$	$\gamma_{M1} = 1.1$

Fig. 2.53: The outline of the girder, load and geometry of cross section

Geometrical characteristics of the cross section used for the longitudinal stiffener are gathered below:

Unequal leg angle $150 \times 100 \times 14$:

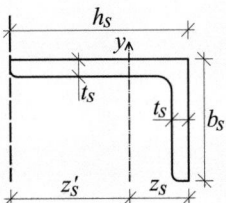

$h_s = 150\,\text{mm} \qquad A_s = 3320\,\text{mm}^2$

$b_s = 100\,\text{mm} \qquad I_{y,s} = 7444000\,\text{mm}^4$

$t_s = 14\,\text{mm} \qquad z_s = 49.8\,\text{mm}$

$z_s' = h_s - z_s = 150 - 49.8 = 100.2\,\text{mm}$

a) EN 1993-1-5 method

In order to obtain the second moment of area of the stiffener including contributing parts of the web $I_{sl,1}$, the following characteristics need to be calculated first:

2. Overview of Design Rules

$$\varepsilon = \sqrt{\frac{235}{f_{yw}}} = \sqrt{\frac{235}{355}} = 0.814$$

$$A_{sl,w} = (2 \cdot 15 \cdot \varepsilon \cdot t_w + t_s) \cdot t_w = (2 \cdot 15 \cdot 0.814 \cdot 10 + 14) \cdot 10 = 2580.9 \, \text{mm}^2$$

$$A_{sl,1} = A_s + A_{sl,w} = 3320 + 2580.9 = 5900.9 \, \text{mm}^2$$

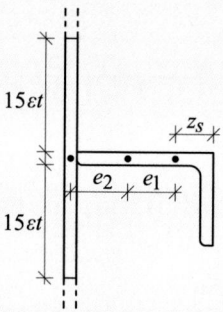

$$e_2 = \frac{\left(z_s' + \frac{t_w}{2}\right) \cdot A_s}{A_{sl,1}} = \frac{\left(100.2 + \frac{10}{2}\right) \cdot 3320}{5900.9} = 59.2 \, \text{mm}$$

$$e_1 = z_s' + \frac{t_w}{2} - e_2 = 100.2 + \frac{10}{2} - 59.2 = 46.0 \, \text{mm}$$

$$I_{sl,1} = \frac{(2 \cdot 15 \cdot \varepsilon \cdot t_w + t_s) \cdot t_w^3}{12} + A_{sl,w} \cdot e_2^2 + I_{y,s} + A_s \cdot e_1^2 =$$

$$= \left[\frac{(2 \cdot 15 \cdot 0.814 \cdot 10 + 14) \cdot 10^3}{12} + \right. \\ \left. + 2580.9 \cdot 59.2^2 + 7444000 + 3320 \cdot 46.0^2 \right] = 2.354 \cdot 10^7 \, \text{mm}^4$$

$$\gamma_s = 10.9 \cdot \frac{I_{sl,1}}{h_w \cdot t_w^3} = 10.9 \cdot \frac{2.354 \cdot 10^7}{1500 \cdot 10^3} = 171.0$$

but

$$\gamma_s = 171.0 \geq 13 \cdot \left(\frac{a}{h_w}\right)^3 + 210 \cdot \left(0.3 - \frac{b_1}{a}\right) =$$

2.6 RESISTANCE TO TRANSVERSE LOADING

$$\geq 13 \cdot \left(\frac{2500}{1500}\right)^3 + 210 \cdot \left(0.3 - \frac{300}{2500}\right) = 98.0 \rightarrow \gamma_s = 98.0$$

The buckling coefficient for a web with longitudinal stiffener k_F may be taken as:

$$k_F = 6 + 2 \cdot \left(\frac{h_w}{a}\right)^2 + \left(5.44 \cdot \frac{b_1}{a} - 0.21\right) \cdot \sqrt{\gamma_s}$$

$$= 6 + 2 \cdot \left(\frac{1500}{2500}\right)^2 + \left(5.44 \cdot \frac{300}{2500} - 0.21\right) \cdot \sqrt{98.0} = 11.1$$

The above formula is valid for:

$$0.05 \leq \frac{b_1}{h_w} = \frac{300}{1500} = 0.2 \leq 0.3 \quad \text{and} \quad \frac{b_1}{a} = \frac{300}{2500} = 0.12 \leq 0.3.$$

If several concentrated forces are closely spaced, such as in the present case, the resistance should be checked for each individual force as well as for the total load with s_s as the centre-to-centre distance between the outer loads.

Resistance check for the scenario with $s_s = 500$ mm and transverse force F_{Ed}:

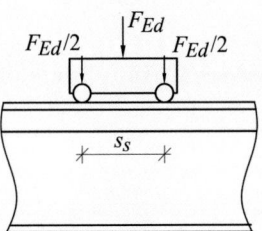

$$F_{cr} = 0.9 \cdot k_F \cdot E \cdot \frac{t_w^3}{h_w} = 0.9 \cdot 11.1 \cdot 210000 \cdot \frac{10^3}{1500} = 1.399 \cdot 10^6 \text{ N}$$

$$l_y = s_s + 2 \cdot t_f \cdot \left(1 + \sqrt{m_1 + m_2}\right)$$

$$= 500 + 2 \cdot 25 \cdot \left(1 + \sqrt{38.9 + 72.0}\right) = 1076.5 \text{ mm} < a = 2500 \text{ mm}$$

2. OVERVIEW OF DESIGN RULES

$$m_1 = \frac{f_{yf} \cdot b_f}{f_{yw} \cdot t_w} = \frac{345 \cdot 400}{355 \cdot 10} = 38.9$$

$$\overline{\lambda}_F = \sqrt{\frac{l_y \cdot t_w \cdot f_{yw}}{F_{cr}}} = \sqrt{\frac{1076.5 \cdot 10 \cdot 355}{1.399 \cdot 10^6}} = 1.653 > 0.5$$

$$\rightarrow m_2 = 0.02 \cdot \left(\frac{h_w}{t_f}\right)^2 = 0.02 \cdot \left(\frac{1500}{25}\right)^2 = 72.0$$

The reduction factor χ_F should be obtained from:

$$\chi_F = \frac{0.5}{\overline{\lambda}_F} = \frac{0.5}{1.653} = 0.303$$

The design resistance of the longitudinally stiffened web should be taken as:

$$F_{Rd} = \chi_F \frac{l_y \cdot t_w \cdot f_{yw}}{\gamma_{M1}} = 0.303 \frac{1076.5 \cdot 10 \cdot 355}{1.1} = 1.051 \cdot 10^6 \text{ N}$$

and the verification check gives:

$$\eta_2 = \frac{F_{Ed}}{F_{Rd}} = \frac{0.950 \cdot 10^6}{1.051 \cdot 10^6} = 0.90$$

Resistance check for the scenario with $s_s = 0$ mm and transverse concentrated force $F_{Ed} / 2$:

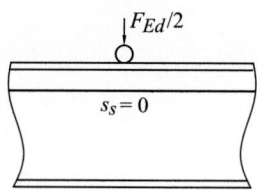

$$l_{y,1} = s_s + 2 \cdot t_f \cdot \left(1 + \sqrt{m_1 + m_2}\right)$$

$$= 0 + 2 \cdot 25 \cdot \left(1 + \sqrt{38.9 + 72.0}\right) = 576.5 \text{ mm} < a = 2500 \text{ mm}$$

$$\bar{\lambda}_{F,1} = \sqrt{\frac{l_{y,1} \cdot t_w \cdot f_{yw}}{F_{cr}}} = \sqrt{\frac{576.5 \cdot 10 \cdot 355}{1.399 \cdot 10^6}} = 1.209 > 0.5$$

$$\chi_{F,1} = \frac{0.5}{\bar{\lambda}_{F,1}} = \frac{0.5}{1.209} = 0.413$$

$$F_{Rd,1} = \chi_F \frac{l_y \cdot t_w \cdot f_{yw}}{\gamma_{M1}} = 0.413 \frac{576.5 \cdot 10 \cdot 355}{1.1} = 0.769 \cdot 10^6 \text{ N}$$

Finally, the verification of resistance to the applied concentrated transverse force is:

$$\eta_{2,1} = \frac{F_{Ed}/2}{F_{Rd,1}} = \frac{0.950 \cdot 10^6 / 2}{0.769 \cdot 10^6} = 0.62 < \eta_2 = \frac{F_{Ed}}{F_{Rd}} = 0.90$$

The result above clearly shows that the second scenario is not decisive in this particular numerical example.

b) Method proposed by Davaine

Elastic critical force:

$$k_{F,2} = \left(0.8 \frac{s_s + 2t_f}{a} + 0.6\right) \left(\frac{a}{b_1}\right)^{0.6\frac{s_s+2t_f}{a}+0.5}$$

$$= \left(0.8 \frac{500 + 2 \cdot 25}{2500} + 0.6\right) \left(\frac{2500}{300}\right)^{0.6\frac{500+2\cdot25}{2500}+0.5} = 2.96$$

$$F_{cr,2} = k_{F,2} \frac{\pi^2 E}{12(1-\nu^2)} \frac{t_w^3}{b_1} = 2.96 \cdot \frac{\pi^2 \cdot 210000}{12(1-0.3^2)} \cdot \frac{10^3}{300} = 1.875 \cdot 10^6 \text{ N}$$

$$F_{cr,1} = F_{cr} = 1.399 \cdot 10^6 \text{ N}$$

$$F_{cr} = \frac{F_{cr,1} F_{cr,2}}{F_{cr,1} + F_{cr,2}} = \frac{1.399 \cdot 10^6 \cdot 1.875 \cdot 10^6}{1.399 \cdot 10^6 + 1.875 \cdot 10^6} = 0.801 \cdot 10^6 \text{ N}$$

2. OVERVIEW OF DESIGN RULES

Slenderness:

In the calculation of l_y it is presumed that $m_2 = 0$.

$$l_y = s_s + 2 \cdot t_f \cdot \left(1 + \sqrt{m_1 + m_2}\right)$$

$$= 500 + 2 \cdot 25 \cdot \left(1 + \sqrt{38.9 + 0}\right) = 861.7 \,\text{mm} < a = 2500 \,\text{mm}$$

$$\overline{\lambda}_F = \sqrt{\frac{l_y \cdot t_w \cdot f_{yw}}{F_{cr}}} = \sqrt{\frac{861.7 \cdot 10 \cdot 355}{0.801 \cdot 10^6}} = 1.954$$

Reduction factor and resistance check:

$$\varphi_F = 0.5\left(1 + 0.21(\overline{\lambda}_F - 0.8) + \overline{\lambda}_F\right)$$

$$= 0.5\left(1 + 0.21(1.954 - 0.8) + 1.954\right) = 1.598$$

$$\chi_F = \frac{1}{\varphi_F + \sqrt{\varphi_F^2 - \overline{\lambda}_F}} = \frac{1}{1.598 + \sqrt{1.598^2 - 1.954}} = 0.421 \leq 1.0$$

$$F_{Rd} = \chi_F \frac{l_y \cdot t_w \cdot f_{yw}}{\gamma_{M1}} = 0.421 \cdot \frac{861.7 \cdot 10 \cdot 355}{1.1} = 1.172 \cdot 10^6 \,\text{N}$$

c) Longitudinally unstiffened web (EN1993-1-5)

In comparison to the previously calculated design resistance of longitudinally stiffened web, the design resistance of the same web without longitudinal stiffener is calculated below.

$$k_F = 6 + 2 \cdot \left(\frac{h_w}{a}\right)^2 = 6 + 2 \cdot \left(\frac{1500}{2500}\right)^2 = 6.72$$

$$F_{cr} = 0.9 \cdot k_F \cdot E \cdot \frac{t_w^3}{h_w} = 0.9 \cdot 6.72 \cdot 210000 \cdot \frac{10^3}{1500} = 8.467 \cdot 10^5 \,\text{N}$$

$l_y = 1076.5 \,\text{mm} < a = 2500 \,\text{mm}$ - see Case a)

$$\overline{\lambda}_F = \sqrt{\frac{l_y \cdot t_w \cdot f_{yw}}{F_{cr}}} = \sqrt{\frac{1076.5 \cdot 10 \cdot 355}{8.467 \cdot 10^5}} = 2.124 > 0.5$$

$$\chi_F = \frac{0.5}{\overline{\lambda}_F} = \frac{0.5}{2.124} = 0.235$$

$$F_{Rd} = \chi_F \frac{l_y \cdot t_w \cdot f_{yw}}{\gamma_{M1}} = 0.235 \frac{1076.5 \cdot 10 \cdot 355}{1.1} = 8.187 \cdot 10^5 \text{ N}$$

The comparison of design resistances to patch loading, calculated according to three different methods, is shown in Table 2.5.

Table 2.5: Design resistance to transverse forces

	Longitudinally stiffened web		Longitudinally unstiffened web
	EN 1993-1-5	Davaine L, 2005	
F_{Rd} [N]	$1.051 \cdot 10^6$	$1.172 \cdot 10^6$	$0.819 \cdot 10^6$

As expected, the EN1993-1-5 method for longitudinally stiffened webs gives (10%) smaller resistance than the method proposed by Davaine. The increase of the resistance in comparison to the unstiffened web is rather substantial: 28% and 43%.

2.7 INTERACTION

As an introduction to this paragraph, it should be reminded that in addition to the interaction requirements, the verifications for each single internal force and moment should also be met.

2.7.1 Interaction between bending moment and shear force in a web panel

EN1993-1-5, clauses 7.1(1) to 7.1(4), deals with I-girder or box-girder section types where two flanges and two transverse stiffeners are the edges

2. Overview of Design Rules

of the web panel where the interaction occurs. The first step of the interaction verification is then to check if the shear force can be resisted by the web alone on the one hand, and if the axial force and the bending moment can be resisted by the flanges alone on the other hand. This is true when the two following criteria are fulfilled:

$$\overline{\eta}_3 = \frac{V_{Ed}}{V_{bw,Rd}} \leq 0.5 \text{ and,} \tag{2.87}$$

$$M_{Ed} \leq M_{f,Rd} \tag{2.88}$$

where

$V_{bw,Rd}$ is the web contribution to the shear design resistance according to EN1993-1-5, clause 5.2, see also sub-chapter 2.5.

$M_{f,Rd}$ is the design plastic resistance of the section consisting of the effective area of the flanges only.

$M_{pl,Rd}$ is the design plastic resistance of the cross section consisting of the effective area of the flanges and the fully effective web irrespective of its section class.

If one of the above criteria is not fulfilled, the following interaction formula should be checked in the web panel of the I-girder or box-girder section types:

$$\overline{\eta}_1 + \left(1 - \frac{M_{f,Rd}}{M_{pl,Rd}}\right)\left(2\overline{\eta}_3 - 1\right)^2 \leq 1.0 \tag{2.89}$$

where

$$\overline{\eta}_1 = \frac{M_{Ed}}{M_{pl,Rd}}.$$

In bridge design, the most common case for which this interaction criterion has to be checked is in the web panel closest to a support of a continuous I-girder or box-girder, see Fig. 2.54. Then the shear force and the bending moment are not constant over the whole web panel. Their maximum

2.7 INTERACTION

values (at support) are usually overestimated because they are calculated by neglecting the beneficial effect of the real width of the support device. Shear buckling ($\bar{\eta}_3$) is a panel failure mode with a buckle usually inclined at an angle of less than 45°, whereas $\bar{\eta}_1$ is a single section criterion. Consequently, EN1993-1-5, clause 7.1(2), indicates that the previous interaction criterion should be met in all sections other than those located at a distance less than $h_w/2$ from a support with vertical stiffeners. This rule is actually valid only for webs without longitudinal stiffeners, which is not stated in EN 1993-1-5. For webs with longitudinal stiffeners it is recommended to use half of the depth of the largest subpanel instead.

With the notations in Fig. 2.54, it should be noticed that $M_{y,Ed,left}$ has to be checked on a gross cross section (elastic resistance) according to sub-chapter 2.4. And in the same way, the panel has to be checked for shear buckling resistance only, assuming that the maximum shear force $V_{Ed,left}$ applies to the entire length of the panel.

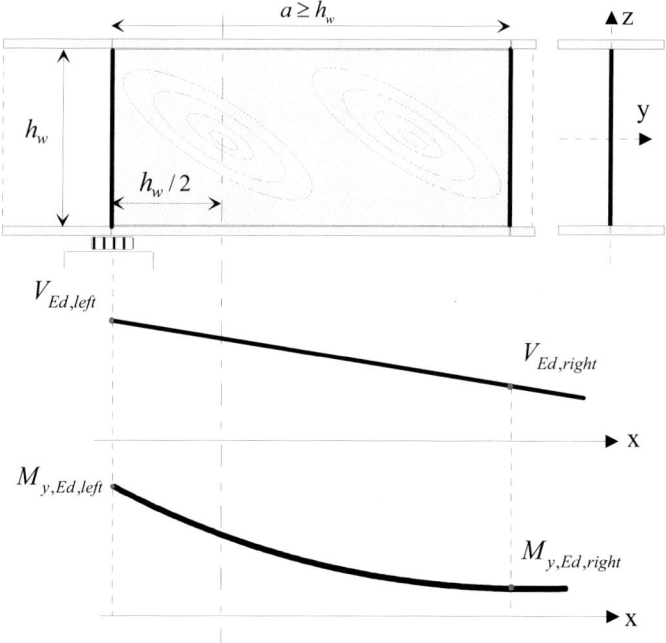

Fig. 2.54: Interaction between bending moment and shear force

2. OVERVIEW OF DESIGN RULES

2.7.2 Interaction between axial force, bending moment and shear force in a web panel

The previous interaction criterion between bending moment and shear force should be corrected if an axial force is present. Two cases have to be considered:

- A part of the web is still in tension, if the axial force N_{Ed} (tension or compression) is applied in addition to the bending moment M_{Ed} or,
- The whole web is in compression, if both N_{Ed} and M_{Ed} are applied.

In the first case, the previous interaction criterion is used with corrected values $M_{N,pl,Rd}$ and $M_{N,f,Rd}$ instead of $M_{pl,Rd}$ and $M_{f,Rd}$ (as defined in the previous paragraph). These corrected values are expressed in clause 6.2.9 of EN1993-1-1.

In the second case, the whole web panel is under compression and it should be treated as a flange of a box-girder (see section 2.7.3 below).

2.7.3 Interaction between axial force, bending moment and shear force in a flange panel

The interaction between bending and shear should be checked not only in the web panels of a box-girder, but also in its flanges. In case of a uniaxial bending moment, these flanges are submitted to a uniform axial force and a shear flow due to the shear force (and possibly an additional contribution from torque).

In such a case, the interaction criterion in the flanges becomes:

$$\eta_1 + \left(2\overline{\eta}_3 - 1\right)^2 \leq 1.0 \qquad (2.90)$$

with η_1 defined in section 2.4.6 and $\overline{\eta}_3$ in sub-chapter 2.5.

V_{Ed} is based on τ_{Ed}, the average shear stress in the whole compression flange, but not less than half of the maximum shear stress in this flange. With the example shown in Fig. 2.55 (stiffened flange), the average shear stress is equal to $\tau_{Ed,max}/2$ for the whole flange and the interaction is verified with $\tau_{Ed,max}/2$. $V_{b,Rd}$ is calculated according to EN1993-1-5, section 5, for the whole compression (possibly stiffened) flange.

In addition, the flange sub-panels should be checked using the average shear stress within the sub-panel and a shear resistance of the sub-panel determined according to EN1993-1-5, section 5, assuming the longitudinal stiffeners to be rigid.

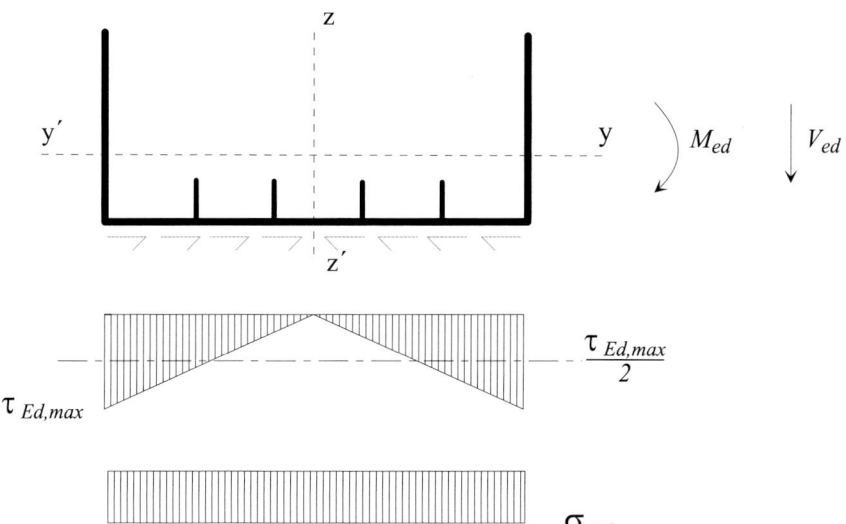

Fig. 2.55: Interaction between bending moment and shear force in a box-girder flange

2.7.4 Interaction between axial force, bending moment and transverse force

The applied transverse force F_{Ed} defines a stress ratio (see sub-chapter 2.6):

$$\eta_2 = \frac{F_{Ed}}{F_{Rd}} = \frac{F_{Ed}}{\dfrac{f_{yw} L_{eff} t_w}{\gamma_{M1}}} \leq 1.0 \qquad (2.91)$$

2. Overview of Design Rules

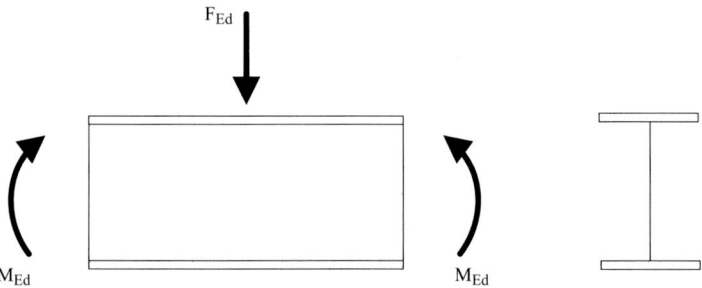

Fig. 2.56: Interaction between bending moment and transverse force in a girder

No interaction has to be considered if the transverse force F_{Ed} is acting on the tension flange of the girder. This is related to the fact that the web zone submitted to the longitudinal compressive stresses (near the compression flange) does not coincide with the web zone submitted to the vertical compressive stresses (near the tension flange where the transverse force is applied). However, if the transverse force acts on the tension flange, a check for yielding should be done according to clause 6.2.1(5) of EN 1993-1-1. On the contrary, if F_{Ed} is acting on the compression flange of the girder, the interaction with an axial force and a bending moment should be verified using η_1 as defined in section 2.4.6:

$$\eta_2 + 0.8 \cdot \eta_1 \leq 1.4 \tag{2.92}$$

As $\eta_2 \leq 1.0$ and $\eta_1 \leq 1.0$ should also be verified, the previous interaction needs not to be checked if $\eta_2 \leq 0.6$ or $\eta_1 \leq 0.5$.

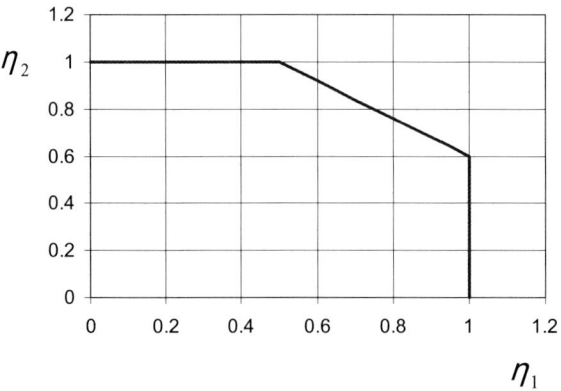

Fig. 2.57: Interaction criterion

2.7 INTERACTION

This interaction criterion also implicitly assumes that the section analysis for η_1 is elastic, which is not always the case. EN1993-1-5 does not give interaction rules for class 1 or 2 cross section, but if no axial force is applied, it is reasonable that η_1 should be replaced by $\overline{\eta}_1$ giving the following criterion:

$$\frac{F_{Ed}}{F_{Rd}} + 0.8 \cdot \frac{M_{Ed}}{M_{pl,Rd}} \leq 1.4 \qquad (2.93)$$

2.7.5 Interaction between shear force and transverse force in a web panel

Currently no formulation for the interaction between transverse force and shear force (F-V) is given. The influence of shear stresses caused by the transverse forces should not be accounted for because it is already included in the patch loading resistance model. Fig. 2.58 shows the basic load cases "pure patch loading" and "pure shear force" which in combination leads to the investigated type of interaction. This sub-division is also the basis on which the interaction equation (2.94) was defined in Kuhlmann et al (2007). This equation was added to the German National Annex as NCCI (Non-Contradictory Complementary Information).

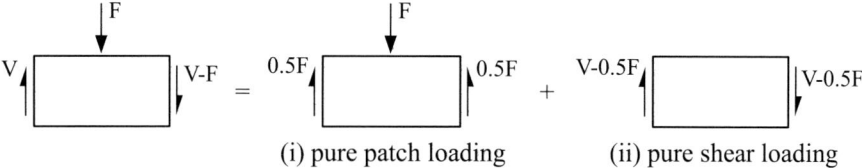

(i) pure patch loading   (ii) pure shear loading

Fig. 2.58: Subdivision of F-V-interaction into basic load cases

In Fig. 2.59 interaction equation (2.94) is compared to experimental and numerical results. The statistical evaluation of the proposed interaction equation was done with the shear resistance model according to section 5, EN1993-1-5. For the patch load resistance, improved models for unstiffened girders (Gozzi, 2007) as well as for longitudinally stiffened girders (Davaine, 2005) were used, which can be transferred to section 6, EN 1993-1-5.

2. OVERVIEW OF DESIGN RULES

The consequences e.g. for bridge construction are shown in Fig. 2.60. In stage a) the introduced patch load is almost equally equilibrated resulting in a pure patch loading situation where the shear is already considered in the patch load model. In stage b) the maximum internal shear force approximates the value of the applied patch load which leads to an asymmetric patch loading condition. Thus, the interaction becomes relevant approximately for the shaded area in Fig. 2.59. However, for the verification of the cross section the interaction load case "patch loading and bending moment" usually governs.

For the interaction between transverse force and shear force, interaction equation (2.94) may be used:

$$\left[\eta_3 \cdot \left(1 - \frac{F_{Ed}}{2 \cdot V_{Ed}}\right)\right]^{1.6} + \eta_2 \leq 1.0 \qquad (2.94)$$

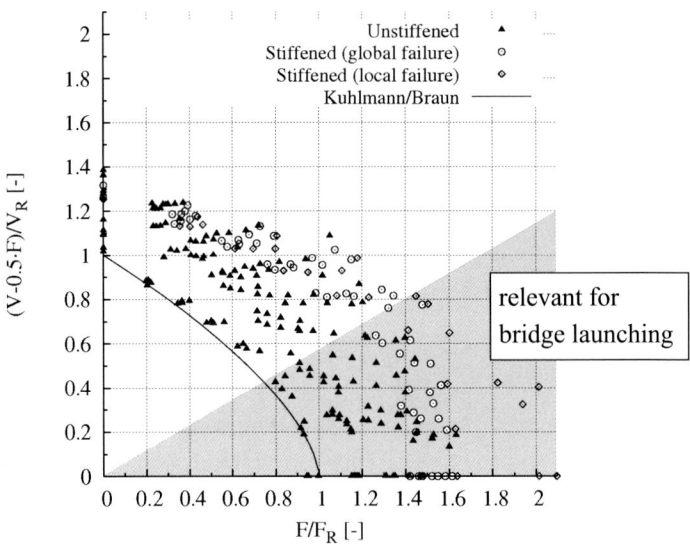

Fig. 2.59: Interaction between transverse force and shear force

2.7 INTERACTION

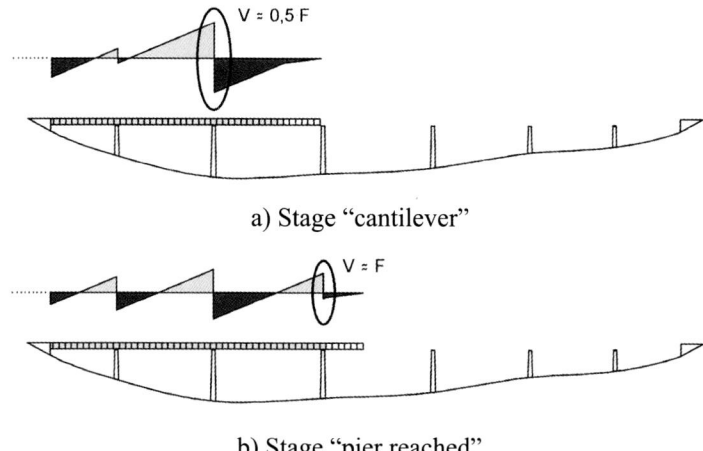

a) Stage "cantilever"

b) Stage "pier reached"

Fig. 2.60: Shear force diagrams for construction stages during bridge launching

2.7.6 Design example

Example 2.7-1: Bending-shear interaction of unstiffened plated girder.

The geometry and basic parameters of the gross cross section of unstiffened plated girder are shown in Fig. 2.32.

$$V_{Ed} = 761 \cdot 10^3 \text{ N}$$

The interaction check may be performed at the distance equal to $0.5h_w$ from the panel edge with the largest moment ($M_{y,Ed,2}$, see Fig. 2.32).

$M_{y,Ed,2} = 5.6 \cdot 10^9$ Nmm and

$A_f = b_f \cdot t_f = 400 \cdot 25 = 10000 \text{ mm}^2$

$h_T = h_w + t_f = 1400 + 25 = 1425 \text{ mm}$

$M_{f,y,Rd} = A_f \cdot h_T \cdot f_y / \gamma_{M0} = 10000 \cdot 1425 \cdot 355 / 1.0 = 5.059 \cdot 10^9$ Nmm

$M_{y,Ed,2} = 5.6 \cdot 10^9$ Nmm $> M_{f,y,Rd} = 5.059 \cdot 10^9$ Nmm,

where
    h_T is the distance between the centroids of the flanges,
    $M_{f,y,Rd}$ is the design plastic moment of the resistance of the section consisting of the effective area of the flanges.

$$\bar{\eta}_3 = \frac{V_{Ed}}{V_{bw,Rd}} = \frac{761 \cdot 10^3}{1.087 \cdot 10^6} = 0.7 \text{ (see 2.5.3)}$$

Since $\bar{\eta}_3 = 0.7 > 0.5$ and $M_{y,Ed,2} > M_{f,y,Rd}$, the interaction effects of bending and shear in the unstiffened web of the plated girder should satisfy the following requirement:

$$\bar{\eta}_1 + \left(1 - \frac{M_{f,y,Rd}}{M_{pl,y,Rd}}\right) \cdot \left(2 \cdot \bar{\eta}_3 - 1\right)^2 \leq 1.0,$$

where
    $M_{pl,y,Rd}$ is the design plastic moment of resistance of the section consisting of the effective area of the flanges and the fully effective web irrespective of its section class.

$$\bar{\eta}_1 = \frac{M_{y,Ed,2}}{M_{pl,y,Rd}} = \frac{5.6 \cdot 10^9}{6.798 \cdot 10^9} = 0.82$$

Finally, the verification of resistance for interaction effects of bending and shear should be performed as follows:

$$0.82 + \left(1 - \frac{5.059 \cdot 10^9}{6.798 \cdot 10^9}\right) \cdot \left(2 \cdot 0.7 - 1\right)^2 = 0.86 \leq 1.0$$

2.8 FLANGE INDUCED BUCKLING

When a girder is subjected to bending, the induced curvature (deformed shape of the girder) combined with the compression in the flange leads to a vertical force applied to the web plane. These vertical deviation forces introduce vertical compressive stresses σ_z into the web. If the web is

2.8 FLANGE INDUCED BUCLING

slender, buckling could occur. This web buckling phenomenon is modelled as the column buckling of a vertical web stripe with a width dx, see Fig. 2.61. The criterion to be verified is then given by:

$$\sigma_z \leq \sigma_{cr} = \frac{\pi^2 E}{12(1-v^2)}\left(\frac{t_w}{h}\right)^2 \tag{2.95}$$

To express the vertical stress σ_z, the following assumptions were made in EN1993-1-5, section 8:

- The girder has a symmetrical I cross section (for calculating the radius of curvature),
- Maximum residual stresses in the flanges are equal to 0.5 f_{yf}, so that the required strain to get yielding over the full flange area is:

$$\varepsilon_y + 0.5\varepsilon_y = 1.5\frac{f_{yf}}{E} \tag{2.96}$$

- The two identical flanges (area A_f) are entirely yielded when buckling occurs.
- The bending resistance is elastic.

These assumptions lead to a web slenderness limit that should not be exceeded in order to avoid flange induced buckling:

$$\frac{3 \cdot A_f \cdot f_{yf}^2}{E \cdot h \cdot t_w} \leq \frac{\pi^2 \cdot E}{12 \cdot (1-v^2)}\left(\frac{t_w}{h}\right)^2 \tag{2.97}$$

also equivalent to:

$$\frac{h}{t_w} \leq k \cdot \frac{E}{f_{yf}} \cdot \sqrt{\frac{h \cdot t_w}{A_f}} \quad \text{with } k = \frac{\pi}{6 \cdot \sqrt{1-v^2}} = 0.55 \tag{2.98}$$

h is the distance between mid-planes of the flanges. The previous k-value (0.55) was obtained with an elastic bending resistance. EN1993-1-5 also proposes different k-values:

2. Overview of Design Rules

- $k = 0.4$ if the plastic bending resistance is utilized,
- $k = 0.3$ if the plastic rotation is utilized.

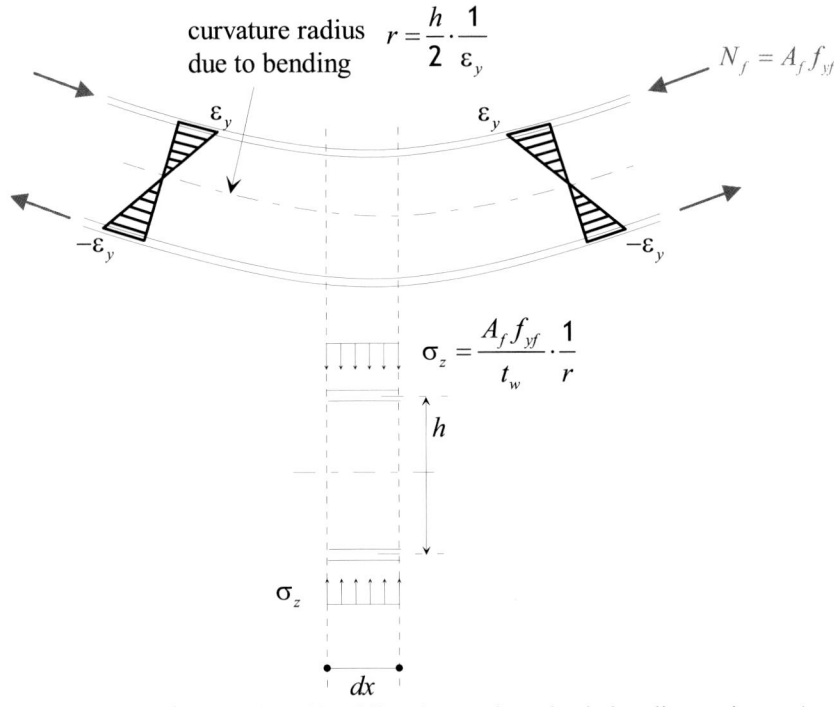

Fig. 2.61: Flange induced buckling (case of an elastic bending resistance)

It should be noticed that this criterion does not apply in the case of an I-girder with a longitudinal stiffener welded to the web and no further information is given in this case.

If the I-girder is initially already curved in elevation with a radius R, the previous formula should be modified according to EN1993-1-5, section 8, as follows:

$$\frac{h}{t_w} \leq \frac{k \cdot \dfrac{E}{f_{yf}} \cdot \sqrt{\dfrac{h \cdot t_w}{A_f}}}{\sqrt{1 + \dfrac{h \cdot E}{3 \cdot R \cdot f_{yf}}}} \tag{2.99}$$

2.9 STIFFENERS AND DETAILING

2.9.1 Introduction

Section 9 of EN 1993-1-5 gives design rules for stiffeners in plated structures and some other detailing rules that are relevant in assessing plate buckling resistance. The most typical elements of plated structures that may be reinforced with stiffeners are flanges of box-girders and webs of plate and box-girders.

Transverse stiffeners increase shear resistance, provide lateral supports to longitudinal stiffeners, carry concentrated transverse forces and together with cross-frames or diaphragms reduce distortional deformations of the cross section. They are usually designed as rigid stiffeners and consequently the panels between two rigid transverse stiffeners may be designed independently without an interaction with adjacent panels. EN 1993-1-5 supports the approach with rigid transverse stiffeners and does not give detailed design rules for the case of flexible transverse stiffeners.

Longitudinal stiffeners increase the shear resistance as well as the resistance to direct stresses and patch loading. They are usually designed to be most effective. Normally this is achieved when a further increase of the stiffener cross section does not significantly increase the resistance of the stiffened plate.

The most typical situations where stiffeners are involved in the design of plated structures are shown in Fig. 2.62. In some cases separate checks are provided in this section and in some cases the stiffener design is incorporated into the design checks of plated elements subjected to direct stresses, shear stress, patch loading, etc.

2. Overview of Design Rules

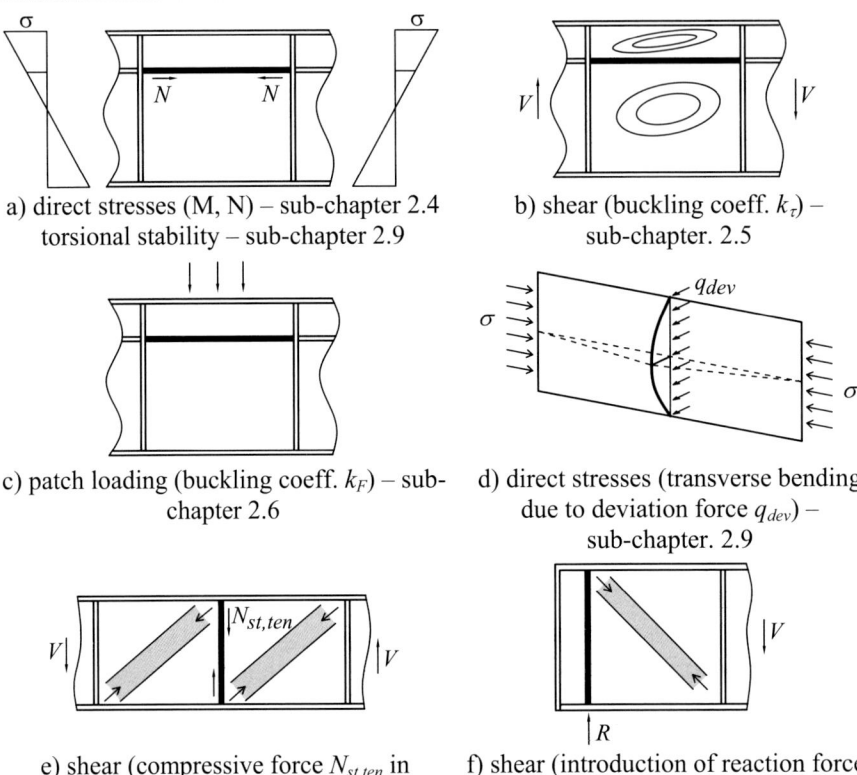

a) direct stresses (M, N) – sub-chapter 2.4 torsional stability – sub-chapter 2.9

b) shear (buckling coeff. k_τ) – sub-chapter. 2.5

c) patch loading (buckling coeff. k_F) – sub-chapter 2.6

d) direct stresses (transverse bending due to deviation force q_{dev}) – sub-chapter 2.9

e) shear (compressive force $N_{st,ten}$ in intermediate transverse stiffener due to the tension field action) – sub-chapter 2.9

f) shear (introduction of reaction forces and end post details) – sub-chapter. 2.9

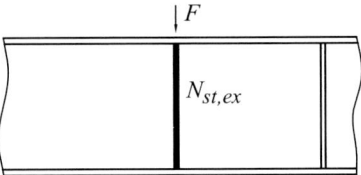

g) external transverse loads (compression force in the transverse stiffener $N_{st,ex}$) – Sub-chapter. 2.9

Fig. 2.62: Typical design situations for longitudinal and transverse stiffeners

When performing independent design checks according to this sub-chapter, the cross section of a longitudinal or transverse stiffener may be taken as composed of the gross area of the stiffener itself A_s and the contributing width of the plate equal to $15\varepsilon t$ on each side of the stiffener (Fig. 2.63). This width should not be more than the actual dimension available, avoiding any overlapping of the contributing widths of adjacent stiffeners.

2.9 STIFFENERS AND DETAILING

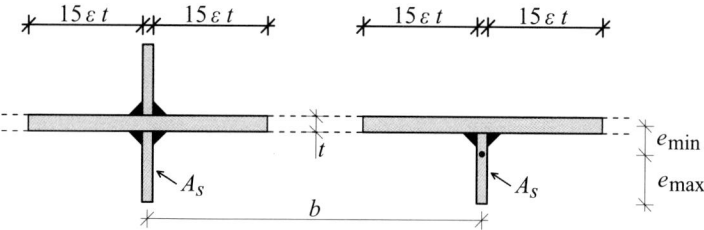

a) No overlapping of contributing plate

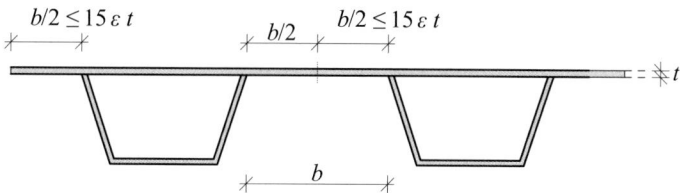

b) Overlapping of contributing plate

Fig. 2.63: Effective cross section of stiffeners

Cross sections of stiffeners may be open or closed and single or double-sided (see Fig. 2.64).

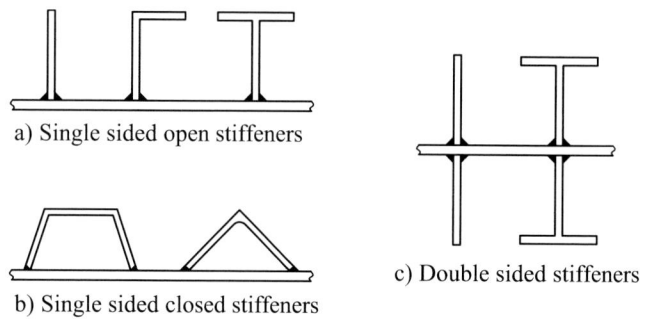

a) Single sided open stiffeners

b) Single sided closed stiffeners

c) Double sided stiffeners

Fig. 2.64: Typical cross sections of stiffeners

Transverse stiffeners are usually flat bars or T profiles. Intermediate transverse stiffeners are usually single-sided, unless they carry large concentrated forces. The stiffeners at supports are always double sided to avoid eccentricity at the introduction of large reaction forces. Longitudinal stiffeners are very often closed trapezoidal stiffeners that have very good torsional rigidity, but may also be open flat bars, T or L shape profiles.

To provide adequate robustness, cross sections of open stiffeners are always designed as Class 3 cross sections or lower. Generally this rule applies also to closed stiffeners. Some new concepts of the stiffened plate design introduce a smaller number of large trapezoidal stiffeners instead of a larger number of smaller stiffners. In this case it may happen that the stiffener belongs to a Class 4 cross section, which should be adequately taken into account in the design procedure.

2.9.2 Transverse stiffeners

2.9.2.1 Direct stresses

Rigid transverse stiffeners are not directly loaded by direct stresses in the plate, but due to inevitable geometrical imperfections they get transverse deviation forces from adjacent compressed panels inducing out of plane bending (Fig. 2.65). To provide rigid support for the plate, they should be designed not only for strength but also for stiffness. Based on a second order analysis the following criteria should be fulfilled:

- maximum stress σ_{max} in the stiffener at the ultimate limit state should not exceed the yield strength:

$$\sigma_{max} \leq \frac{f_y}{\gamma_{M1}} \qquad (2.100)$$

- additional lateral deflection w at the ultimate limit state should not exceed:

$$w \leq \frac{b}{300} \qquad (2.101)$$

where b is the plate width (see Fig. 2.65).

The mechanical model to be used in checking transverse stiffeners is given in Fig. 2.65. The transverse stiffener under consideration has a

2.9 STIFFENERS AND DETAILING

sinusoidal geometric imperfection with amplitude w_0. Both adjacent transverse stiffeners are supposed to be straight and rigid and the adjacent compressed panels including longitudinal stiffeners, if any, are considered to be simply supported along the transverse stiffeners. Axial forces in the stiffener from external loading or from tension field action should be included in the mechanical model if present.

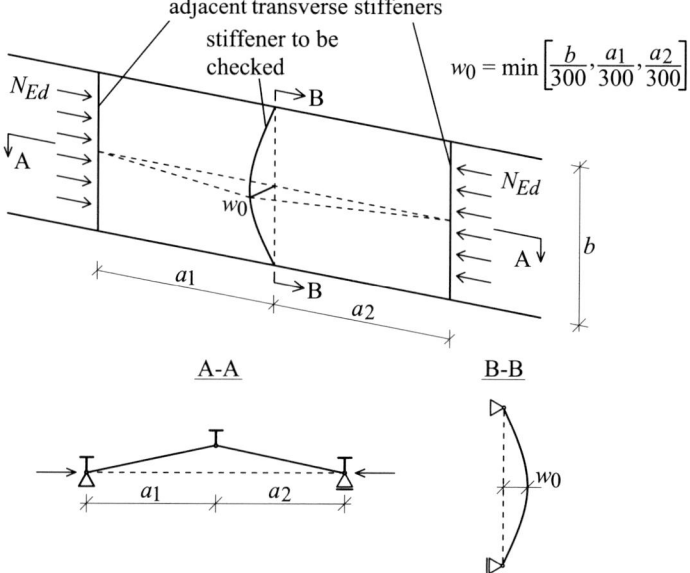

Fig. 2.65: Mechanical model for rigid transverse stiffeners

When only deviation forces act on the transverse stiffener (e.g. webs of plate girders in the mid-span region, bottom flanges of box-girders near intermediate supports if there is no significant effect of torsion), the requirements (2.100) and (2.101) may be rewritten in the form of a minimum required second moment of area I_{st}:

$$I_{st,act} \geq I_{st} = \frac{\sigma_m}{E}\left(\frac{b}{\pi}\right)^4\left(1 + w_0 \frac{300}{b} u\right) \qquad (2.102)$$

$$\sigma_m = \frac{\sigma_{cr,c}}{\sigma_{cr,p}} \frac{N_{Ed}}{b}\left(\frac{1}{a_1} + \frac{1}{a_2}\right) \qquad (2.103)$$

2. OVERVIEW OF DESIGN RULES

$$u = \frac{\pi^2 \cdot E \cdot e_{max}}{\dfrac{f_y \cdot 300 \cdot b}{\gamma_{M1}}} \geq 1.0 \tag{2.104}$$

where

$I_{st,act}$ is the second moment of area of the transverse stiffener

I_{st} is the minimum required second moment of area of the transverse stiffener to be considered as rigid

e_{max} is the maximum distance from the edge of the stiffener to the centroid of the stiffener (see Fig. 2.63)

N_{Ed} is the maximum compressive force of both adjacent panels. It represents the resultant of direct compression stresses and should not be taken as less than the maximum compressive stress at the edge of the panel times half of the effective^p compressive area of the panel $A_{c,eff}$ (see section 2.4.5)

$\sigma_{cr,c}$, $\sigma_{cr,p}$ elastic critical stresses for column- and plate-like buckling (see sections 2.4.3 and 2.4.4).

At larger aspect ratios, the ratio $\sigma_{cr,c}/\sigma_{cr,p}$ may become very small. In order to avoid underestimation of σ_m, this ratio should be limited according to (2.105):

$$0.5 \leq \frac{\sigma_{cr,c}}{\sigma_{cr,p}} \leq 1.0 \tag{2.105}$$

When u (see equation (2.104)) is less than 1.0, a displacement check is decisive and u is taken as 1.0. Otherwise a strength check governs.

Another possibility of verifying the requirements (2.100) and (2.101), if transverse stiffeners are not loaded axially but only with deviation forces, is to perform a first order elastic analysis on the stiffener loaded laterally with the equivalent uniformly distributed deviation forces

$$q_{dev,Ed} = \frac{\pi}{4} \sigma_m (w_0 + w_{el}) \tag{2.106}$$

where

    σ_m is defined in (2.103)
    w_0 is defined in Fig. 2.65
    w_{el} is the elastic deflection of the stiffener. w_{el} may be determined iteratively or it may be taken as the maximum permitted deflection $b/300$.

In the absence of axial forces both approaches (2.102) and (2.106) are equally valid for single and double-sided stiffeners and they lead to reasonable sizes of stiffeners.

2.9.2.2 Shear

Shear in the plate influences transverse stiffeners in two different ways:

- At plate buckling in shear, rigid transverse stiffeners should ensure that there are no lateral movements of the plate at the position of the stiffener. Therefore, adjacent transverse stiffeners should have appropriate stiffness. The check of stiffness is necessary only for intermediate stiffeners, because stiffeners at supports are much stronger by definition.
- In the postcritical state the diagonal tension field develops in the plate (see section 2.5.1). Tension field action induces additional axial forces in the transverse stiffeners (see Fig. 2.68) and additional bending moments in end posts (end supports) due to anchorage of the tension field at plate girder ends. Separate checks for additional axial forces are necessary only at intermediate transverse stiffeners. At stiffeners above the supports all axial actions are summed up in the reaction forces that are relevant for their design.

Rigid end posts

Rigid end posts should have the form of a vertical I profile at the end of the profile. Two double-sided stiffeners or an inserted hot rolled profile may be used for this purpose (see Fig. 2.66).

2. OVERVIEW OF DESIGN RULES

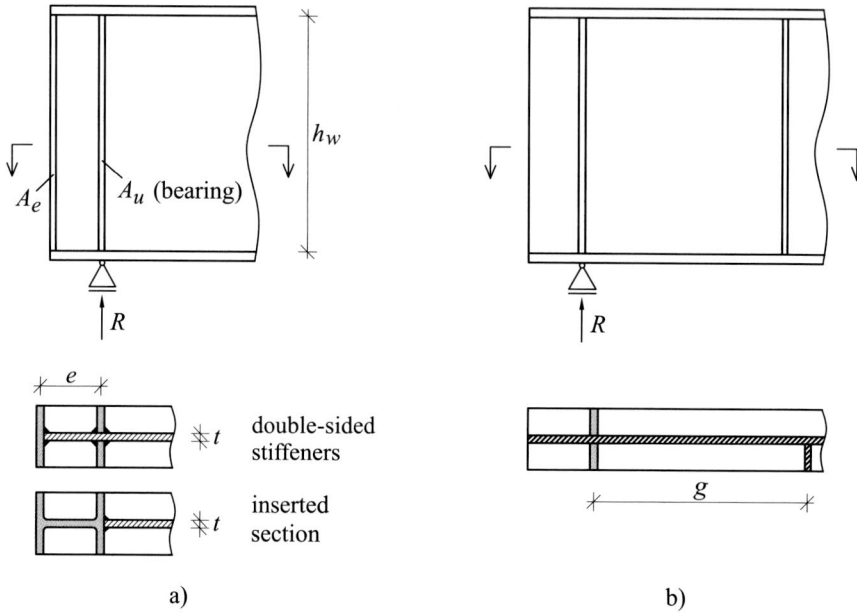

Fig. 2.66: Rigid end post details

To ensure adequate stiffness and strength of the end post (Fig. 2.66a)) the following two requirements should be fulfilled:

$$e > 0.1 \cdot h_w \quad (2.107)$$

$$A_e > \frac{4 \cdot h_w \cdot t^2}{e} \quad (2.108)$$

where e is the centre to centre distance between the stiffeners.

The other flange of an end post with cross section A_u should be checked also as a bearing stiffener to carry reaction force R.

When inserted profiles are used as end posts, the section modulus of such profiles should not be less than $4h_w t^2$ (for bending around the horizontal axis perpendicular to the web).

Another possibility to create a rigid end post is to limit the length g of the panel at the end support such that the panel resists shear loading for the non-rigid end post conditions (Fig. 2.66b).

Non-rigid end posts

When design criteria for rigid end posts are not fulfilled, the end post should be considered as non-rigid (see Fig. 2.67), and the reduced shear resistance of the end panels should be determined according to Eq. (2.52).

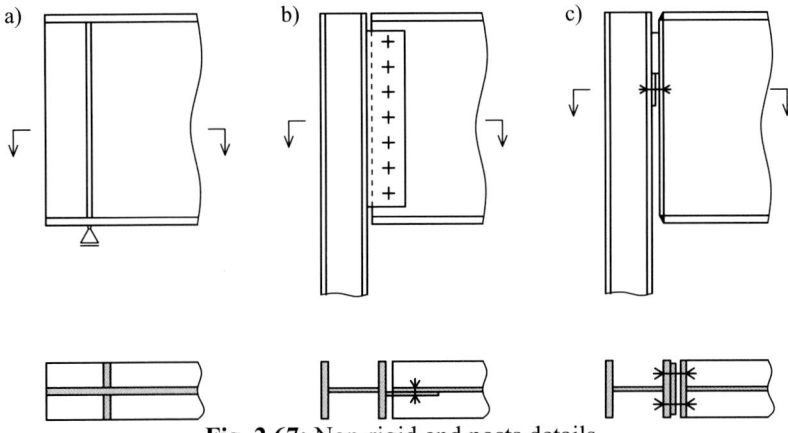

Fig. 2.67: Non-rigid end posts details

Generally single and double-sided stiffeners may be used as non-rigid end posts. If they also act as bearing stiffeners (e.g. Fig. 2.67a)), they should be double-sided.

Intermediate transverse stiffeners

To consider an intermediate transverse stiffener rigid for shear buckling of the plate, the following requirement has to be fulfilled:

$$I_{st} \geq \frac{1.5 h_w^3 t^3}{a^2} \quad \text{for} \quad \alpha = \frac{a}{h_w} < \sqrt{2}$$

$$I_{st} \geq 0.75 h_w t^3 \quad \text{for} \quad \alpha = \frac{a}{h_w} \geq \sqrt{2}$$

(2.109)

where

I_{st} is the second moment of the area of a stiffener for a cross section, defined in Fig. 2.63, for the axis parallel to the web plate.

The requirement (2.109) usually does not demand very strong stiffeners.

Axial force $N_{st,ten}$ in the intermediate stiffener imposed by the tension field action (Fig. 2.68) is calculated as:

$$N_{st,ten} = V_{Ed} - \frac{1}{\overline{\lambda}_w^2} t \cdot h_w \frac{f_y}{\sqrt{3} \cdot \gamma_{M1}} \qquad (2.110)$$

where

V_{Ed} is a design shear force in the adjacent panels. At variable shear forces V_{Ed} is taken at the distance $0.5\ h_w$ from the edge of the panel with the largest shear force (see Fig. 2.68).

$\overline{\lambda}_w$ is a slenderness of the panel adjacent to the stiffener (see Eq. (2.57)).

According to the available test results and numerical simulations (Presta, 2007; Basler et al, 1960; Evans and Tang, 1981) Eq. (2.110) is very conservative (by a factor 2 or more) and overestimates the level of the axial force. This may be problematic, especially for single-sided stiffeners where eccentric introduction of the axial force should be taken into account. When Eq. (2.110) gives a negative value, $N_{st,ten} = 0$. For S355 and shear force equal to the shear design resistance V_{Rd} this happens at $\overline{\lambda}_w = 1.22$ for rigid end posts and $\overline{\lambda}_w = 1.33$ for non-rigid end posts. At larger slenderness $N_{st,ten}$ quickly increases. This problem may be avoided by omitting the transverse stiffeners when possible and reducing the fabrication costs at the same time.

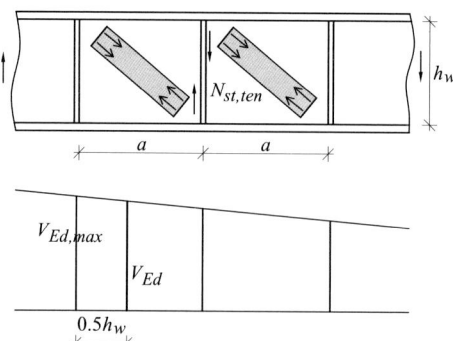

Fig. 2.68: Development of axial force in the intermediate transverse stiffener

2.9.2.3 Simultaneous action of direct stresses and shear

According to EN 1993-1-5 interaction of transverse deviation forces coming from direct stresses in the plate and axial forces in the stiffener coming from shear in the plate and/or external loading (see Fig. 2.62) should be checked and the requirements (2.100) and (2.101) should be fulfilled for each transverse stiffener, but no detailed rules are given.

It can be shown that the effect of deviation forces can be transformed into an additional axial force in the stiffener $\Delta N_{st,\,Ed}$ (Johansson et al, 2007):

$$\Delta N_{st,Ed} = \frac{\sigma_m h_w^2}{\pi^2} \qquad (2.111)$$

This expression considers a stiffener as an axially loaded simply supported and geometrically imperfect column. Certainly, $\Delta N_{st,\,Ed}$ influences only the second order effects in the stiffener increasing bending moments and deflections, but it does not contribute to the increase of uniform direct stresses in the stiffener from axial forces. At single sided stiffeners the additional eccentricity of the axial force should be considered. A simple verification for single and double sided stiffeners can be presented in the form of beam-column interaction formula. Because the model for the deviation force is based on the full web depth h_w, it is not possible to reduce the buckling length due to declining distribution of the axial force $N_{st,ex}$ in the stiffener coming from the concentrated external force F (see sub-section 2.9.2.4). An approximate solution model would be to consider a constant value of axial force $N_{st,ex} = 0.6\,F$.

Double-sided stiffeners

A mechanical model for double-sided stiffeners is shown in Fig. 2.69 including the stiffness and strength checks by Eq. (2.112) and Eq. (2.113):

2. Overview of Design Rules

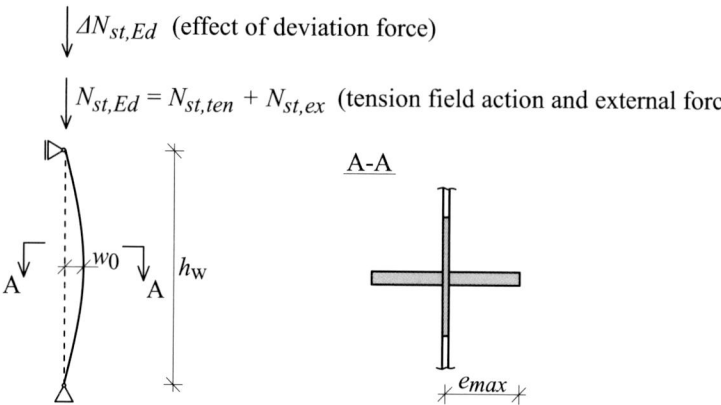

Fig. 2.69: Mechanical model for a double-sided stiffener

$$w = w_0 \frac{1}{\frac{N_{cr,st}}{\sum N_{st,Ed}} - 1} \leq \frac{h_w}{300} \qquad (2.112)$$

$$\sigma_{max} = \frac{N_{st,Ed}}{A_{st}} + \frac{\sum N_{st,Ed} \cdot e_{max}}{I_{st}} w_0 \frac{1}{1 - \frac{\sum N_{st,Ed}}{N_{cr,st}}} \leq \frac{f_y}{\gamma_{M1}} \qquad (2.113)$$

where

w_0 equivalent geometric imperfection of the stiffener according to Fig. 2.65

$N_{cr,st}$ Euler elastic critical force of the stiffener ($N_{cr,st} = \frac{\pi^2 E I_{st}}{h_w^2}$)

$N_{st,Ed}$ = $N_{st,ten} + N_{st,ex}$ (sum of axial forces from the tension field action and from external forces)

$\sum N_{st,Ed}$ = $N_{st,Ed} + \Delta N_{st,Ed}$

A_{st}, I_{st} cross section area and second moment of area of the effective cross section of the stiffener (see Fig. 2.63)

e_{max} the maximum distance from the edge of the stiffener to the centroid of the stiffener (see Fig. 2.69).

Single-sided stiffeners

A mechanical model for a single-sided stiffener is shown in Fig. 2.70.

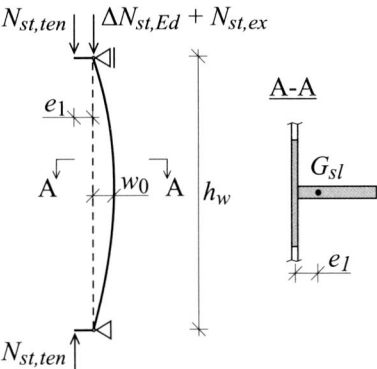

Fig. 2.70: Mechanical model for a single-sided stiffener

Because e_1 is normally much larger than w_0, the opposite orientation of bow imperfection w_0 than that given in Fig. 2.70 is not relevant. The exact analytical solution for the mechanical model in Fig. 2.70 is very complicated. A fairly accurate approximation was developed by Beg and Dujc (2007), see also Johansson et al (2007):

$$w = w_0 \frac{1}{\frac{N_{cr,st}}{\sum N_{st,Ed}} - 1}(1+1.25\delta_m) \le \frac{h_w}{300} \qquad (2.114)$$

$$\sigma_{max} = \left[\frac{\frac{N_{st,Ed}}{A_{st}} + \frac{\sum N_{st,Ed} \cdot e_1}{I_{st}} w_0}{1 - \frac{\sum N_{st,Ed}}{N_{cr,st}}}(1+1.11\delta_m) \right] \le \frac{f_y}{\gamma_{M1}} \qquad (2.115)$$

where

e_1 see Fig. 2.70

$$\delta_m = \frac{N_{st,ten} \cdot e_1}{\sum N_{st,Ed} \cdot w_0}$$

For single-sided stiffeners, expressions (2.114) and (2.115) are not easy to satisfy. This is not because the expressions are very conservative, but because the axial force $N_{st,ten}$ from the tension field action given by Eq.

2. OVERVIEW OF DESIGN RULES

(2.110) is overestimated.

General case

To fulfil the requirements (2.100) and (2.101) the stiffener can also be analysed by FEM taking into account second order effects and relevant imperfections and loadings (deviation and axial forces). The mechanical model is given in Fig. 2.71 and for double-sided stiffeners $e_1 = 0$.

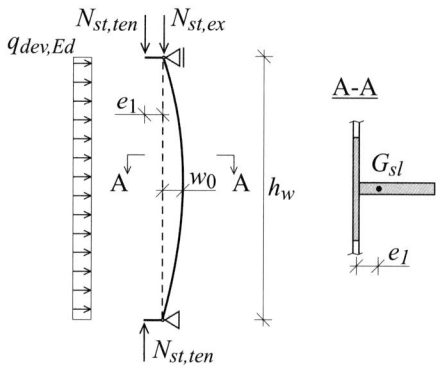

Fig. 2.71: Mechanical model for the general case

$q_{dev.Ed}$ is given by Eq. (2.106) and as a simplification w_{el} may be taken as $b/300$ (the maximum permitted additional deflection). Certainly the actual deflection should be less than $b/300$.

2.9.2.4 Introduction of reaction forces and other large transverse forces

For concentrated loads acting on the flanges of plate or box girders, a transverse stiffener should be provided at the location of a concentrated force if the patch loading resistance in the web is exceeded. The stiffener should be checked for out of plane buckling. If both ends are assumed to be supported laterally, the equivalent buckling length may be taken as $0.75\ h_w$ (see Fig. 2.72). At the intermediate transverse stiffeners the axial force from the tension field action (Eq. (2.110)) should also be included. In the presence of relevant deviation forces from direct stresses in the plate the design checks should be performed according to sub-section 2.9.2.3.

2.9 STIFFENERS AND DETAILING

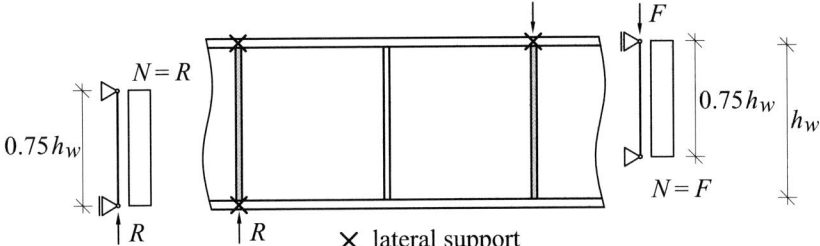

Fig. 2.72: Transverse stiffeners loaded by concentrated loads

The buckling resistance should be determined according to EN 1993-1-1, using buckling curve c. A buckling length larger than $0.75\ h_w$ should be used if less lateral restraint is provided or if the concentrated load acts on both stiffener ends. If a stiffener has a cut-out at the loaded end, the cross section resistance should be checked at that end. Any eccentricity either from single sided stiffener or from other asymmetric stiffener should be accounted for using clauses 6.3.3 or 6.3.4 of EN 1993-1-1 or by the simplified approach of sub-section 2.9.2.3.

2.9.3 Longitudinal stiffeners

2.9.3.1 Direct stresses

Design of longitudinal stiffeners subject to direct stresses is fully incorporated into the design procedures for longitudinally stiffened panels and an additional check of the stiffeners alone is not necessary (see sub-chapter 2.4).

Longitudinal stiffeners may be continuous or discontinuous. They are continuous when they pass through the openings made in the transverse stiffeners or when they are connected to either side of the transverse stiffener (the first solution provides better fatigue performance). They may also run through on the opposite side of a web which is stiffened by a single sided transverse stiffener, see Fig. 2.73c). The cross section of continuous stiffeners can be taken as part of the effective cross section A_{eff} (see sub-chapter 2.4). In all other cases stiffeners have to be considered as discontinuous. Such stiffeners increase the bending stiffness in view of buckling resistance, but they are not considered as part of the cross section to

2. OVERVIEW OF DESIGN RULES

transfer direct stresses due to bending moment or axial force.

EN 1993-1-5 imposes the following limitations to discontinuous stiffeners:

- To be used only for webs (i.e. not allowed in flanges)
- To be neglected in global analysis
- To be neglected in the calculation of stresses
- To be considered in the calculation of effective[p] widths of sub-panels
- To be considered in the calculation of the critical stresses $\sigma_{cr,p}$ and $\sigma_{cr,c}$ (see sub-section 2.4.3.2 and 2.4.4.2).

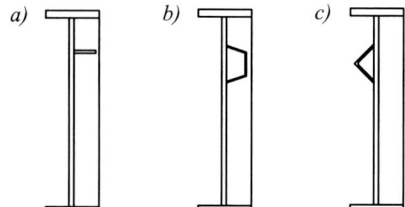

Fig. 2.73: Position of longitudinal stiffeners

To avoid undesirable local failure modes in the plating it is important that discontinuous stiffeners terminate close to the transverse stiffeners, see Fig. 2.74.

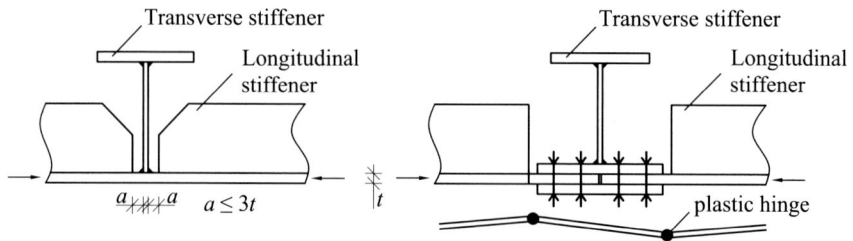

Fig. 2.74: Discontinuity of longitudinal stiffeners

The condition $a \leq 3t$ in Fig. 2.74 is not given in EN 1993-1-5, but is recommended in Johansson et al (2007).

For aesthetic reasons, longitudinal stiffeners are usually installed on the same side of the web as single-sided intermediate transverse stiffeners (inside box-girders, internal sides of twin girders that are facing each other), Fig. 2.73a, and Fig. 2.73b.

Easier fabrication and better fatigue details may be achieved by putting single-sided transverse stiffeners on one side of the web and longitudinal stiffeners on the other side (Fig. 2.73c). This arrangement is possible only with closed longitudinal stiffeners, because at the intersection with transverse stiffeners the latter do not provide torsional restraint for open longitudinal stiffeners.

2.9.3.2 Shear

When stiffened plates are loaded in shear, no special design checks are needed for longitudinal stiffeners. The influence of longitudinal stiffeners is reflected in the calculation of the shear buckling coefficient of a stiffened panel, Eq. (2.59) or (2.60). The presence of longitudinal stiffeners certainly increases the plate shear resistance.

2.9.4 Torsional buckling of stiffeners

Design rules for stiffened plates and stiffeners assume that torsional buckling of longitudinal and transverse stiffeners is completely prevented when loaded axially. This concerns only open stiffeners, because closed stiffeners are not susceptible to torsional buckling. EN 1993-1-5 gives only the general criterion to avoid torsional buckling and a specific rule for flat stiffeners. Generally the following requirement should be fulfilled:

$$\sigma_{cr} \geq \theta f_y \qquad (2.116)$$

where

- σ_{cr} is the elastic critical stress of a stiffener at torsional buckling
- θ = 2 for flat stiffeners
- θ = 6 for other open stiffeners that possess also warping stiffness (T, Γ, etc.).

Parameter θ defines the length of the plateau of the buckling curve where torsional buckling does not occur. At $\theta = 2$ the slenderness of the end of the plateau is 0.7 (as for local buckling) and at $\theta = 6$ this value is 0.4 (as for lateral torsional buckling).

2. OVERVIEW OF DESIGN RULES

For flat stiffeners the requirement (2.116) may be rewritten as

$$\frac{I_t}{I_p} \geq 5.3 \frac{f_y}{E} \qquad (2.117)$$

where

I_t is the St. Venant torsional constant of the stiffener alone (without contributing plating)

I_p is the polar second moment area of the stiffener alone around the edge fixed to the plate

Considering the dimensions of a flat stiffener the requirement (2.117) may be further simplified (Fig. 2.75) and the limiting width to thickness ratio for standard steel grades is given in Table 2.6.

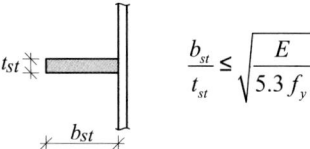

Fig. 2.75: Torsional buckling of flat stiffeners

Table 2.6: Limit ratio b_{st}/t_{st} for flat stiffeners to prevent torsional buckling

Steel grade	235	275	355	420	460
$b_{st}/t_{st} \leq$	13.0	12.0	10.6	9.7	9.3

For the stiffeners with warping stiffness conservatively the requirement (2.117) may be applied or a more accurate expression for σ_{cr} may be taken from the literature (e.g. Iyengar, 1988):

$$\sigma_{cr} = \frac{1}{I_p}\left(\frac{\pi^2 EI_w}{l^2} + GI_t\right) \qquad (2.118)$$

where

I_w is the warping cross section constant of the stiffener alone around the edge fixed to the plate

l is the length of the stiffener (transverse stiffeners are usually torsionally restrained at both ends and longitudinal stiffeners

2.9 STIFFENERS AND DETAILING

at intersection with transverse stiffeners)
G   is the shear elastic modulus

The problem is that for longer stiffeners the effect of the warping stiffness becomes small and the ratio I_t/I_p is small anyway. For shorter stiffeners where warping torsion prevails the ratio I_w/I_p does not always increase significantly if the cross section of the stiffener is increased (see Fig. 2.76).

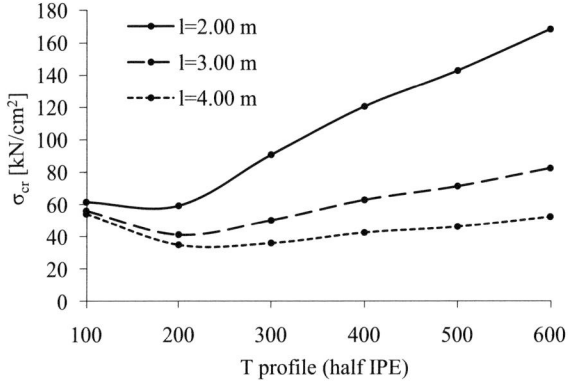

Fig. 2.76: σ_{cr} for T profile (half of IPE) for different profile sizes

For these reasons the requirement (2.116) with $\theta = 6$ is not easy to fulfil. There are two fairly simple ways to overcome the problem:

- Relaxing the requirement (2.116) by replacing f_y with the maximum actual stress $\sigma_{act,Ed}$ that occurs in the stiffener under consideration. This may work for intermediate transverse stiffeners that are never loaded axially close to the plastic loading and for longitudinal stiffeners in webs, if the stiffeners are located away from the most stressed edge of the plate. However, in the flanges, longitudinal stiffeners may be easily stressed close to f_y.
- Increasing σ_{cr} by taking advantage of the contributing plating (Johansson et al, 2007) acting as a continuous elastic support c_θ (continuous rotational stiffness), see Fig. 2.77 for two typical stiffener arrangements. For other cases the calculation of c_θ is straightforward.

2. Overview of Design Rules

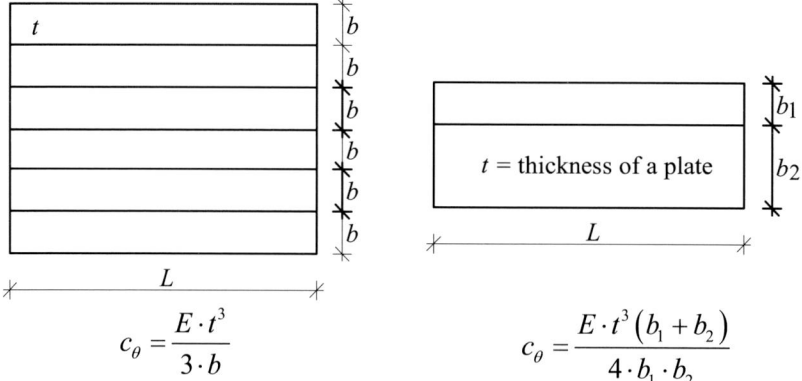

Fig. 2.77: c_θ for two typical stiffener arrangements

In this case σ_{cr} is given as follows:

$$\sigma_{cr} = \frac{1}{I_p}\left(\frac{\pi^2 EI_w}{l^2} + GI_t + \frac{c_\theta l^2}{\pi^2}\right) \quad \text{for } l < l_{cr} \qquad (2.119)$$

$$\sigma_{cr} = \frac{1}{I_p}\left(2\sqrt{c_\theta EI_w} - GI_t\right) \quad \text{for } l > l_{cr} \qquad (2.120)$$

where

$$l_{cr} = \pi \sqrt[4]{\frac{EI_w}{c_\theta}} \qquad (2.121)$$

2.9.5 Structural detailing related to plate buckling

2.9.5.1 Transverse welds in the plate

When the plate thickness is changed, the transverse weld in the plate should be sufficiently close to the transverse stiffener so that the effect of eccentricity may be disregarded. The distance of the weld from the transverse stiffener should fulfil the requirement given in Fig. 2.78 or the effect of eccentricity should be accounted for in the design of the plate.

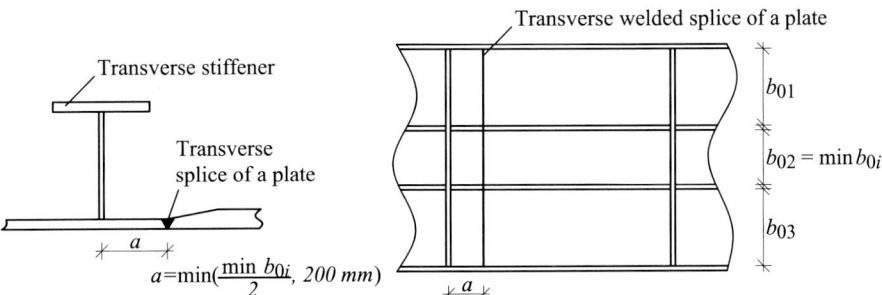

Fig. 2.78: Location of the transverse weld in the plate

2.9.5.2 Cut-outs in stiffeners

Cut-outs in longitudinal stiffeners should be limited in length and depth to prevent plate buckling and to control the net section resistance, see Fig. 2.79.

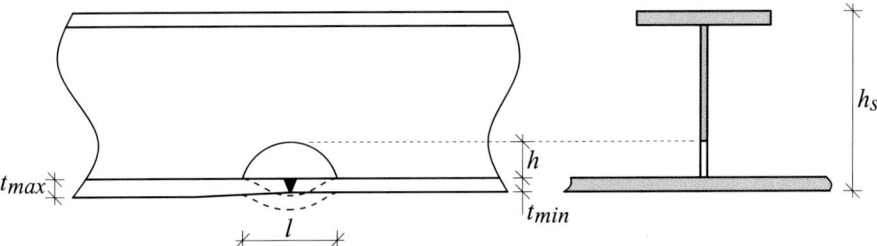

Fig. 2.79: Cut-outs in longitudinal stiffeners

Length l and depth h of the cut-out should not exceed:
$l \leq 6\ t_{min}$ for flat stiffeners in compression,
$l \leq 8\ t_{min}$ for other stiffeners in compression,
$l \leq 15\ t_{min}$ for stiffeners without compression,
$h \leq \min(h_s/4,\ 40\ mm)$.

The limiting value of the hole length l for stiffeners in compression may be increased with the factor $\sqrt{\sigma_{x,Rd}/\sigma_{x,Ed}}$ up to $15\ t_{min}$, where $\sigma_{x,Rd}$ and $\sigma_{x,Ed}$ are the stress at design resistance and the actual stress at the location of the cut-out, respectively (calculated according to beam theory). The dimensions of cut-outs in transverse stiffeners should be as shown in Fig. 2.80.

2. OVERVIEW OF DESIGN RULES

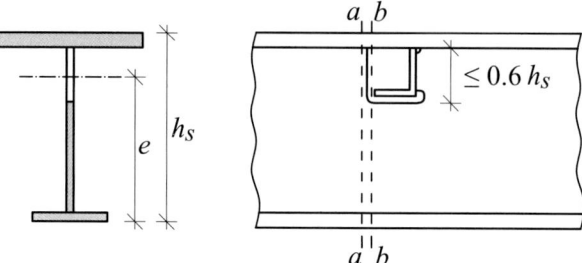

Fig. 2.80: Cut-outs in transverse stiffeners

Additionally, the gross cross section of the web a-a adjacent to the cut-out should resist a shear force V_{Ed}:

$$V_{Ed} = \frac{I_{net}}{e} \frac{f_y \pi}{\gamma_{M0} b_G} \tag{2.122}$$

where

I_{net} is the second moment of area for the net section of the transverse stiffener b-b, see Fig. 2.80

e is the maximum distance from the neutral axis of the net section to the outmost fibre of the stiffener

b_G is the length of the transverse stiffener (for web stiffeners the distance between flanges, for flange stiffeners of box girders the distance between adjacent webs).

2.9.5.3 Welds

Web to flange weld should be designed for the shear flow v_{Ed} as follows (see also section 2.5.2):

$$v_{Ed} = \frac{V_{Ed}}{h_w} \qquad \text{when} \quad V_{Ed} \leq V_{bw,Rd} \tag{2.123}$$

$$v_{Ed} = \eta \cdot t \frac{f_y}{\sqrt{3} \cdot \gamma_{M1}} \qquad \text{when} \quad V_{Ed} > V_{bw,Rd} \tag{2.124}$$

2.9.6 Design examples

Example 2.9-1: Torsional buckling of stiffeners.

According to EN1993-1-5, clauses 9.2.1.(8) and 9.2.1.(9) torsional buckling of stiffeners should be completely prevented by fulfilling the following requirement (2.116):

$$\sigma_{cr} > \theta f_y$$

In some cases this requirement may be very stringent. To solve the problem the stiffness of the plate may be taken into account when calculating σ_{cr} or f_y may be replaced with the maximum design value of the stress in the stiffeners.

a) Transverse stiffener in a web

$a = 4000$ mm
$h_w = l = 3000$ mm
$t_w = 15$ mm

$b_1 = 200$ mm
$b_2 = 200$ mm
$t_1 = 10$ mm
$t_2 = 10$ mm

S355 $f_y = 355$ N/mm² $V_{Ed} = 2000$ kN   (See Fig. 2.68)

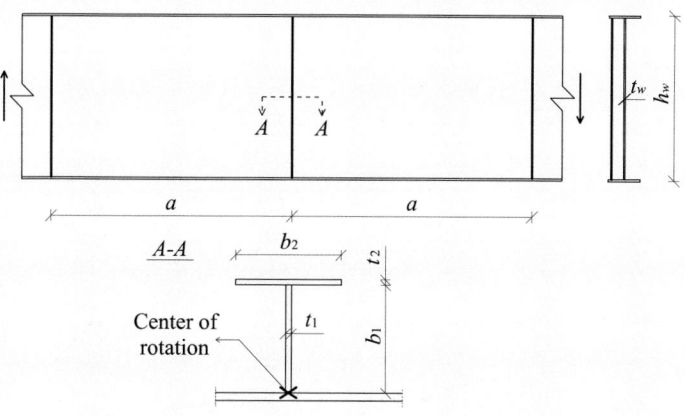

2. Overview of Design Rules

$$A = b_1 \cdot t_1 + b_2 \cdot t_2 = 200 \cdot 10 + 200 \cdot 10 = 4000 \text{ mm}^2$$

$$I_t = \frac{b_1 \cdot t_1^3}{3} + \frac{b_2 \cdot t_2^3}{3} = \frac{200 \cdot 10^3}{3} + \frac{200 \cdot 10^3}{3} = 1.333 \times 10^5 \text{ mm}^4$$

$$I_p = \frac{b_1^3 \cdot t_1}{3} + b_2 \cdot t_2 \cdot \left(b_1 + \frac{t_2}{2}\right)^2 + \frac{b_2^3 \cdot t_2}{12} =$$

$$= \frac{200^3 \cdot 12}{3} + 200 \cdot 10 \cdot \left(200 + \frac{10}{2}\right)^2 + \frac{200^3 \cdot 10}{12} = 1.174 \times 10^8 \text{ mm}^4$$

$$I_w = \frac{b_2^3 \cdot t_2 \left(b_1 + \frac{t_2}{2}\right)^2}{12} = \frac{200^3 \cdot 10 \cdot \left(200 + \frac{10}{2}\right)^2}{12} = 2.802 \times 10^{11} \text{ mm}^6$$

I_p and I_w are calculated for the stiffener alone taking the stiffener - plate connection line as the reference axis.

Four different approaches are applied to fulfil the requirement (2.116):

Case 1: Neglecting the warping stiffness

$$\sigma_{cr} \geq 2 f_y$$

$$\sigma_{cr} = \frac{G \cdot I_t}{I_p} = \frac{81000 \cdot 1.333 \times 10^5}{1.174 \times 10^8} =$$

$$= 91.98 \text{ N/mm}^2 < 2 \cdot f_y = 2 \cdot 355 = 710 \text{ N/mm}^2$$

The expression above is only a more general form of (2.117). Generally, this requirement is difficult to fulfil even if a much larger stiffener is employed (for a T stiffener it is practically impossible) and the warping stiffness should be taken into account.

Case 2: Taking warping stiffness into account

$$\sigma_{cr} \geq 6 f_y$$

2.9 STIFFENERS AND DETAILING

$$\sigma_{cr} = \frac{1}{I_p}\left(\frac{\pi^2 \cdot E \cdot I_w}{l^2} + G \cdot I_t\right) =$$

$$= \left[\frac{1}{1.174 \times 10^8}\left(\frac{\pi^2 \cdot 210000 \cdot 2.802 \times 10^{11}}{3000^2} + 81000 \cdot 1.333 \times 10^5\right)\right] =$$

$$= 642 \text{ N/mm}^2 < 6 \cdot f_y = 6 \cdot 355 = 2130 \text{ N/mm}^2$$

A larger stiffener is required to fulfil this requirement. A stiffener with $b_1/t_1 = b_2/t_2 = 400\,\text{mm}/20\,\text{mm}$ gives

$$\sigma_{cr} = 2290 \text{ N/mm}^2 > 6 \cdot f_y = 6 \cdot 355 = 2130 \text{ N/mm}^2 \checkmark$$

Case 3: Taking account of the real design axial stress in the stiffener

Axial force from the tension field action may be calculated according to Eq. (2.110). For the web panel between two transverse stiffeners a relative stenderness $\overline{\lambda}_w$ is calculated as follows:

$$\alpha = \frac{a}{h_w} = \frac{4000}{3000} = 1.33$$

$$\varepsilon = \sqrt{\frac{235}{f_y}} = \sqrt{\frac{235}{355}} = 0.814$$

$$k_\tau = 5.34 + \frac{4}{\alpha^2} = 5.34 + \frac{4}{1.33^2} = 7.59$$

$$\overline{\lambda}_w = \frac{h_w}{t_w} \cdot \frac{1}{37.4 \cdot \varepsilon \cdot \sqrt{k_\tau}} = \frac{3000}{15} \cdot \frac{1}{37.4 \cdot 0.814 \cdot \sqrt{7.59}} = 2.39$$

$$N_{Ed} = V_{Ed} - \frac{1}{\overline{\lambda}_w^2} \cdot \frac{h_w \cdot t_w \cdot f_y}{\sqrt{3} \cdot \gamma_{M1}} =$$

$$= 2000 \cdot 10^3 - \frac{1}{2.39^2} \cdot \frac{3000 \cdot 15 \cdot 355}{\sqrt{3} \cdot 1.0} = 385.3 \times 10^3 \text{ N}$$

$$\sigma_{Ed,act} = \frac{N_{Ed}}{A} = \frac{385.3 \cdot 10^3}{4000} = 96.3 \text{ N/mm}^2$$

If design axial force is small or even zero, it is advisable to consider a suitable lower limit of $\sigma_{Ed,act}$. A value $0.3 f_y$ is recommended here:

$$\sigma_{Ed,act} = 96.3 \text{ N/mm}^2 < 0.3 \cdot f_y = 0.3 \cdot 355 = 106.5 \text{ N/mm}^2$$

$$\sigma_{cr} = 642 > 6 \cdot \sigma_{Ed,act} = 6 \cdot 106.5 = 639 \text{ N/mm}^2 \checkmark$$

This approach is not allowed explicitly by EN1993-1-5 but is in line with similar situations where the actual stress is employed instead of f_y (see plate buckling in EN 1993-1-5, clause 4.4(4)).

Case 4: Taking account of the stiffness of the plate (acting as a rotational spring)

$$c_\theta = \frac{E \cdot t_w^3}{3 \cdot a} = \frac{210000 \cdot 15^3}{3 \cdot 4000} = 59.1 \times 10^3 \text{ N}$$

$$l_{cr} = \pi \sqrt[4]{\frac{E \cdot I_w}{c_\theta}} = \pi \sqrt[4]{\frac{210000 \cdot 2.802 \times 10^{11}}{59.1 \times 10^3}} = 3135.7 \text{ mm}$$

$$l_{cr} = 3135.7 \text{ mm} > l = 3000 \text{ mm}$$

$$\sigma_{cr} = \frac{1}{I_p} \left(\frac{\pi^2 \cdot E \cdot I_w}{l^2} + G \cdot I_t + \frac{c_\theta l^2}{\pi^2} \right) =$$

$$= \frac{1}{1.174 \times 10^8} \left[\begin{array}{c} \dfrac{\pi^2 \cdot 210000 \cdot 2.802 \times 10^{11}}{3000^2} + \\ + 81000 \cdot 1.333 \times 10^5 + \dfrac{59.1 \times 10^3 \cdot 3000^2}{\pi^2} \end{array} \right] =$$

$$= 1100.7 \text{ N/mm}^2 < 6 \cdot f_y = 6 \cdot 355 = 2130 \text{ N/mm}^2$$

For a transverse stiffener the contribution of the plate is important only if the plate thickness is large enough as the distance of transverse stiffeners a is rather large.

2.9 STIFFENERS AND DETAILING

b) Longitudinal stiffeners in the flange of a box girder

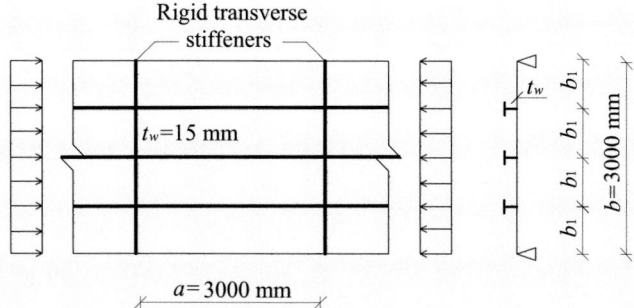

$\sigma_{Ed,act} = 312 \text{ N/mm}^2$

$b_1 = \dfrac{b}{4} = 750 \text{ mm}$

$a = l = 3000 \text{ mm}$

The stiffener has the same geometry as the transverse stiffener in the previous numerical example a). In this case the four options for preventing torsional buckling give the following results:

Case 1: Neglecting the warping stiffness

The same result as in a) Case 1:

$\sigma_{cr} = 91.98 \text{ N/mm}^2 < 2 \cdot f_y = 2 \cdot 355 = 710 \text{ N/mm}^2$

Case 2: Taking warping stiffness into account

The same result as in a) Case 2:

$\sigma_{cr} = 642 \text{ N/mm}^2 < 6 \cdot f_y = 6 \cdot 355 = 2130 \text{ N/mm}^2$

For larger stiffener with $b_1/t_1 = b_2/t_2 = 400 \text{ mm}/20 \text{ mm}$:

$\sigma_{cr} = 2290 \text{ N/mm}^2 > 6 \cdot f_y = 6 \cdot 355 = 2130 \text{ N/mm}^2$ ✓

2. OVERVIEW OF DESIGN RULES

Case 3: Taking account of a real design axial stress in the stiffener

$$\sigma_{Ed,act} = 312 \text{ N/mm}^2$$

$$\sigma_{cr} = 642 \text{ N/mm}^2 < 6 \cdot \sigma_{Ed,act} = 6 \cdot 312 = 1875 \text{ N/mm}^2$$

When the actual stress is close to f_y, this case is not very helpful.

Case 4: Taking account of stiffness of a plate (acting as a rotational spring)

$$c_\theta = \frac{E \cdot t_w^3}{3 \cdot b_1} = \frac{210000 \cdot 15^3}{3 \cdot 750} = 315 \times 10^3 \text{ N}$$

$$l_{cr} = \pi \sqrt[4]{\frac{E \cdot I_w}{c_\theta}} = \pi \sqrt[4]{\frac{210000 \cdot 2.802 \cdot 10^{11}}{315.10^3}} = 2065.4 \text{ mm}$$

$$l_{cr} = 2065.4 \text{ mm} < l = 3000 \text{ mm}$$

$$\sigma_{cr} = \frac{1}{I_p}\left(2\sqrt{c_\theta \cdot E \cdot I_w} - G \cdot I_t\right) =$$

$$= \left[\frac{1}{1.174 \times 10^8}\left(2\sqrt{315 \times 10^3 \cdot 210000 \cdot 2.802 \times 10^{11}} - 81000 \cdot 1.333 \times 10^5\right)\right] =$$

$$= 2227.4 \text{ N/mm}^2 > 6 \cdot f_y = 6 \cdot 355 = 2130 \text{ N/mm}^2 \checkmark$$

More closely spaced longitudinal stiffeners help to increase the continuous elastic support of the plate c_θ and the requirement for torsional buckling is fulfilled.

Example 2.9-2: Intermediate transverse stiffeners

In this numerical example the intermediate transverse stiffeners are checked at two relevant locations:

2.9 STIFFENERS AND DETAILING

- Near midspan, where only deviation forces from direct stresses (sagging moments) act on the transverse stiffener;
- Near the internal support, where besides deviation forces from direct stresses (hogging moments) also the axial force from the tension field action (shear) acts on the transverse stiffener.

In all cases the strength and the stiffness requirement at the ultimate limit state should be fulfilled (see sub-section 2.9.2.1):

$$\sigma_{st,\max} \leq \frac{f_y}{\gamma_{M1}}, \quad w \leq \frac{b}{300}.$$

2.9-2.1 Data

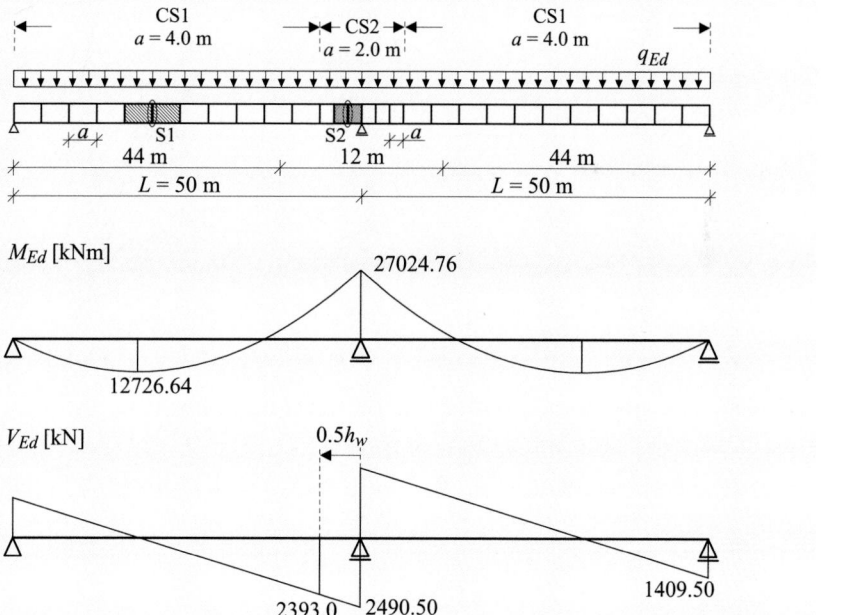

Fig. 2.81: The outline of the plated girder, transverse stiffeners, load and distribution of internal forces

2. OVERVIEW OF DESIGN RULES

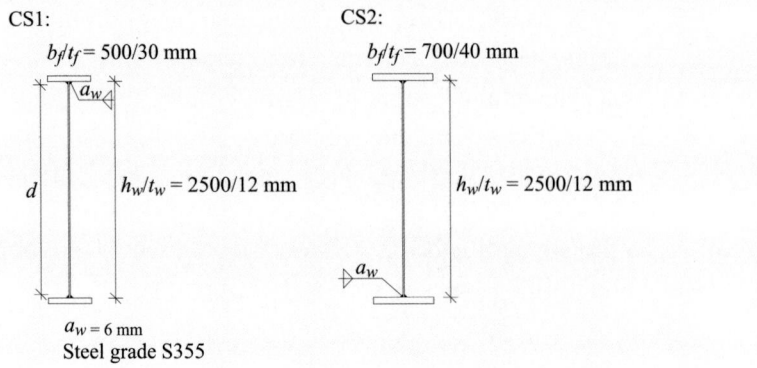

$a_w = 6$ mm
Steel grade S355

Fig. 2.82: The geometry of cross sections

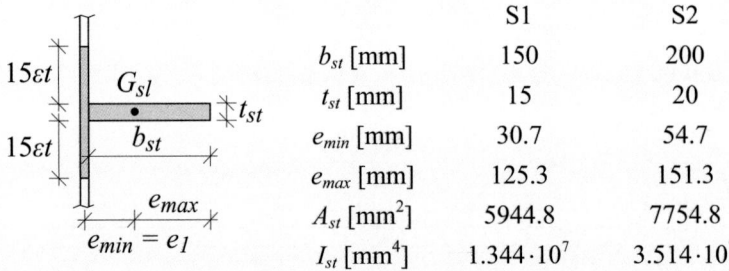

	S1	S2
b_{st} [mm]	150	200
t_{st} [mm]	15	20
e_{min} [mm]	30.7	54.7
e_{max} [mm]	125.3	151.3
A_{st} [mm^2]	5944.8	7754.8
I_{st} [mm^4]	$1.344 \cdot 10^7$	$3.514 \cdot 10^7$

Fig. 2.83: Geometric characteristics of single-sided flat transverse stiffener S1 and S2

2.9-2.2 Transverse stiffener in the mid-span region

Single-sided flat stiffener 150/15

EN 1993-1-5 provides two methods for checking transverse stiffeners (in the absence of the axial force in the stiffener):
 - direct calculation of the required second moment of area of the stiffener $I_{st,req}$;
 - bending check due to equivalent deviation $q_{dev,Ed}$.

a) Direct calculation of $I_{st,req}$

The web of both cross sections is of Class 4. The calculation of the effective widths of the web (equal for both cross sections, S1 and S2) is needed to determine the equivalent axial force N_{Ed} in the web.

2.9 Stiffeners and Detailing

$$\psi = -1 \Rightarrow k_\sigma = 23.9$$

$$d = h_w - 2a_w\sqrt{2} = 2500 - 2 \cdot 6 \cdot \sqrt{2} = 2483.0 \text{ mm}$$

$$\overline{\lambda}_p = \frac{d/t_w}{28.4 \cdot \varepsilon \cdot \sqrt{k_\sigma}} = \frac{2483.0/12}{28.4 \cdot 0.814 \cdot \sqrt{23.9}} = 1.832$$

$$\overline{\lambda}_p = 1.832 > 0.5 + \sqrt{0.085 - 0.055 \cdot \psi} = 0.5 + \sqrt{0.085 + 0.055 \cdot 1} = 0.874$$

$$\rho = \frac{\overline{\lambda}_p - 0.055 \cdot (3+\psi)}{\overline{\lambda}_p^2} = \frac{1.832 - 0.055 \cdot (3-1)}{1.832^2} = 0.513$$

$$b_c = \frac{d}{(1-\psi)} = \frac{2483.0}{(1+1)} = 1241.5 \text{ mm}$$

$$b_{eff} = \rho \cdot b_c = 0.513 \cdot 1241.5 = 637.1 \text{ mm}$$

$$b_{e1} = 0.4 \cdot b_{eff} + a_w\sqrt{2} = 0.4 \cdot 637.1 + 6 \cdot \sqrt{2} = 263.3 \text{ mm}$$

$$b_{e2} = 0.6 \cdot b_{eff} = 0.6 \cdot 637.1 = 382.2 \text{ mm}$$

The centroid of the effective section moves downwards by 94.1 mm and the new b_{e2} and b_c are (see Fig. 2.84):

$$b_{e2} = 476.4 \text{ mm}$$

$$b_c = 1335.6 \text{ mm}$$

Effective second moment of area for the cross section CS1 under pure bending:

$$I_{eff} = 5.955 \cdot 10^{10} \text{ mm}^4$$

The effective section moduli for the compression edge of the girder's web:

$$W_{eff} = \frac{I_{eff}}{b_c + a_w\sqrt{2}} = \frac{5.955 \cdot 10^{10}}{1335.6 + 6\sqrt{2}} = 4.430 \cdot 10^7 \text{ mm}^3,$$

The maximum compressive stress at the edge of the web panel:

2. OVERVIEW OF DESIGN RULES

$$\sigma_{max,Ed} = \frac{M_{max}}{W_{eff}} = \frac{12.727 \cdot 10^9}{4.430 \cdot 10^7} = 287.3 \, \text{N/mm}^2$$

The following criterion for second moment of area should be fulfilled:

$$I_{st,act} \geq I_{st} = \frac{\sigma_m}{E} \left(\frac{b}{\pi}\right)^4 \left(1 + w_0 \frac{300}{b} u\right)$$

$$a_1 = a_2 = 4000 \, \text{mm}, \, b = h_w = 2500 \, \text{mm}$$

Equivalent axial force in the web N_{Ed} represents the resultant of compression direct stresses and should not be taken as less than the maximum compressive stress at the edge of the panel times half of the effective[p] compressive area of the panel:

$$N_{Ed} \geq \frac{A_{c,eff}^p}{2} \sigma_{max,Ed}$$

Calculation of the stress resultant N_{Ed}:

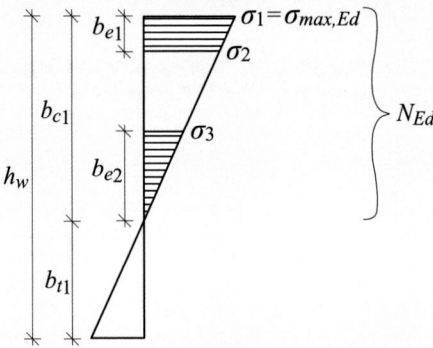

Fig. 2.84: Stress distribution on the effective cross section of the girder's web

$$b_{c,1} = b_c + a_w \sqrt{2} = 1335.6 + 6\sqrt{2} = 1344.1 \, \text{mm}$$

$$b_{t,1} = b_t + a_w \sqrt{2} = 1147.4 + 6\sqrt{2} = 1155.9 \, \text{mm}$$

Stresses σ_1, σ_2, σ_3 can be expressed as:

$$\sigma_1 = \sigma_{max,Ed} = 287.3 \, \text{N/mm}^2$$

$$\sigma_2 = \sigma_1 - \left(\sigma_1 \frac{b_{e1}}{b_{c1}}\right) = 287.3 - \left(287.3 \frac{263.3}{1344.1}\right) = 231.0 \, \text{N/mm}^2$$

$$\sigma_3 = \sigma_1 \frac{b_{e2}}{b_{c1}} = 287.3 \frac{476.4}{1344.1} = 101.8 \, \text{N/mm}^2$$

Equivalent axial force in the web N_{Ed}:

$$N_{Ed} = \left(b_{e1} \frac{\sigma_1 + \sigma_2}{2} + b_{e2} \frac{\sigma_3}{2}\right) t_w$$

$$= \left(263.3 \frac{287.3 + 231.0}{2} + 476.4 \frac{101.8}{2}\right) \cdot 12 = 1.110 \cdot 10^6 \, \text{N}$$

$$A^p_{c,eff} = (b_{e1} + b_{e2}) t_w = (263.3 + 476.4) 12 = 8876.2 \, \text{mm}^2$$

$$N_{Ed} = 1.110 \cdot 10^6 \, \text{N} < \frac{A^p_{c,eff}}{2} \cdot \sigma_{max,Ed} = \frac{8876.2}{2} \cdot 287.3 = 1.275 \cdot 10^6 \, \text{N}$$

$$\rightarrow N_{Ed} = 1.275 \cdot 10^6 \, \text{N}$$

$$\sigma_{cr,c} = \frac{\pi^2 \cdot E \cdot t_w^2}{12(1-v^2)a^2} = \frac{\pi^2 \cdot 210000 \cdot 12^2}{12(1-0.3^2)4000^2} = 1.7 \, \text{N/mm}^2$$

$$\sigma_{cr,p} = k_\sigma \frac{\pi^2 \cdot E \cdot t_w^2}{12(1-v^2)b^2} = 23.9 \frac{\pi^2 \cdot 210000 \cdot 12^2}{12(1-0.3^2)2500^2} = 104.5 \, \text{N/mm}^2$$

$$\frac{\sigma_{cr,c}}{\sigma_{cr,p}} = \frac{1.7}{104.5} = 0.02 < 0.5 \rightarrow \frac{\sigma_{cr,c}}{\sigma_{cr,p}} = 0.5$$

$$\sigma_m = \frac{\sigma_{cr,c}}{\sigma_{cr,p}} \frac{N_{Ed}}{b} \left(\frac{1}{a_1} + \frac{1}{a_2}\right) = 0.5 \cdot \frac{1.275 \cdot 10^6}{2500} \left(\frac{2}{4000}\right) = 0.127 \, \text{N/mm}^2$$

$$e_{max} = 125.3 \, \text{mm}$$

$$u = \frac{\pi^2 \cdot E \cdot e_{max}}{\frac{f_y \cdot 300 \cdot b}{\gamma_{M1}}} = \frac{\pi^2 \cdot 210000 \cdot 125.3}{\frac{355 \cdot 300 \cdot 2500}{1.1}} = 1.07$$

2. OVERVIEW OF DESIGN RULES

$u = 1.07 \geq 1.0$

$$w_0 = \min\left[\frac{b}{300}, \frac{a}{300}\right] = \min\left[\frac{2500}{300}, \frac{4000}{300}\right] = \frac{2500}{300} = 8.3 \text{ mm}$$

$$I_{st,act} \geq I_{st} = \frac{\sigma_m}{E}\left(\frac{b}{\pi}\right)^4\left(1 + w_0 \frac{300}{b} u\right)$$

$$= \frac{0.127}{210000}\left(\frac{2500}{\pi}\right)^4\left(1 + 8.3\frac{300}{2500} \cdot 1.07\right) = 0.050 \cdot 10^7 \text{ mm}^4$$

$$I_{st,act} = 1.344 \cdot 10^7 \text{ mm}^4 \geq I_{st,req} = 0.050 \cdot 10^7 \text{ mm}^4 \checkmark$$

b) Bending check due to equivalent deviation force $q_{dev,Ed}$

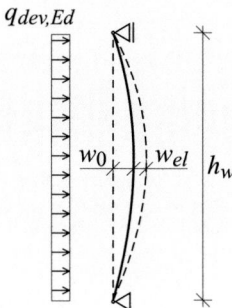

Fig. 2.85: Mechanical model for transverse stiffener

$$q_{dev,Ed} = \frac{\pi}{4}\sigma_m(w_0 + w_{el}) = \frac{\pi}{4} \cdot 0.127(2 \cdot 8.3) = 1.669 \text{ N/mm}$$

For the sake of simplicity for w_{el} the maximum allowable value $b/300 = 8.3$ mm was taken. Otherwise an iterative procedure is required.

$$M_{max} = \frac{q_{dev,Ed} \cdot b^2}{8} = \frac{1.669 \cdot 2500^2}{8} = 1.304 \cdot 10^6 \text{ Nmm}$$

$$w_{max} = \frac{5 \cdot q_{dev,Ed} \cdot b^4}{384 \cdot E \cdot I_{st,act}} = \frac{5 \cdot 1.669 \cdot 2500^4}{384 \cdot 210000 \cdot 1.344 \cdot 10^7} = 0.3 \text{ mm}$$

2.9 STIFFENERS AND DETAILING

$$\sigma_{st,max} = \frac{M_{max} \cdot e_{max}}{I_{st,act}} = \frac{1.304 \cdot 10^6 \cdot 125.3}{1.344 \cdot 10^7} = 12.2\,\text{N}/\text{mm}^2$$

$$\sigma_{st,max} = 12.2\,\text{N}/\text{mm}^2 < \frac{f_y}{\gamma_{M1}} = \frac{355}{1.1} = 322.7\,\text{N}/\text{mm}^2 \checkmark$$

$$w_{max} = 0.3\,\text{mm} < w_{el} = 8.3\,\text{mm},\checkmark$$

where w_{max} is the maximum stiffener deflection at midspan.

In this case the required second moment of area of the stiffener is small. Usually simplifications related to the calculation of N_{Ed} (taking f_y/γ_{M0} instead of $\sigma_{max,Ed}$) and w_{el} (assuming that w_{el} is equal to the maximum allowable displacement $b/300$ and avoiding the iterative procedure) do not increase significantly the demands for the second moment of area of the stiffener.

2.9-2.3 Transverse stiffener close to the internal support

Single-sided flat stiffener 200/20

Torsional buckling check of the flat stiffener (acc. to Table 2.6)

$$\frac{b_{st}}{t_{st}} = \frac{200}{20} = 10 \leq 10.6 \checkmark$$

Torsional buckling of the stiffener is prevented.

a) **Simplified stability check according to Beg and Dujc (2007)**

$$a_1 = a_2 = 2000\,\text{mm},\ b = h_w = 2500\,\text{mm}$$

Minimum required second moment of area of the stiffener to prevent shear buckling:

$$\alpha = \frac{a}{b} = \frac{2000}{2500} = 0.8 < \sqrt{2}$$

2. OVERVIEW OF DESIGN RULES

$$I_{st} \geq I_{st,req} = \frac{1.5 \cdot b^3 \cdot t^3}{a^2}$$

$$I_{st,req} = \frac{1.5 \cdot b^3 \cdot t^3}{a^2} = \frac{1.5 \cdot 2500^3 \cdot 12^3}{2000^2} = 1.013 \cdot 10^7 \text{ mm}^4$$

$$I_{st} = 3.514 \cdot 10^7 \text{ mm}^4 > I_{st,req} = 1.013 \cdot 10^7 \text{ mm}^4 \checkmark$$

For single sided stiffener the following two criteria should be fulfilled (interaction of direct and shear stresses in the web):

$$w = w_0 \frac{1}{\frac{N_{cr,st}}{\sum N_{st,Ed}} - 1} (1 + 1.25 \delta_m) \leq \frac{b}{300}$$

$$\sigma_{max} = \left[\frac{\frac{N_{st,Ed}}{A_{st}} + \frac{\sum N_{st,Ed} \cdot e_1}{I_{st}} w_0}{1 - \frac{\sum N_{st,Ed}}{N_{cr,st}}} (1 + 1.11 \delta_m) \right] \leq \frac{f_y}{\gamma_{M1}}$$

Axial force in the stiffener from the tension field:

Design shear force in adjacent panel is taken at the distance $0.5\ b = 1250$ mm from the inner support (Fig. 2.81):

$$V_{Ed} = 2.393 \cdot 10^6 \text{ N}$$

$$N_{st,ten} = V_{Ed} - \frac{1}{\lambda_w^2} t_w \cdot b \frac{f_y}{\sqrt{3} \cdot \gamma_{M1}}$$

$$= 2.393 \cdot 10^6 - \frac{1}{1.935^2} 12 \cdot 2500 \frac{355}{\sqrt{3} \cdot 1.1} = 0.901 \cdot 10^6 \text{ N}$$

$$N_{st,Ed} = N_{st,ten} = 0.901 \cdot 10^6 \text{ N}$$

2.9 STIFFENERS AND DETAILING

Additional axial force in the stiffener $\Delta N_{st,Ed}$ due to deviation forces:

Here, for the sake of simplicity, yield strength divided by safety factor γ_{M0} is used for the value of maximum compressive stress (actual maximum stress amounts 347.8 N/mm²) when calculating N_{Ed}.

The effective compression area was calculated as:

$$A^p_{c,eff} = (b_{e1} + b_{e2})t_w = (363.3 + 445.3)12 = 8503.3 \, \text{mm}^2$$

$$N_{Ed} = \frac{A^p_{c,eff}}{2} \cdot \frac{f_y}{\gamma_{M0}} = \frac{8503.3}{2} \cdot \frac{355}{1.0} = 1.509 \cdot 10^6 \, \text{N}$$

$$\sigma_{cr,c} = \frac{\pi^2 \cdot E \cdot t_w^2}{12(1-v^2)a^2} = \frac{\pi^2 \cdot 210000 \cdot 12^2}{12(1-0.3^2)2000^2} = 6.8 \, \text{N/mm}^2$$

$$\sigma_{cr,p} = k_\sigma \frac{\pi^2 \cdot E \cdot t_w^2}{12(1-v^2)b^2} = 23.9 \frac{\pi^2 \cdot 210000 \cdot 12^2}{12(1-0.3^2)2500^2} = 104.5 \, \text{N/mm}^2$$

$$\frac{\sigma_{cr,c}}{\sigma_{cr,p}} = \frac{6.8}{104.5} = 0.07 < 0.5 \rightarrow \frac{\sigma_{cr,c}}{\sigma_{cr,p}} = 0.5$$

$$\sigma_m = \frac{\sigma_{cr,c}}{\sigma_{cr,p}} \frac{N_{Ed}}{b}\left(\frac{1}{a_1} + \frac{1}{a_2}\right) = 0.5 \cdot \frac{1.509 \cdot 10^6}{2500}\left(\frac{2}{2000}\right) = 0.302 \, \text{N/mm}^2$$

$$\Delta N_{st,Ed} = \frac{\sigma_m b^2}{\pi^2} = \frac{0.302 \cdot 2500^2}{\pi^2} = 1.912 \cdot 10^5 \, \text{N}$$

$$\sum N_{st,Ed} = N_{st,Ed} + \Delta N_{st,Ed} = 0.901 \cdot 10^6 + 0.191 \cdot 10^6 = 1.092 \cdot 10^6 \, \text{N}$$

Euler elastic critical force of the stiffener $N_{cr,st}$:

$$N_{cr,st} = \frac{\pi^2 E I_{st}}{b^2} = \frac{\pi^2 \cdot 210000 \cdot 3.514 \cdot 10^7}{2500^2} = 1.165 \cdot 10^7 \, \text{N}$$

$$e_1 = e_{min} = 54.7 \, \text{mm}$$

2. OVERVIEW OF DESIGN RULES

$$w_0 = \min\left[\frac{b}{300}, \frac{a}{300}\right] = \min\left[\frac{2500}{300}, \frac{2000}{300}\right] = \frac{2000}{300} = 6.7\,\text{mm}$$

$$\delta_m = \frac{N_{st,Ed} \cdot e_1}{\sum N_{st,Ed} \cdot w_0} = \frac{0.901 \cdot 10^6 \cdot 54.7}{1.092 \cdot 10^6 \cdot 6.7} = 6.77$$

Deflection of transverse stiffener:

$$w = 6.7 \frac{1}{\dfrac{1.165 \cdot 10^7}{1.092 \cdot 10^6} - 1}(1+1.25 \cdot 6.77) = 6.5\,\text{mm}$$

$$w = 6.5\,\text{mm} < \frac{b}{300} = \frac{2500}{300} = 8.3\,\text{mm} \;\checkmark$$

Maximal stress in the transverse stiffener:

$$\sigma_{st,\max} = \left[\frac{\dfrac{N_{st,Ed}}{A_{st}} + \dfrac{\sum N_{st,Ed} \cdot e_1}{I_{st}} w_0}{1 - \dfrac{\sum N_{st,Ed}}{N_{cr,st}}}(1+1.11\delta_m)\right]$$

$$= \left[\frac{\dfrac{0.901 \cdot 10^6}{7754.8} + \dfrac{1.092 \cdot 10^6 \cdot 54.7}{3.514 \cdot 10^7} 6.7 \cdot}{1 - \dfrac{1.092 \cdot 10^6}{1.165 \cdot 10^7}}(1+1.11 \cdot 6.77)\right] = 222.5\,\text{N/mm}^2$$

$$\sigma_{st,\max} = 222.5\,\text{N/mm}^2 \leq \frac{355}{1.1} = 322.7\,\text{N/mm}^2 \;\checkmark$$

b)   General case

A second order elastic analysis on the stiffener loaded with deviation and axial forces, taking account of relevant imperfection and eccentricities, was performed with the FEM software ("Abaqus FEA", 2007).

2.9 STIFFENERS AND DETAILING

$$q_{dev,Ed} = \frac{\pi}{4}\sigma_m(w_0 + w_{el}) = \frac{\pi}{4} \cdot 0.302(6.7+8.3) = 3.556 \text{ N/mm}$$

$$N_{st,Ed} = N_{st,ten} = 0.901 \cdot 10^6 \text{ N}$$

For w_{el} the maximum allowable value $b/300 = 8.3$ mm was taken. Otherwise an iterative procedure is required.

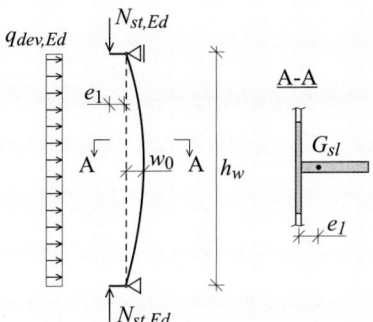

Fig. 2.86: Mechanical model for the general case

Results from the Abaqus FE analysis:

$$M_{max} = 65.497 \cdot 10^6 \text{ Nmm}$$

$$N = 9.01 \cdot 10^5 \text{ N}$$

$$w_{max} = 6.64 \text{ mm}$$

Maximum compressive stress in the web plate centreline:

$$\sigma_{st,max} = \frac{N}{A_{st}} + \frac{M_{max} \cdot e_1}{I_{st}} = \frac{9.01 \cdot 10^5}{7754.8} + \frac{65.497 \cdot 10^6 \cdot 54.7}{3.514 \cdot 10^7}$$

$$= 218.1 \text{ N/mm}^2$$

$$\sigma_{st,max} = 218.1 \text{ N/mm}^2 < \frac{f_y}{\gamma_{M1}} = \frac{355}{1.1} = 322.7 \text{ N/mm}^2 \checkmark$$

$$w_{max} = 6.6 \text{ mm} < \frac{b}{300} = 8.3 \text{ mm} \checkmark$$

2. OVERVIEW OF DESIGN RULES

Stress at the free edge of the stiffener (not relevant):

$$\sigma_{st,free} = \frac{N}{A_{st}} - \frac{M_{max} \cdot e_{max}}{I_{st}} = \frac{9.008 \cdot 10^5}{7754.8} - \frac{65.497 \cdot 10^6 \cdot 151.3}{3.514 \cdot 10^7}$$

$$= -165.9 \, \text{N/mm}^2 \text{ (tension stress)}$$

Results of the alternative iterative procedure are shown in Table 2.7.

Table 2.7: Results of the iterative procedure

iteration	w_{el} [mm] assumed	$\geq$	w_{max} [mm] calculated	σ_{max} [n/mm²] calculated	$\leq$	f_y/γ_{M1} [N/mm²]
1.	8.33	>	6.64	218.1	<	
2.	6.64	>	6.61	217.5	<	322.7
3.	6.61	$\geq$	6.61	217.5	<	

$$w_{max}^{(3)} = 6.61 \, \text{mm} < \frac{b}{300} = 8.3 \, \text{mm} \checkmark$$

Also in this case assuming that w_{el} is equal to the maximum allowable displacement $b/300$ and avoiding the iteration procedure did not visibly affect the final result.

2.10 REDUCED STRESS METHOD (INCLUDING ANNEXES A AND B WHERE APPLICABLE)

2.10.1 General

Besides the effective width method (sections 4 to 7, EN 1993-1-5), EN 1993-1-5 also provides the reduced stress method in section 10. The reduced stress method applies not only for standard steel plated cross sections such as I- and box-girders according to the conditions in clause 4.1, EN1993-1-5, but also for members with non-parallel flanges and webs with regular or irregular openings and non-orthogonal stiffeners.

In contrast to the effective width method, the reduced stress method assumes a linear stress distribution up to the stress limit of the plate element which buckles first. Until this stress limit has been reached, the cross section

2.10 REDUCED STRESS METHOD

is fully effective[p]. Thus, cross sections verified according to section 10, EN 1993-1-5, can be categorised as Class 3 members assuming no load shedding between cross sectional elements. For a single plate element the reduced stress method fully corresponds to the effective width method. However, for steel plated cross sections the reduced stress method does not take into account load shedding from highly stressed to less stressed plate elements. As a result, the weakest plate element in a steel plated cross section governs the resistance of the entire cross section.

The reduced stress method uses the von Mises criterion to take into account interaction between different stress types. In contrast to the effective width method, a verification of each load type followed by a combination of these load types by means of an interaction equation is not necessary. Instead, the resistance is determined in a single verification step, see Fig. 2.87. The verification of the plate subject to the complete stress field is:

$$\sqrt{\left(\frac{\sigma_{x,Ed}}{\rho_x \cdot f_y / \gamma_{M1}}\right)^2 + \left(\frac{\sigma_{z,Ed}}{\rho_z \cdot f_y / \gamma_{M1}}\right)^2 - \left(\frac{\sigma_{x,Ed}}{\rho_x \cdot f_y / \gamma_{M1}}\right)\left(\frac{\sigma_{z,Ed}}{\rho_z \cdot f_y / \gamma_{M1}}\right) + 3 \cdot \left(\frac{\tau_{Ed}}{\chi_w \cdot f_y / \gamma_{M1}}\right)^2} \leq 1 \quad (2.125)$$

where

$\sigma_{x,Ed}$; $\sigma_{z,Ed}$; τ_{Ed}	design stresses (load)
f_y	yield strength (resistance)
ρ_x; ρ_z; χ_w	reduction factors
γ_{M1}	partial safety factor

Conservatively, if only the minimum reduction factor ρ is taken as a basis, Eq. (2.125) simplifies to:

$$\sqrt{\left(\frac{\sigma_{x,Ed}}{f_y / \gamma_{M1}}\right)^2 + \left(\frac{\sigma_{z,Ed}}{f_y / \gamma_{M1}}\right)^2 - \left(\frac{\sigma_{x,Ed}}{f_y / \gamma_{M1}}\right)\left(\frac{\sigma_{z,Ed}}{f_y / \gamma_{M1}}\right) + 3 \cdot \left(\frac{\tau_{Ed}}{f_y / \gamma_{M1}}\right)^2} \leq \rho$$

i. e. $\alpha_{Rd} = \dfrac{\rho \cdot \alpha_{ult,k}}{\gamma_{M1}} \geq 1$ \quad (2.126)

2. OVERVIEW OF DESIGN RULES

where

$$\rho = \min(\rho_x; \rho_z; \chi_w)$$

$\alpha_{ult,k}$ load amplifier according to Eq. (2.129)

The reduction factors are determined only with one plate slenderness $\overline{\lambda}_p$ according to Eq. (2.127). Column-like behaviour has to be accounted for when relevant. $\overline{\lambda}_p$ is calculated as follows:

$$\overline{\lambda}_p = \sqrt{\frac{\alpha_{ult,k}}{\alpha_{cr}}} \qquad (2.127)$$

where

$\alpha_{ult,k}$ minimum load amplifier for the design loads to reach the characteristic value of the resistance according to Eq. (2.129)

α_{cr} minimum load amplifier for the design loads to reach the elastic critical value of the plate according to Eq. (2.132)

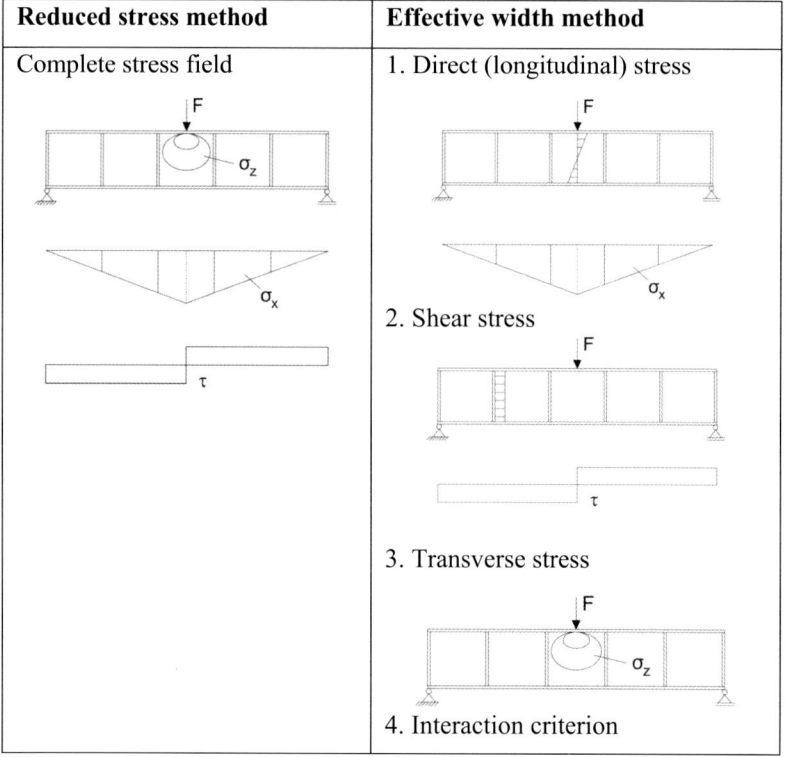

Fig. 2.87: Comparison of reduced stress method and effective width method

2.10 REDUCED STRESS METHOD

For simple cases the load amplifiers $\alpha_{ult,k}$ and α_{cr} can be determined by hand calculations or based on adequate literature, see e.g. (Klöppel and Scheer, 1960) and (Klöppel and Möller, 1968). Below the equivalent stress $\sigma_{eq,Ed}$ is used to illustrate the procedure. Assuming a plane stress field, $\sigma_{eq,Ed}$ is defined as follows:

$$\sigma_{eq,Ed} = \sqrt{\sigma_{x,Ed}^2 + \sigma_{z,Ed}^2 - \sigma_{x,Ed}\cdot\sigma_{z,Ed} + 3\cdot\tau_{Ed}^2} \quad (2.128)$$

The load amplifier $\alpha_{ult,k}$ is the smallest factor for which the design equivalent stress $\sigma_{eq,Ed}$ has to be increased to reach the characteristic yield strength f_y. It can be written according to Eq. (2.129) or (2.130).

$$\frac{1}{\alpha_{ult,k}^2} = \left(\frac{\sigma_{x,Ed}}{f_y}\right)^2 + \left(\frac{\sigma_{z,Ed}}{f_y}\right)^2 - \left(\frac{\sigma_{x,Ed}}{f_y}\right)\cdot\left(\frac{\sigma_{z,Ed}}{f_y}\right) + 3\cdot\left(\frac{\tau_{Ed}}{f_y}\right)^2 \quad (2.129)$$

or

$$\alpha_{ult,k} = \frac{f_y}{\sigma_{eq,Ed}} \quad (2.130)$$

The load amplifier α_{cr} is the smallest factor for which the design equivalent stress $\sigma_{eq,Ed}$ has to be increased to reach the elastic critical equivalent stress $\sigma_{eq,cr}$. It can be written according to Eq. (2.131).

$$\alpha_{cr} = \frac{1}{\frac{1+\psi_x}{4\cdot\alpha_{cr,x}} + \frac{1+\psi_z}{4\cdot\alpha_{cr,z}} + \sqrt{\left(\frac{1+\psi_x}{4\cdot\alpha_{cr,x}} + \frac{1+\psi_z}{4\cdot\alpha_{cr,z}}\right)^2 + \frac{1-\psi_x}{2\cdot\alpha_{cr,x}^2} + \frac{1-\psi_z}{2\cdot\alpha_{cr,z}^2} + \frac{1}{\alpha_{cr,\tau}^2}}} \quad (2.131)$$

or

$$\alpha_{cr} = \frac{\sigma_{eq,cr}}{\sigma_{eq,Ed}} \quad (2.132)$$

where

$$\alpha_{cr,x} = \frac{\sigma_{cr,x}}{\sigma_{x,Ed}} \; ; \; \alpha_{cr,z} = \frac{\sigma_{cr,z}}{\sigma_{z,Ed}} \; ; \; \alpha_{cr,\tau} = \frac{\tau_{cr}}{\tau_{Ed}}$$

2. OVERVIEW OF DESIGN RULES

$\sigma_{cr,x}$; $\sigma_{cr,z}$; τ_{cr} elastic critical buckling stress
ψ_x; ψ_z stress ratio along longitudinal and transverse edges
$\sigma_{eq,cr}$ equivalent elastic critical stress

The advantage of the reduced stress method lies in the fact that the minimum load amplifiers $\alpha_{ult,k}$ and α_{cr} may be determined by means of numerical methods in a single step according to Eqs. (2.130) and (2.132), e.g. by *EBPlate* (EBplate, 2007) or commercial finite element software. This allows fairly simple calculation of complex geometries and boundary conditions. Annex C, EN 1993-1-5, gives recommendations for the determination of $\alpha_{ult,k}$ and α_{cr} via the finite element method. If the use of numerical methods is not possible or if a hand calculation is desired, $\alpha_{ult,k}$ and α_{cr} may be determined from the design stresses $\sigma_{x,Ed}$, $\sigma_{z,Ed}$ and τ_{Ed}, as well as elastic critical stresses $\sigma_{cr,x}$, $\sigma_{cr,z}$ and τ_{cr} according to Eqs. (2.129) and (2.131).

It should be noted however that the reduced stress method allows no stress redistribution i.e. the weakest cross sectional element governs the design. The practical consequence is that the slenderness of each plate is usually determined in such a way that the buckling strength is close to the yield strength for economic reasons. This is usually achieved by adding stiffeners to the plate, thus consequently increasing the costs. Such situation is typical for plate girders with slender webs in bending.

2.10.2 Choice of reduction factors

The reduction factors in section 10, EN 1993-1-5, may be determined either from sections 4 and 5 or from Annex B. Reduction factors according to sections 4 and 5 try to utilise as much of the post-critical reserve as possible. In contrast to this, Annex B provides buckling curves on the basis of a generalised format which does not fully account for the post-critical reserve, in favour of a reduced number of buckling curves. When determining the reduction factors, column-like behaviour has to be considered where relevant. This procedure is analogue to the one used for the effective width method, i.e. the reduction factor χ_c to consider column-like behaviour is determined according to clause 6.3.1, EN 1993-1-1 (CEN,

2005).

The reduction factors according to sections 4 and 5 are different for each loading, i.e. longitudinal, shear or transverse stresses. Section 6 should generally not be applied due to consistency of the slenderness definition. Paragraph 10(5), EN 1993-1-5, says that the reduction factor ρ_z for transverse stresses acting only partially along the flange should be determined according to clause 4.5.4(1). However, the application of clause 4.5.4(1) and the interpolation between plate-like and column-like behaviour may lead to unsafe results as shown in (Kuhlman et al, 2009), because the transferability of the reduction factor ρ_x to the transverse direction is not fully justified. Thus, in the third edition of German DIN-Fachbericht 103 (DIN-Fachbericht 103, 2009) the determination of the reduction factor ρ_z was changed according to Annex B.1(3), EN 1993-1-5, which is also recommended in this book. Thus, the reduction factors can be summarized as shown in Table 2.8. The verification equation interpolates these reduction factors on the basis of the von Mises-criterion, see Eq. (2.125).

Table 2.8: Use of reduction factors with section 10, EN 1993-1-5

Loading	Reduction factor
Direct stress	ρ_x according to 4.5.4(1), EN1993-1-5 taking into account column-like behaviour when relevant
Shear stress	χ_w according to 5.3(1), EN1993-1-5
Transverse stress	ρ_z according to B.1(3), NOTE, EN1993-1-5 taking into account column like behaviour when relevant

The reduction factors according to Annex B are based on a harmonised mathematical format according to Eqs. (2.133) and (2.134). Müller (2003) developed so called "generalised buckling curves" and determined coefficients $\overline{\lambda}_{p0}$ and α_p, given in Table 2.9. It can be shown that for most load cases a single reduction factor is sufficient, which in particular facilitates the use of Eq. (2.126).

$$\rho_z = \frac{1}{\varphi_p + \sqrt{\varphi_p^2 - \overline{\lambda}_p}} \leq 1 \qquad (2.133)$$

2. OVERVIEW OF DESIGN RULES

with

$$\varphi_p = 0.5 \cdot \left[1 + \alpha_p \cdot \left(\overline{\lambda}_p - \overline{\lambda}_{p0} \right) + \overline{\lambda}_p \right] \quad (2.134)$$

Table 2.9: Alternative use of reduction factors with section 10, EN 1993-1-5: Values for $\overline{\lambda}_{p0}$ and α_p to be used with Eqs. (2.133) and (2.134)

Product	Predominant buckling mode	α_p	$\overline{\lambda}_{p0}$
Hot rolled	Direct stress for $\psi \geq 0$		0.70
	Direct stress for $\psi < 0$	0.13	0.80
	Shear stress		0.80
	Transverse stress		0.80
welded or cold-formed	Direct stress for $\psi \geq 0$		0.70
	Direct stress for $\psi < 0$	0.34	0.80
	Shear stress		0.80
	Transverse stress		0.80

An example calculation for an unstiffened girder is given in the framework of the crane runway beam example in sub-chapter 3.7. For a girder with longitudinal stiffener an example calculation is provided in the framework of the box-girder bridge example, see chapter 4.

2.11 FEM

2.11.1 Introduction

In steel construction, due to the computer technology and user-friendly software developments in the past decades, the use of Finite Element Methods (FEM) of analysis is now widely spread in design offices and is no longer restricted to research purposes. To take this trend into account, the informative Annex C in EN1993-1-5 proposes some recommendations for a "good FE analysis" of **_steel plated structures_**. Note that another ECCS Design Manual is under preparation to deal only with the FEM, going very deep in its application to steel structures (beams, frames, plates and shells, solids). The purpose of this sub-chapter of the Design

Manual is very limited and only concerns the information given by Annex C in EN1993-1-5.

The most common applications of FEM for steel plated structures are:

- The first-order linear elastic analysis:
  The structure is modelled with its theoretical initial geometry without any imperfections, the steel behaviour is elastic and the influence of the deformed structure shape on the load definition is not taken into account when the load is increasing (first-order theory). Calculation examples: elastic shear lag effect, elastic resistance.
- The first-order linear plastic analysis (coefficient $\alpha_{ult} = F_y / F_{Ed}$):
  In comparison to the previous point of this list, only the steel behaviour is modified to take into account the influence of its yield strength. Such analysis is used to calculate the plastic resistance of a steel structure at ULS.
- The calculation of the critical buckling modes (coefficient $\alpha_{crit} = F_{cr} / F_{Ed}$):
  The steel plated structure is modelled with its theoretical geometry, no imperfections are introduced and the steel behaviour is elastic. The aim is to know the different modal shapes of the steel structure under a given load case, for determining the slenderness used in the conventional design rules. For this kind of analysis, the use of global FE software is justified if the geometry of the structure is complicated. If not, the critical buckling modes of a simple stiffened plate can be more easily determined using simple freeware, e.g. EBPlate® (EBplate, 2007).
- The second-order linear elastic analysis:
  Initial imperfections are introduced in the FE model, the steel behaviour is elastic and the influence of the deformed structure shape on the load definition is taken into account by a step by step analysis (second-order theory). For instance: elastic plate buckling resistance.

- The non-linear analysis:
  This is the most general case where imperfections, geometrical as

2. OVERVIEW OF DESIGN RULES

well as residual stresses, are introduced in the FE model with also a non-linear behaviour of the steel material. The analysis is performed step by step as a second order analysis. Nowadays this kind of FE use is mainly reserved to research purposes, but as FE software is becoming more and more user-friendly, the use of this analysis in design offices could become wide spread in the future.

2.11.2 Modelling

The FE modelling is out of the scope of this Design Manual and many references can be found in the literature (for instance in Zienkiewicz *et al*, 2005) dealing with the good choices in meshing, element types, mesh size and refinement, degree of freedom, sub-modelling,... Note that the accuracy of the results is closely linked to these modelling choices. The boundary conditions for supports, interfaces and applied loads should be chosen such that the obtained results are conservative, or at best correct. Very often this leads to applying simply supported edges around the analyzed plate.

2.11.3 Definition of initial imperfections in the FE model

Imperfections are from two different origins:

- **Geometric imperfections** due to fabrication and construction tolerances.
  They are modelled by a deformed shape of the theoretical structure and by the definition of maximum amplitudes for this deformed shape. Annex C of EN1993-1-5 recommends the shapes based on the critical plate buckling modes and amplitudes equal to 80% of the fabrication tolerances. Note that the fabrication tolerances are defined by European Standard EN1090 Part 2 for steel structures (CEN, 2008).
- **Residual stresses** due to the fabrication process (steel plate rolling, flame cutting, welding)
  They are represented by a self-equilibrated stress pattern in each plate of the structure. In a FEM model the residual stresses are

difficult to model so that the simplified approach of an equivalent geometric imperfection is often used. As information, Fig. 2.88 gives the definition adopted by the Swedish Code for the residual stress patterns (Johansson et al, 2007). Further information about residual stress patterns can also be found in literature, e.g. (ECCS, 1977).

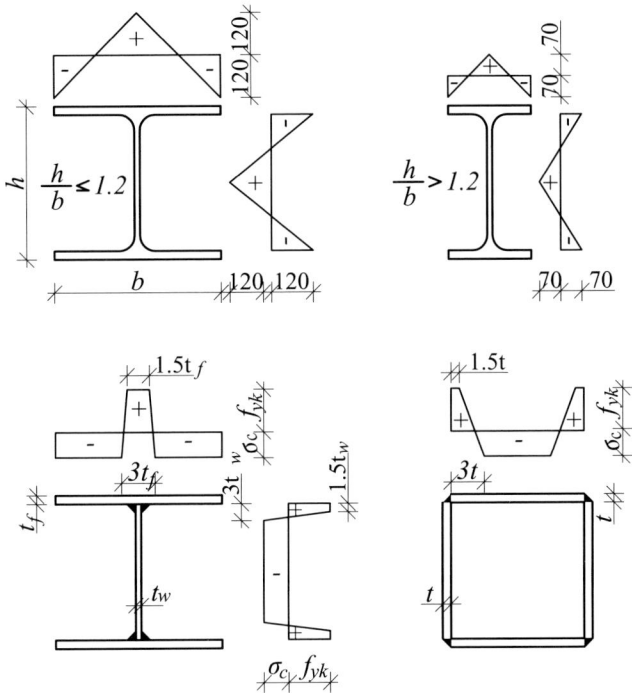

Fig. 2.88: Residual stress patterns from Swedish design code BSK

To combine both effects, the equivalent geometric imperfection method may be applied, consisting of increasing the amplitude of the geometric imperfections in order to cover also the residual stresses. The application of this method is much simpler than modelling of the residual stress pattern, but also less accurate. The effects of the residual stresses are in many cases quite different from those of geometrical imperfections. For some basic cases, Table C.2 and Figure C.1 from EN1993-1-5 give recommendations for defining the deformed shapes and the amplitudes of these equivalent imperfections.

2. OVERVIEW OF DESIGN RULES

Type of imperfection	Component	Shape	Magnitude
global	member with length ℓ	bow	see EN 1993-1-1, Table 5.1
global	longitudinal stiffener with length a	bow	min (a/400, b/400)
local	panel or sub-panel with short span a or b	buckling shape	min (a/200, b/200)
local	stiffener or flange subject to twist	bow twist	1 / 50

Fig. 2.89: Extract from Annex C of EN1993-1-5 (Table C.2)

The elementary imperfection shapes in Fig. 2.90 can be obtained by using the buckling modes of the structure taken from a previous linear bifurcation analysis. An appropriate combination of these shapes should be used. For instance, a global imperfection of a stiffened web panel can be added to the twist imperfection in its longitudinal stiffener. EN1993-1-5, C.5 (5), indicates that a leading imperfection should be chosen and then the accompanying imperfections may have their values reduced by 70%. Then the main problem for the engineer is that every combination should be checked in order to get a conservative result, i.e. the minimum value of the resistance of the steel structure. This is a tedious work with numerous cases to compute. Moreover, it is very difficult to get directly the most unfavourable equivalent imperfection and even more difficult to prove that this is really the most unfavourable one.

Type of imperfection	Component
global member with length ℓ	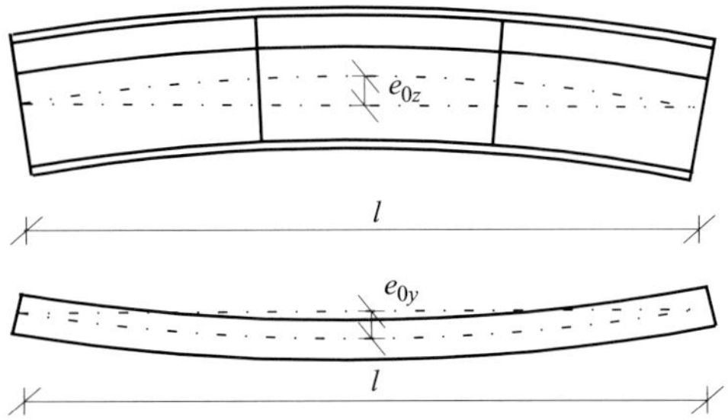 e_{0z}, l / e_{0y}, l
global longitudinal stiffener with length a	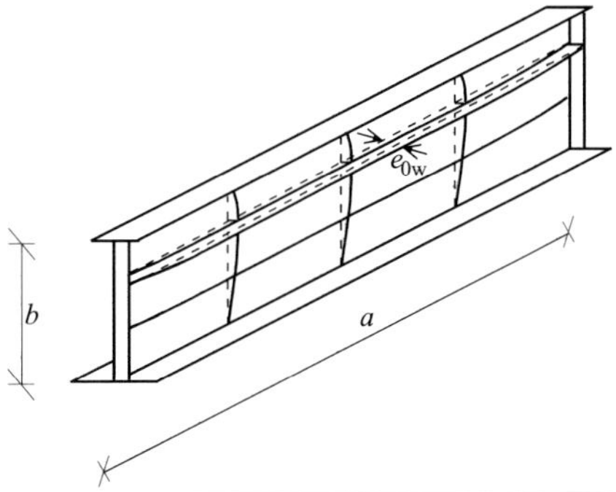 e_{0w}, a, b
local panel or sub-panel	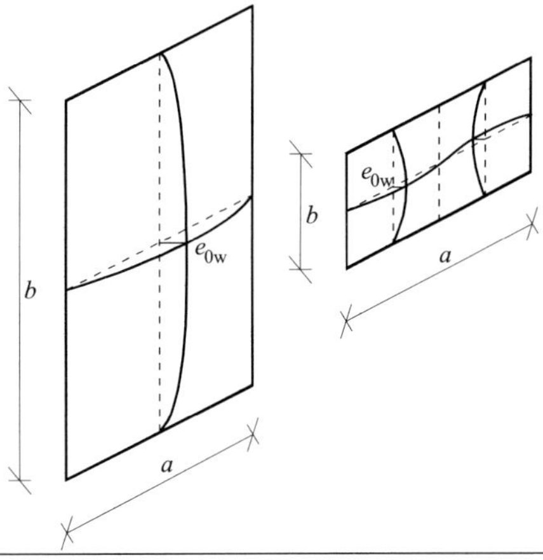 e_{0w}, a, b
local stiffener or flange subject to twist	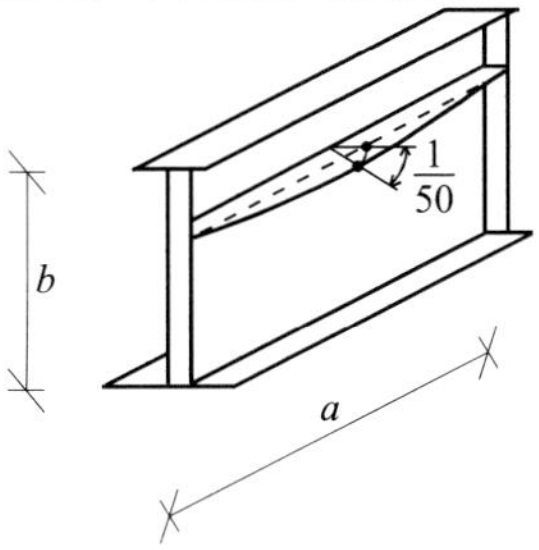 $\frac{1}{50}$, a, b

Fig. 2.90: Modelling of equivalent geometrical imperfections (from EN1993-1-5, Figure C1)

2. OVERVIEW OF DESIGN RULES

2.11.4 Definition of material behaviour in the FE model

The question is how to define a steel stress-strain curve for taking the characteristic yield strength f_y and possibly the strain hardening into account.

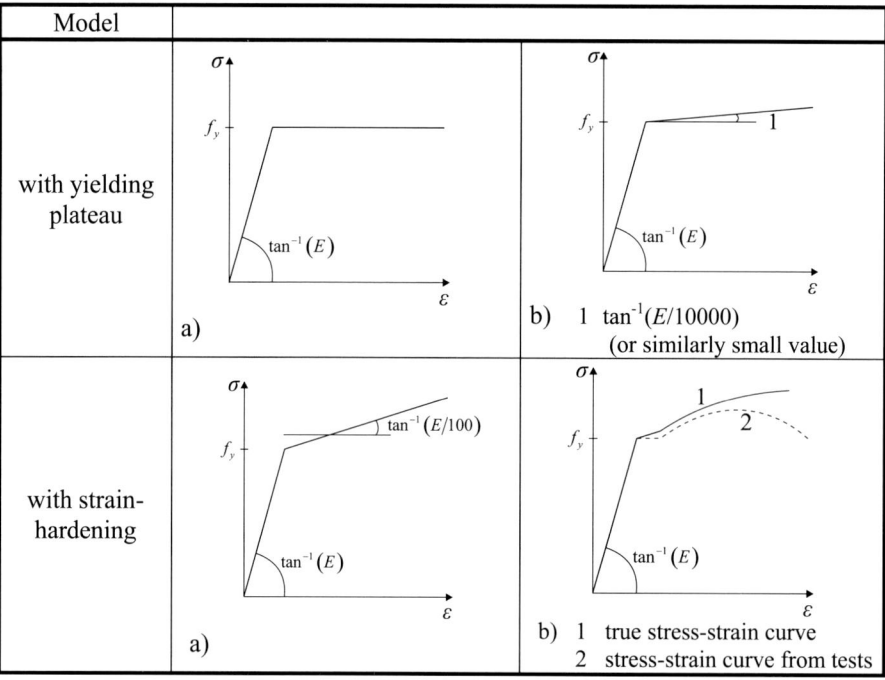

Fig. 2.91: Modelling of material behaviour (from EN1993-1-5)

EN1993-1-5 recommends 5 stress-strain curves:

- Option a) is the easiest one: the strain hardening is not taken into account and the yield plateau is horizontal.
- To avoid possible problems with numerical instability when a horizontal yield plateau is employed, option b) may be used with a very small slope (E/10000) for the yield plateau.
- Option c) considers strain hardening by using a slope (E/100) and neglecting the yield plateau.
- Options d1) and d2) represent most realistic stress-strain curves (that may be obtained by tests). The difference between d1) and d2) is the influence of the reduction of area during the tensile test which is taken into account in d1) and not in d2) where the stress is

calculated on the basis of the initial area of the test coupon.

In practice, modern FE-software has a database of material stress-strain laws and their introduction in the computation does not represent a difficulty. What is more problematic for the engineer is the definition of the relevant limit state of the modelled structure on the basis of the FE results. Different criteria should be checked:

- The maximum load in the load-deformation curve for compression elements susceptible to buckling
- The limiting value of the principal membrane strain (a recommended value is 0.05 (Johansson *et al*, 2007)). This criterion is also relevant for compression, for instance if option c) is used
- The limiting value of displacements (when the two previous criteria do not govern).

2.11.5 Design examples

Example 2.11-1: Finite element analysis.

The finite element analysis (FEM) considering geometric and material non-linearity and initial imperfections (GMNIA) is used to determine the resistance of a stiffened panel in pure compression. The panel consists of a thin plate stiffened with three flat stiffeners (see Fig 2.86). This numerical example is of rather academic nature, because in reality such a compressed panel (as part of a more complex cross section) should usually have a smaller plate slenderness and stronger stiffeners.

When using FEM tools, special attention should be paid to the modelling of the structural component, the choice of software, the use of imperfections, the modelling of material properties, boundary conditions and loads.

Imperfection modelling will be based both on eigenmode shapes and equivalent geometric imperfection, as proposed in EN 1993-1-5. Both procedures are compared at the end.

2. OVERVIEW OF DESIGN RULES

A linear bifurcation analysis is performed to get the buckling shapes which will be used as initial imperfections in the nonlinear analysis. The material used in the linear bifurcation analysis is linear with an elastic modulus of $E = 210000 \text{ N/mm}^2$. The numerical model with its boundary conditions is shown in Fig. 2.92.

The sensitivity analysis considering mesh discretisation was first performed. In Fig. 2.93 the ultimate force and maximal out of plane displacement were compared for a plate meshed with average finite element lengths of 200, 100, 50, 25 and 10 mm. For further analysis the plate was meshed using the average finite element length of 25 mm.

In Fig. 2.94 the first six buckling modes are plotted. For further analysis the 1st buckling mode and the 2nd buckling mode are used as initial imperfection to assess the elastoplastic resistance at ULS

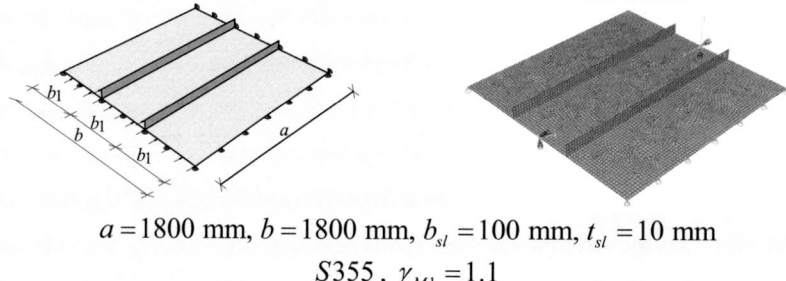

$a = 1800$ mm, $b = 1800$ mm, $b_{sl} = 100$ mm, $t_{sl} = 10$ mm

$S355$, $\gamma_{M1} = 1.1$

Fig. 2.92: Numerical model with boundary conditions

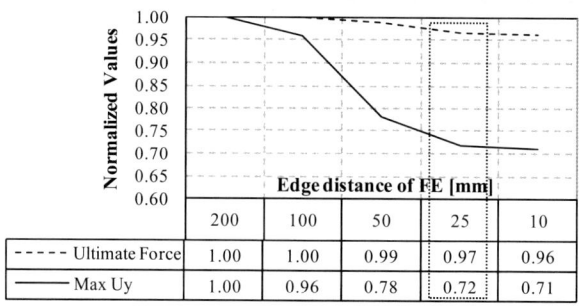

	Edge distance of FE [mm]				
	200	100	50	25	10
----- Ultimate Force	1.00	1.00	0.99	0.97	0.96
——— Max Uy	1.00	0.96	0.78	0.72	0.71

Fig. 2.93: Behaviour of the plate considering different mesh discretisations

The mathematical model for nonlinear analysis is the same as for linear buckling analysis, with the exception of material properties. The material is modelled as elastoplastic with strain-hardening according to C.6 of EN 1993-1-5. The hardening module is equal to $E/100$ and the yield stress is equal to $f_y = 355$ N/mm^2. The stress-strain curve is shown in the figure below. True stress – logarithmic strain material model is used in numerical simulations.

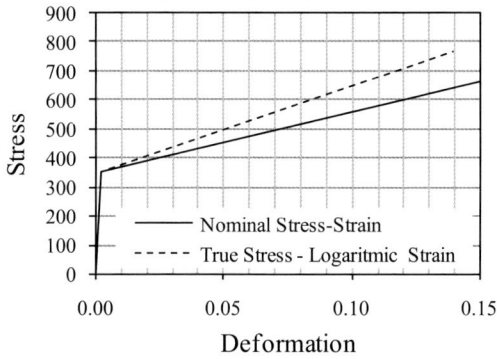

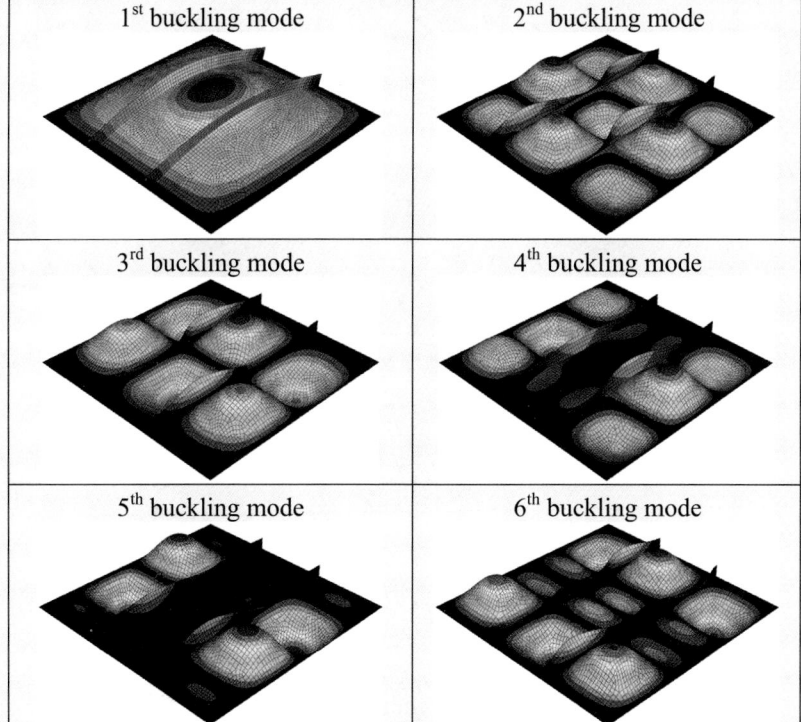

Fig. 2.94: Buckling modes of stiffened plate

2. OVERVIEW OF DESIGN RULES

The non-linear analysis is performed with the following imperfections (amplitudes according to EN 1993-1-5, Annex C):

- IMP 1 - 1st buckling mode with amplitude:
  $w_1 = \min(a/400,\ b/400) = \min(1800/400,\ 1800/400) = 4.5$ mm,
- IMP 2 - 2nd buckling mode with amplitude:
  $w_2 = \min(a/200,\ b_1/200) = \min(1800/200,\ 600/200) = 3$ mm,
- IMP 3 - global panel imperfection according to Fig. 2.90:

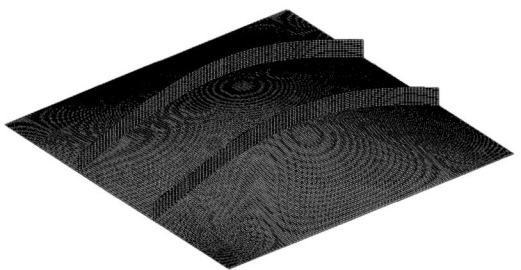

$$w_3 = \min(a/400,\ b/400) \cdot \cos\left(\frac{\pi \cdot x}{b}\right) \cdot \sin\left(\frac{\pi \cdot z}{b}\right),$$

- IMP 4 - local sub-panel imperfection according to Fig. 2.90:

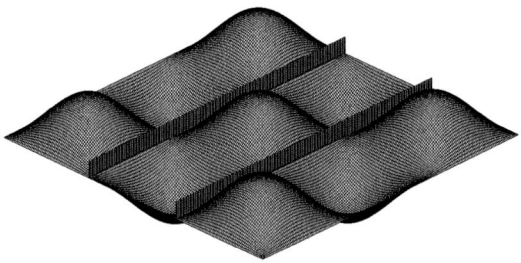

$$w_4 = \min(a/200,\ b_1/200) \cdot \cos\left(\frac{\pi \cdot x}{b_1}\right) \cdot \sin\left(\frac{\pi \cdot z}{b_1}\right) \text{ and}$$

- IMP 5 - local stiffener subjected to twist according to Fig. 2.90 with amplitude 1/50:

$$v_5 = \frac{y}{50} \cdot \sin\left(\frac{\pi \cdot z}{b}\right).$$

The first and the second imperfections used in the analysis are determined by using buckling mode analysis. The imperfection according to the first buckling mode comprises global imperfection of the plate and local twist of the stiffener, while the imperfection according to the second buckling mode consists of local buckling mode and local twist of the stiffener.

The imperfections IMP3-IMP5 are modelled according to Annex C5 of EN 1993-1-5. In these cases only global or local imperfection is determined. Further on, combinations of these three basic imperfections are done according to EN 1993-1-5, C5(5), where IMP 3 is the leading imperfection, and IMP 4 and IMP 5 are the accompanying imperfections with reduced values of amplitudes (70% of the nominal value).

The results (ultimate load, failure mode and force-displacement curves) of the non-linear analysis are gathered in Table 2.10.

The table below shows that a global imperfection (IMP 1 and IMP 3) has the highest influence on the capacity of the plate. The global initial imperfection (IMP3) according to Fig. 2.90 results in the smallest resistance of the plate. Similar results are obtained for the girder with an initial imperfection according to the 1st global buckling mode (IMP1). On the other hand, local imperfections (IMP 2, IMP 4, IMP 5) do not significantly affect the capacity of the plate.

2. OVERVIEW OF DESIGN RULES

Table 2.10: Considered imperfections and corresponding ultimate forces

IMPERFECTION	Ultimate Force	Deviation [%]
-	$3.977 \cdot 10^6$ N Acc. EN 1993-1-5	0.00
No imperfection	$5.128 \cdot 10^6$ N	28.94
IMP 1	$4.424 \cdot 10^6$ N	11.23
IMP 2	$5.223 \cdot 10^6$ N	31.31
IMP 3	$\mathbf{4.386 \cdot 10^6}$ **N**	**10.28**
IMP 4	$5.001 \cdot 10^6$ N	25.75
IMP 5	$5.131 \cdot 10^6$ N	29.02
IMP 3 + 0.7 · IMP 4	$4.518 \cdot 10^6$ N	13.60
IMP 3 + 0.7 · IMP 5	$4.387 \cdot 10^6$ N	10.31
IMP 3 + 0.7 · (IMP 4 + IMP 5)	$4.519 \cdot 10^6$ N	13.63

In general it is very important what kind of imperfection will be applied in the numerical model if the FEM tool is used to define nonlinear ultimate resistance of the plate.

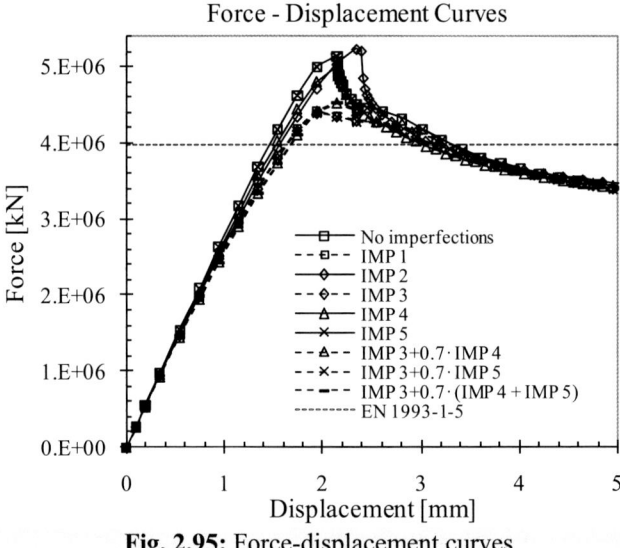

Fig. 2.95: Force-displacement curves

The resistance of the plate is then calculated considering factor α_1, which covers the model uncertainty of the FE-modelling, and α_2, which covers the scatter of the loading and resistance models and is equal to γ_{M1} if global instability governs the resistance and γ_{M2} if fracture governs the resistance.

From the deformed shape of the plate and from the load–displacement diagram it is evident that the failure mode is plate buckling and the relevant partial factor is $\gamma_{M1} = 1.1$ (bridges).

Factor α_1 can be determined by comparing the FEM results to other similar cases for which the buckling resistance is known (benchmarking) or by comparing the FEM results to the available test results. The above mentioned comparison does not mean only comparison of the resistance of the performed study, but also comparison of rigidity, material behaviour, failure mode, post-buckling behaviour and imperfection sensitivity.

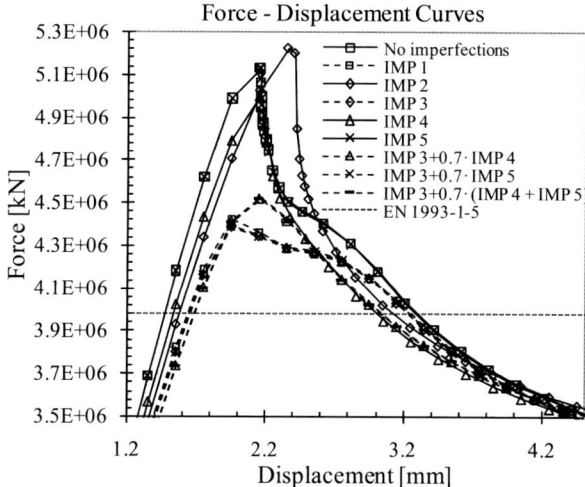

Fig. 2.96: Peak region of force-displacement diagram

In this numerical example factor α_1 is assumed to be equal to 1. In German National Annex to EN 1993-1-5 for well-built FEM models the value 1.05 is recommended for α_1. Finally, the resistance is given by:

$$F_{Rd,GMNIA} = \frac{F_{GMNIA}}{\alpha_u} = \frac{F_{GMNIA}}{\alpha_1 \cdot \alpha_2} = \frac{4386 \cdot 10^6}{1 \cdot 1.1} = 3987 \cdot 10^6 \text{ N},$$

with $\alpha_1 = 1.0$ and $\alpha_2 = \gamma_{M1} = 1.1$.

For bridge design ($\gamma_{M1} = 1.1$) this leads to some inconsistency because in EN 1993-1-5, equation 4.14, the resistance of unstiffened or stiffened plates is based on the partial factor γ_{M0} with the recommended value 1.0. For

2. Overview of Design Rules

buildings where $\gamma_{M1} = 1.0$, this inconsistency vanishes.

For $\gamma_{M1} = 1.1$ the minimum design resistance from the FEM analysis is almost equal to the EN 1993-1-5 design resistance and for $\gamma_{M1} = 1.0$ it is 10% higher (the characteristic resistance from the FEM analysis is in this example 10% higher than the characteristic resistance according EN 1993-1-5).

Chapter 3

CRANE RUNWAY BEAM EXAMPLE

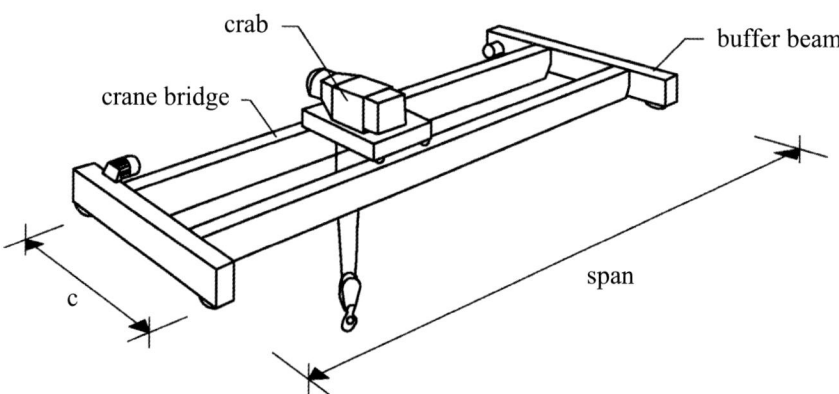

Fig. 3.1: Double-girder overhead travelling crane

3.1 DESCRIPTION OF THE CRANE

The crane supplier specified the following data for the crane (80 tons) shown in Fig. 3.1:

- Double-girder overhead travelling crane with grab operation
- Hoisting class HC4, loading class S3
- Carriage system IFF
- Self-weight Q_c = 259 kN
- Hoist load Q_h = 824 kN
- Steady hoisting speed v_h = 2.2 m/min
- Wheel base c = 4.5 m

3. CRANE RUNWAY BEAM EXAMPLE

- Max. wheel load $Q_{r,max} = 554$ kN
- Min. wheel load $Q_{r,min} = 63$ kN

Horizontal and buffer forces were omitted because only vertical forces are relevant in this example. These forces are usually also provided by the crane supplier.

3.2 DESCRIPTION OF THE CRANE RUNWAY BEAM

3.2.1 Geometry

The crane runway has a single span as shown in Fig. 3.3. The crane runway is located inside a hydroelectric power plant lifting heavy loads but with a low number of cycles over its lifetime. In Fig. 3.4 the welded cross section is shown. The self-weight of the crane runway beam with rail is $g = 5.0$ kN/m.

Crane rail properties:

- Crane rail with foot flange, type A100 according to DIN 536-1 (DIN 536-1, 1991)
- Nominal values: $b_{fr} = 200$ mm, $h_r = 95$ mm, $I_r = 856$ cm^4
- Values taking wear into account: $h_{r,wear} = 85$ mm, $I_{r,wear} = 629$ cm^4

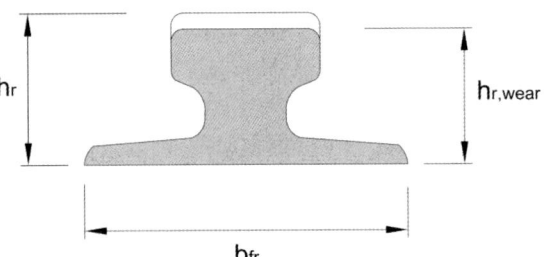

Fig. 3.2: Crane rail properties

Cross section properties of the crane runway beam:

$A = 472$ cm^2; $I_y = 1\,294\,060$ cm^4
$z_s = 548$ mm; $z_{s,pl} = 475$ mm
$W_{y,1} = 22\,027$ cm^4; $W_{y,2} = 22\,803$ cm^4; $W_{y,3} = 23\,636$ cm^4

3.2 DESCRIPTION OF THE CRANE RUNWAY BEAM

$W_{y,4} = 19\,832$ cm^4; $W_{y,5} = 19\,243$ cm^4; $W_{y,6} = 18\,687$ cm^4
Transverse stiffeners at the supports

For the location $i = 1$ to 6 of the section modulus $W_{y,i}$ see Fig. 3.4.

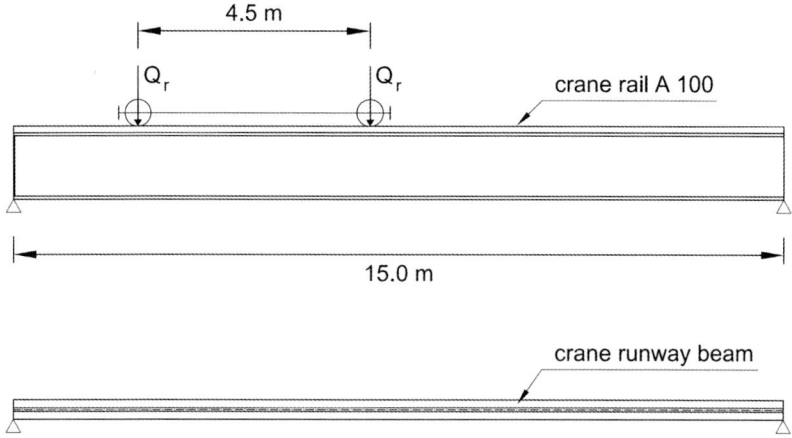

Fig. 3.3: Elevation and top view of the crane runway beam

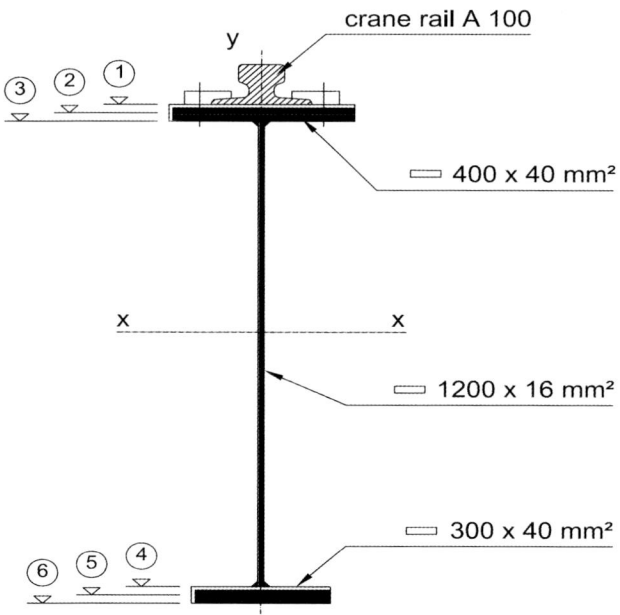

Fig. 3.4: Cross section of the crane runway beam

3. CRANE RUNWAY BEAM EXAMPLE

3.2.2 Material properties and material partial factors

Steel grade S235 with material properties according to Table 3.1 is used for the crane runway beam.

Table 3.1: Yield and ultimate strength of S235 according to EN 10025-2

plate thickness [mm]	f_y [N/mm²]	f_u [N/mm²]	E [N/mm²]
≤ 16	235	360	210000
> 16 ≤ 40	225	360	210000

$\gamma_{M0} = \gamma_{M1} = 1.0$ as recommended in clause 6.1(1), EN 1993-6. Note that National Annexes do give different partial factors!

3.2.3 Cross section classification

The classification of the web is done according to the c/t-limits given in Table 3.2.

$$\alpha = \frac{z_{s,pl}}{h_w} = \frac{475}{1200} = 0.396$$

$$\frac{1200}{16} \leq \frac{36 \cdot \sqrt{\frac{235}{235}}}{0.396} \quad \text{for Class 1}$$

$$75.0 < 90.9 \quad \text{OK.}$$

The web is in Class 1, so that the plate buckling check due to direct stresses is not required.

The web should be checked against shear buckling when $h_w/t > 72 \cdot \varepsilon/\eta$:

3.2 DESCRIPTION OF THE CRANE RUNWAY BEAM

$$\frac{1200}{16} > 72 \cdot \frac{\sqrt{\frac{235}{235}}}{1.2} \quad \text{where} \quad \eta = 1.2$$

$$75.0 > 60.0 \quad \rightarrow \quad \text{slender web.}$$

The shear buckling resistance of the web has to be checked.

Table 3.2: Maximum width-to-thickness ratios for internal elements under compression and bending ($\alpha \leq 0.5$; $\psi \leq -1$) according to Table 5.2, EN 1993-1-1

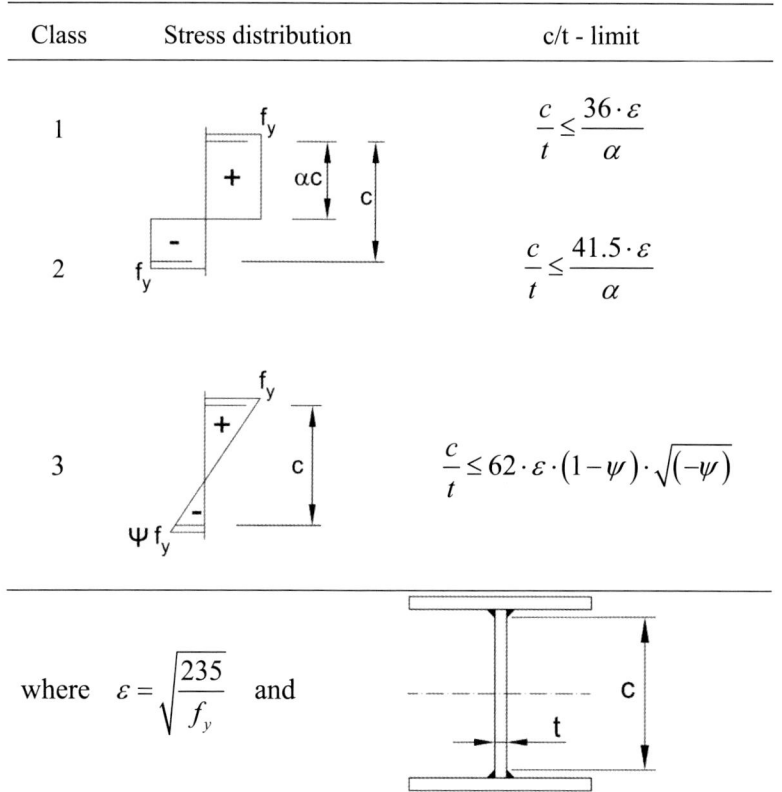

Class	Stress distribution	c/t - limit
1		$\dfrac{c}{t} \leq \dfrac{36 \cdot \varepsilon}{\alpha}$
2		$\dfrac{c}{t} \leq \dfrac{41.5 \cdot \varepsilon}{\alpha}$
3		$\dfrac{c}{t} \leq 62 \cdot \varepsilon \cdot (1-\psi) \cdot \sqrt{(-\psi)}$

where $\varepsilon = \sqrt{\dfrac{235}{f_y}}$ and

The classification of the flanges is done according to the *c/t*-limits given in Table 3.3.

$$\frac{(400-16)/2}{40} \leq 9 \cdot \sqrt{\frac{235}{225}}$$

3. CRANE RUNWAY BEAM EXAMPLE

$$4.8 < 9.2 \quad \text{OK}.$$

The flanges are in Class 1, so that the plate buckling check due to direct stresses is not required.

The whole cross section is in Class 1.

Table 3.3: Maximum width-to-thickness ratios for outstand flanges under uniform compression according to Table 5.2, EN 1993-1-1

Class	c/t - limit
1	$\dfrac{c}{t} \leq 9 \cdot \varepsilon$
2	$\dfrac{c}{t} \leq 10 \cdot \varepsilon$
3	$\dfrac{c}{t} \leq 14 \cdot \varepsilon$

where

$$\varepsilon = \sqrt{\dfrac{235}{f_y}}$$

3.3 ACTIONS AND LOAD PARTIAL FACTORS

3.3.1 General

A crane runway beam is subjected to general actions, i.e. non-crane loads, for which the relevant parts of EN 1991-1 "Actions on structures – General actions" are presumed to be known. In addition to that, crane actions act on the crane runway beam according to EN 1991-3 "Actions on structures – Actions induced by cranes and machinery" (CEN, 2006c), addressed in section 3.3.2.

For each critical load case the design values of the action effects in combination need to be determined. At ultimate limit state, the partial factor for self-weight is γ_G = 1.35. The partial factor for unfavourable crane action according to Table 3.4 is γ_Q = 1.35. For crane actions in combination with non-crane loads the relevant ψ-factors according to Table 3.5 shall be applied. Here, ψ = 1.0 because the governing load combination is self-weight of the crane runway beam and crane action from load group 1, see section 3.3.2. Thus, the load combination becomes here:

$$\gamma_G \cdot G_k + \gamma_Q \cdot Q_k = 1.35 \cdot G_k + 1.35 \cdot Q_k$$

Table 3.4: Recommended values of γ-factors for unfavourable crane actions according to Table A.1 and A.3.2, EN 1991-3, and clause 2.8, EN 1993-6

Unfavourable actions	Persistent and transient situation	Accidental situation
Crane actions (ULS*)	$\gamma_Q = 1.35$	$\gamma_A = 1.00$
Crane test loads (ULS*)	$\gamma_{F,test} = 1.10$	$\gamma_A = 1.00$
Crane actions (SLS*)	$\gamma_{Q,ser} = 1.00$	—
Crane actions (Fatigue)	$\gamma_Q = 1.00$	—

* ULS: Ultimate Limit State; SLS: Serviceability Limit State

Table 3.5: ψ-factors for crane actions according to Table A.2, EN 1991-3

Action	Ψ_0	Ψ_1	Ψ_2
Single crane or group of loads induced by cranes	1.0	0.9	$\dfrac{\text{Permanent crane action}}{\text{Total crane action}}$

3.3.2 Crane actions

Crane actions are actions on the crane runway beam induced by the wheels of the crane and possibly by guide rollers or other guidance devices. These actions are usually separated in vertical crane actions caused by the self-weight of the crane and the hoist load, and in horizontal crane actions caused by acceleration and deceleration, by skewing and other dynamic effects. The different actions induced by cranes are taken into account by combining them in groups of loads according to Table 3.6. In terms of EN 1990 (CEN, 2002), such a load group is considered as one characteristic crane action.

3. CRANE RUNWAY BEAM EXAMPLE

Table 3.6: Groups of loads and dynamic factors to be considered as one characteristic crane action at Ultimate Limit State (ULS) according to Table 2.2, EN 1991-3

#	Description	Symbol	Groups of load at ULS						
			1	2	3	4	5	6	7
1	Self-weight of crane	Q_c	φ_1	φ_1	1	φ_4	φ_4	φ_4	1
2	Hoist load	Q_h	φ_2	φ_3	-	φ_4	φ_4	φ_4	η^*
3	Acceleration of crane bride	H_L, H_T	φ_5	φ_5	φ_5	φ_5	-	-	-
4	Skewing of crane bridge	H_S	-	-	-	-	1	-	-
5	Acceleration or braking of crab or hoist block	H_{T3}	-	-	-	-	-	1	-
6	In service wind	F_w^*	1	1	1	1	1	-	-

* η is the ratio of the hoist load that remains when the payload is removed, but is not included in the self-weight of the crane

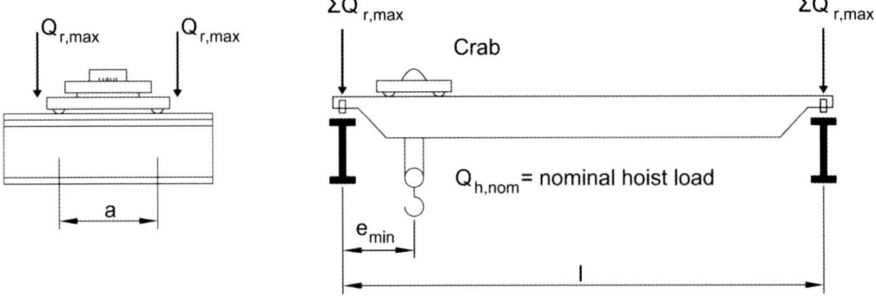

Fig. 3.5: Load arrangement of the loaded crane to obtain the maximum wheel load $Q_{r,max}$ on the runway beam according to Fig. 2.1, EN 1991-3

For the plate buckling verifications of the beam, the vertical forces induced by the self-weight and hoist load are relevant. Usually load group 1 governs the design under the wheel load, which is also the case here. The maximum wheel load $Q_{r,max}$ comprises static and dynamic components which are represented by the dynamic factors φ_1 and φ_2 according to Table 3.6. $Q_{r,max}$ is determined according to the load arrangement shown in Fig. 3.5 and it is usually provided by the crane supplier, see sub-chapter 3.1.

3.4 INTERNAL FORCES AND STRESSES

3.4.1 General

For the plate buckling verifications, section 3.4.2 to section 3.4.4 summarise the relevant internal forces and stresses. Based on the cross section classification, plate buckling verifications are required for both the shear resistance and the patch loading resistance under wheel load. In Fig. 3.6 the characteristic bending moment and shear force distributions due to self-weight of the crane runway beam are shown.

The maximum internal forces induced by the wheel loads occur at different locations since it is a moving load which can travel along the crane runway beam. Due to the pair of wheel loads, the maximum bending moment does not occur at mid-span but at location x_1 = 6.375 m, see Fig. 3.7. The maximum shear force is determined for the wheel load position at x_2 = $h_w/2$ = 0.6 m next to the support, as shown in Fig. 3.8. For a smaller wheel load distance from the support the maximum shear force would increase slightly, but the average shear force in the web plate near the support, relevant for shear buckling, would clearly decrease.

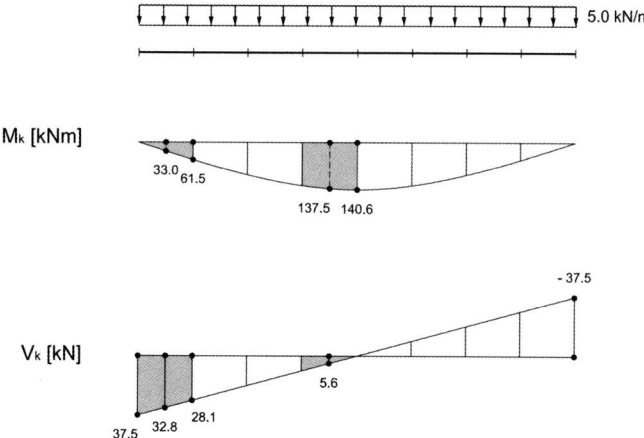

Fig. 3.6: Characteristic internal forces due to self-weight of the crane runway beam

3. Crane Runway Beam Example

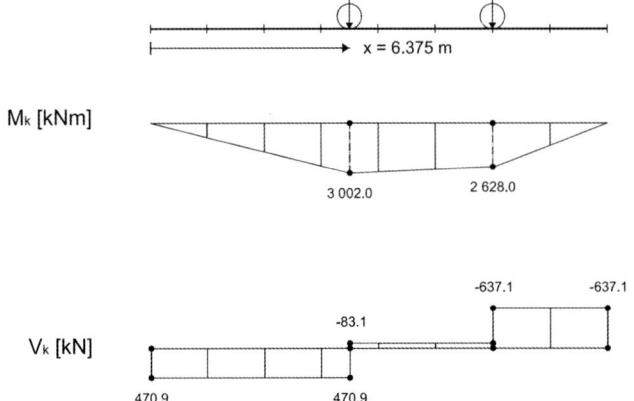

Fig. 3.7: Characteristic internal forces due to wheel loads at location $x_1 = 6.375$ m

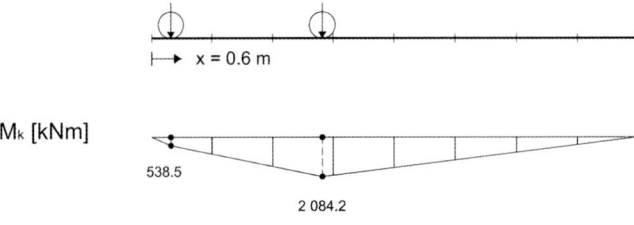

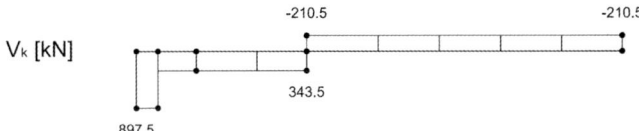

Fig. 3.8: Characteristic internal forces due to wheel loads at location $x_2 = 0.6$ m

3.4.2 Transverse forces and stresses

The transverse force $F_{z,Ed}$ exerted on the crane runway beam is the design value of the maximum wheel load $Q_{r,max}$.

$$F_{z,Ed} = \gamma_Q \cdot Q_{r,max} = 1.35 \cdot 554 = 748 \text{ kN}$$

The local vertical compressive stress $\sigma_{z,Ed}$ at the underside of the top flange should be determined according to clause 5.7.1(1), EN 1993-6 (CEN, 2007):

3.4 INTERNAL FORCES AND STRESSES

$$\sigma_{z,Ed} = \frac{F_{z,Ed}}{\ell_{eff} \cdot t_w}$$

The effective loaded length ℓ_{eff} should be calculated according to Table 3.7 for the present case of a crane rail not rigidly fixed to the flange. Taking wear into account, $h_{r,wear}$ is 85 mm and the effective flange width becomes:

$$b_{eff} = b_{fr} + h_{r,wear} + t_f \leq b$$

$$b_{eff} = 200 + 85 + 40 = 325 \text{ mm} < 400 \text{ mm}$$

Table 3.7: Effective loaded length ℓ_{eff} according to Table 5.1, EN 1993-6

Case	Description of crane rail	Effective loaded length ℓ_{eff}
(a)	Rigidly fixed to the flange	$\ell_{eff} = 3.25 \cdot \left(\dfrac{I_{rf}}{t_w}\right)^{\frac{1}{3}}$
(b)	Not rigidly fixed to the flange	$\ell_{eff} = 3.25 \cdot \left(\dfrac{I_r + I_{f,eff}}{t_w}\right)^{\frac{1}{3}}$
(c)	Mounted on a suitable resilient elastomeric bearing pad at least 6 mm thick	$\ell_{eff} = 4.25 \cdot \left(\dfrac{I_r + I_{f,eff}}{t_w}\right)^{\frac{1}{3}}$

where $I_{f,eff}$ second moment of area of a flange with an effective width b_{eff}
I_r second moment of area of the rail
I_{rf} second moment of the combined cross section comprising the rail and a flange with an effective width b_{eff}
t_w web thickness

The second moment of inertia of the flange is then:

$$I_{f,eff} = \frac{b_{eff} \cdot t_f^3}{12} = \frac{325 \cdot 40^3}{12} \cdot 10^{-4} = 173 \text{ cm}^4$$

With the second moment of inertia of the rail, $I_r = 629$ cm^4 taking wear into account, the effective loaded length ℓ_{eff} becomes:

$$\ell_{\text{eff}} = 3.25 \cdot \left(\frac{I_{r,\text{wear}} + I_{f,\text{eff}}}{t_w} \right)^{\frac{1}{3}} = 3.25 \cdot \left(\frac{629 \cdot 10^4 + 173 \cdot 10^4}{16} \right)^{\frac{1}{3}} = 258 \text{ mm}$$

Finally, the local vertical compressive stress $\sigma_{z,Ed}$ at the underside of the top flange becomes:

$$\sigma_{z,Ed} = \frac{748 \cdot 10^3}{258 \cdot 16} = 181.2 \text{ N/mm}^2$$

3.4.3 Maximum bending moments and stresses

The maximum bending moment under wheel loads is at location $x_1 = 6.375$ m:

$$M_{Q,k,\text{max}} = \frac{x_1^2}{L} \cdot 2 \cdot Q_{r,\text{max}} = \frac{6.375^2}{15} \cdot 2 \cdot 554 = 3002.0 \text{ kNm}$$

The maximum bending moments under self-weight at mid-span and at location $x_1 = 6.375$ m are:

$$M_{g,k,\text{max}} = \frac{g \cdot L^2}{8} = \frac{5.0 \cdot 15^2}{8} = 140.6 \text{ kNm}$$

$$M_{g,k,x1} = 137.5 \text{ kNm}$$

Thus, the design value of maximum bending moment becomes at location $x_1 = 6.375$ m:

$$M_{Ed,\text{max}} = \gamma_G \cdot M_{g,k,x1} + \gamma_Q \cdot M_{g,k,\text{max}} =$$

$$= 1.35 \cdot 137.5 + 1.35 \cdot 3002.0 = 4238 \text{ kNm}$$

The longitudinal stresses at the web-to-flange-junctions following the numbering of Fig. 3.4 become:

3.4 INTERNAL FORCES AND STRESSES

$$\sigma_{3,x,Ed} = \frac{M_{Ed,max}}{W_3} = \frac{4238 \cdot 10^6}{23636 \cdot 10^3} = 179.4 \text{ N/mm}^2$$

$$\sigma_{4,x,Ed} = \frac{M_{Ed,max}}{W_4} = \frac{4238 \cdot 10^6}{19832 \cdot 10^3} = -213.7 \text{ N/mm}^2$$

Note that compression is taken as positive according to the sign convention of EN 1993-1-5.

With the shear force under self-weight $V_{g,k} = 5.6$ kN and the maximum shear force under wheel loads $V_{Q,k,max} = 470.9$ kN, the design value of the shear force at the location of the wheel load becomes:

$$V_{Ed} = \gamma_g \cdot V_{g,k} + \gamma_Q \cdot V_{Q,k,max} = 1.35 \cdot 5.6 + 1.35 \cdot 470.9 = 643 \text{ kN}$$

The design values of shear force and stress at location $x_1 = 6.375$ m become:

$$V_{Ed,avg} = V_{Ed} - \frac{F_{z,Ed}}{2} = 643 - \frac{748}{2} = 269 \text{ kN}$$

$$\tau_{Ed} = \frac{V_{Ed,avg}}{h_w \cdot t_w} = \frac{199.5 \cdot 10^3}{1200 \cdot 16} = 14.0 \text{ N/mm}^2$$

3.4.4 Maximum shear forces and stresses

The maximum shear force under wheel loads at location $x_3 = 0.6$ m next to the support is:

$$V_{Q,k,max} = 897.5 \text{ kN}$$

Note that for fatigue verifications also local shear stresses acting at each side of the wheel load position have to be taken into account, see clause 9.3.3, EN 1993-6.

The maximum shear forces under self-weight at the support and at location $x_2 = 0.6$ m are:

3. CRANE RUNWAY BEAM EXAMPLE

$$V_{g,k,max} = \frac{g \cdot L}{2} = \frac{5 \cdot 15}{2} = 37.5 \text{ kN}$$

$$V_{g,k,x2} = 34.5 \text{ kN}$$

Thus, the design value of maximum shear force becomes at location $x_2 = 0.6$ m:

$$V_{Ed,max} = \gamma_G \cdot V_{G,k,x2} + \gamma_Q \cdot V_{Q,k,max} = 1.35 \cdot 34.5 + 1.35 \cdot 897.5 = 1\,258 \text{ kN}$$

The design value of shear stress at location $x_2 = 0.6$ m becomes:

$$\tau_{Ed} = \frac{V_{Ed,max}}{h_w \cdot t_w} = \frac{1{,}258 \cdot 10^3}{1200 \cdot 16} = 65.5 \text{ N/mm}^2$$

3.5 VERIFICATIONS IN GENERAL

The crane runway beam has to meet ultimate limit state verifications such as general stress verifications and lateral torsional buckling verifications. Besides that, also fatigue verifications and serviceability verifications have to be checked.

In this example, only the plate buckling verifications at ultimate limit state are addressed. According to clause 6.5.1(2), EN 1993-6, the lateral eccentricity of the wheel loads does not need to be considered in the plate buckling verifications.

3.6 BUCKLING VERIFICATIONS ACCORDING TO SECTIONS 4 TO 7, EN 1993-1-5

Below, the procedure according to sections 4 to 7, EN 1993-1-5, is illustrated, which is the recommended standard procedure in clause 6.5.1(3), EN 1993-6. Alternatively, the verification method according to section 10, EN 1993-1-5, may be used, as explained in sub-chapter 2.10.

3.6 BUCKLING VERIFICATIONS ACCORDING TO SECTIONS 4 TO 7, EN 1993-1-5

3.6.1 Resistance to shear forces

According to section 3.2.3, the web has to be checked against shear buckling. The design resistance to shear forces should be taken as:

$$V_{b,Rd} = V_{bw,Rd} + V_{bf,Rd} \leq V_{pl,Rd} = h_w \cdot t_w \cdot \frac{\eta \cdot f_{yw}}{\sqrt{3} \cdot \gamma_{M1}}$$

Next the contribution of the web is determined. With the shear buckling coefficient

$$k_\tau = 5.34 + 4 \cdot \left(\frac{h_w}{a}\right)^2 = 5.34 + 4 \cdot \left(\frac{1200}{15000}\right)^2 = 5.366$$

the slenderness becomes:

$$\overline{\lambda}_w = \frac{h_w}{37.4 \cdot t_w \cdot \varepsilon \cdot \sqrt{k_\tau}} = \frac{1200}{37.4 \cdot 16 \cdot 1.0 \cdot \sqrt{5.366}} = 0.866$$

For a non-rigid end support and with $\eta = 1.2$ the reduction factor becomes:

$$\chi_w = \frac{0.83}{\overline{\lambda}_w} = \frac{0.83}{0.866} = 0.959 \text{ for } \overline{\lambda}_w > 0.83/\eta = 0.692$$

Finally, the contribution of the web is:

$$V_{bw,Rd} = \chi_w \cdot h_w \cdot t_w \cdot \frac{f_{yw}}{\sqrt{3} \cdot \gamma_{M1}} =$$

$$= 0.959 \cdot 1200 \cdot 16 \cdot \frac{235}{\sqrt{3} \cdot 1.0} \cdot 10^{-3} = 2498 \text{ kN}$$

It may be reasonable to add the contribution of the flanges when the flange resistance is not completely utilised in resisting the bending moment and the increase in resistance is needed. Here the resistance of the web alone is already enough, but for the sake of completeness the contribution of the

3. Crane Runway Beam Example

flanges is determined. Firstly, the bending moment resistance of the cross section consisting only of the effective area of the flanges without the web is calculated. The flange widths $b_{f,1} = 400$ mm and $b_{f,2} = 300$ mm do not exceed the value of twice $15 \cdot \varepsilon \cdot t = 15 \cdot 1.0 \cdot 40 = 600$ mm, so that with a distance between mid-plane of flanges $h_f = 1240$ mm:

$$M_{f,k} = \min\left(A_{f,1} \cdot f_{yf,1} \cdot h_f ; A_{f,2} \cdot f_{yf,2} \cdot h_f\right)$$

$$M_{f,k} = \min\left(400 \cdot 40 \cdot 225 \cdot 1240 \cdot 10^{-6} ; 400 \cdot 40 \cdot 225 \cdot 1240 \cdot 10^{-6}\right) =$$

$$= \min(4464; 3348) = 3348 \text{ kNm}$$

$$M_{f,Rd} = \frac{M_{f,k}}{\gamma_{M0}} = \frac{3348}{1.0} = 3348 \text{ kNm}$$

With $M_{Ed} = 1.35 \cdot (538.5 + 33.0) = 771.5$ kNm the flanges are utilised up to 23 % so that generally some contribution of the flanges can be expected. For girders without transverse stiffeners the applicability of the formulae for the contribution of flanges is not obvious and anyway these formulae give practically negligible additional resistance. This contribution is determined based on the distance c of the plastic hinges in the flange

$$c = a \cdot \left(0.25 + \frac{1.6 \cdot b_f \cdot t_f^2 \cdot f_{yf}}{t_w \cdot h_w^2 \cdot f_{yw}}\right) =$$

$$= 15\,000 \cdot \left(0.25 + \frac{1.6 \cdot 300 \cdot 40^2 \cdot 225}{16 \cdot 1200^2 \cdot 235}\right) = 4229 \text{ mm}$$

Finally, the contribution of the flanges is:

$$V_{bf,Rd} = \frac{b_f \cdot t_f^2}{c} \cdot \frac{f_{yf}}{\gamma_{M1}} \left[1 - \left(\frac{M_{Ed}}{M_{f,Rd}}\right)^2\right] =$$

$$= \frac{300 \cdot 40^2}{4229} \cdot \frac{225}{1.0} \left[1 - \left(\frac{771.5}{3348}\right)^2\right] = 24.2 \text{ kN}$$

3.6 BUCKLING VERIFICATIONS ACCORDING TO SECTIONS 4 TO 7, EN 1993-1-5

With $\eta = 1.2$ the verification becomes:

$$V_{b,Rd} = V_{bw,Rd} + V_{bf,Rd} = 2522 \text{ kN} < V_{pl,Rd} = 3126 \text{ kN}$$

where $V_{pl,Rd} = h_w \cdot t_w \cdot \dfrac{\eta \cdot f_{yw}}{\sqrt{3} \cdot \gamma_{M1}} = 1200 \cdot 16 \cdot \dfrac{1.2 \cdot 235}{\sqrt{3} \cdot 1.0} = 3126 \text{ kNm}$

$$\eta_3 = \dfrac{V_{Ed}}{V_{b,Rd}} = \dfrac{1258}{2522} = 0.499 \quad \text{OK.}$$

3.6.2 Resistance to transverse forces

The length of stiff bearing s_s according to clause 6.3, EN 1993-1-5, refers to the upperside of the loaded flange. This length should be determined from the effective loaded length ℓ_{eff}, calculated in section 3.4.2, according to clause 6.5.2(1), EN 1993-6:

$$s_s = \ell_{eff} - 2 \cdot t_f = 258 - 2 \cdot 40 = 178 \text{ mm}$$

The critical load F_{cr} is calculated based on the buckling value k_F. The determination of the buckling value has to be strictly based on Fig. 6.1, EN 1993-1-5, because the reduction curve $\chi_F(\overline{\lambda}_F)$ was calibrated based on that formula.

$$k_F = 6 + 2 \cdot \left(\dfrac{h_w}{a}\right)^2 = 6 + 2 \cdot \left(\dfrac{1200}{15000}\right)^2 = 6.031$$

$$F_{cr} = 0.9 \cdot k_F \cdot E \cdot \dfrac{t_w^3}{h_w} = 0.9 \cdot 6.031 \cdot 210{,}000 \cdot \dfrac{16^3}{1200} \cdot 10^{-3} = 3879 \text{ kN}$$

The yield load F_y is determined based on the effective loaded length ℓ_y. Note that this effective loaded length is different from the effective length according to EN1993-6, determined in section 3.4.2.

$$\ell_y = s_s + 2 \cdot t_f \cdot \left(1 + \sqrt{m_1 + m_2}\right) \leq a$$

3. Crane Runway Beam Example

$$m_1 = \frac{f_{yf} \cdot b_f}{f_{yw} \cdot t_w} = \frac{225 \cdot 400}{235 \cdot 16} = 23.9$$

$$m_2 = 0.02 \cdot \left(\frac{h_w}{t_f}\right)^2 = 0.02 \cdot \left(\frac{1200}{40}\right)^2 = 18.0 \text{ for } \overline{\lambda}_F > 0.5$$

In case $\overline{\lambda}_F \leq 0.5$, the calculation for the yield load should be redone with $m_2 = 0$.

$$\ell_y = 258 + 2 \cdot 40 \cdot \left(1 + \sqrt{23.9 + 18.0}\right) = 776 \text{ mm} \quad < \quad 1875 \text{ mm}$$

The yield load becomes:

$$F_y = \ell_y \cdot t_w \cdot f_{yw} = 776 \cdot 16 \cdot 235 \cdot 10^{-3} = 2919 \text{ kN}$$

Finally, the slenderness can be determined:

$$\overline{\lambda}_F = \sqrt{\frac{F_y}{F_{cr}}} = \sqrt{\frac{2919}{3879}} = 0.867$$

Because $\overline{\lambda}_F > 0.5$, no recalculation of m_2 is necessary.

The reduction factor which is applied to the yield load becomes

$$\chi_F = \frac{0.5}{\overline{\lambda}_F} = \frac{0.5}{0.867} = 0.576 \quad < \quad 1$$

so that the resistance to transverse forces can be determined.

$$F_{Rd} = \chi_F \cdot \frac{F_y}{\gamma_{M1}} = 0.576 \cdot \frac{2919}{1.0} = 1682 \text{ kN}$$

Finally, the verification becomes:

$$\eta_2 = \frac{F_{Ed}}{F_{Rd}} = \frac{748}{1682} = 0.445 \quad < \quad 1$$

3.6.3 Interaction checks

At location $x_1 = 6.375$ m, the resistance to transverse forces requires an interaction check with bending moment. There the bending moment reaches a maximum: $M_{Ed} = 4238$ kNm. However, according to clause 7.2, EN 1993-1-5, the interaction between transverse force and bending moment is only necessary if both of the following conditions are fulfilled:

$$\eta_2 = \frac{F_{Ed}}{F_{Rd}} > 0.5 \quad \text{and} \quad \eta_1 = \frac{M_{Ed}}{M_{Rd}} > 0.6$$

Here $\eta_2 < 0.5$, so that the interaction check is not necessary. For the sake of completeness, the verification is shown below.

The bending moment utilisation is:

$$\eta_1 = \frac{M_{Ed}}{W_{y,5} \cdot f_{yf} / \gamma_{M0}} = \frac{4\,238 \cdot 10^6}{19\,243 \cdot 10^3 \cdot 225 / 1.0} = 0.979 < 1$$

The interaction verification becomes:

$$\eta_2 + 0.8 \cdot \eta_1 \leq 1.4$$

$$0.445 + 0.8 \cdot 0.979 = 1.2 < 1.4 \quad \text{OK}.$$

At location $x_3 = 0.6$ m, the resistance to transverse forces should be checked against interaction with shear force. However, section 7, EN 1993-1-5, does not account for this type of interaction. In the framework of the COMBRI research project (Kuhlmann et al, 2007), the following interaction equation was developed:

$$\left(\frac{V_{Ed} - F_{z,Ed}/2}{V_{b,Rd}}\right)^{1.6} + \eta_2 \leq 1.0$$

With $V_{Ed,avg} = V_{Ed} - F_{z,Ed}/2 = 1258 - 748/2 = 884$ kN and $V_{b,Rd} = 2522$ kN the verification becomes:

$$\left(\frac{884}{2522}\right)^{1.6} + 0.445 < 1.0$$

3. CRANE RUNWAY BEAM EXAMPLE

$$0.632 < 1.0 \quad \text{OK.}$$

3.7 BUCKLING VERIFICATIONS ACCORDING TO SECTION 10, EN 1993-1-5

In this section, the alternative verification method according to section 10, EN 1993-1-5, is explained for location $x_1 = 6.375$ m. Note that the recommended standard procedure in clause 6.5.1(3), EN 1993-6, corresponds to the procedures according to sections 4 to 7, EN 1993-1-5, which were applied in sub-chapter 3.6.

According to clause 6.5.1(2), EN 1993-6, the lateral eccentricity of the wheel loads does not need to be considered in the plate buckling verifications. The loading length used here corresponds to the value at the underside of the loaded flange, which was calculated as effective loaded length ℓ_{eff} in section 3.4.2. The stress field acting at the considered location is shown in Fig. 3.9. The stresses are taken from this critical cross section and are applied as constant along the whole girder length, which is a good approximation of the real conditions.

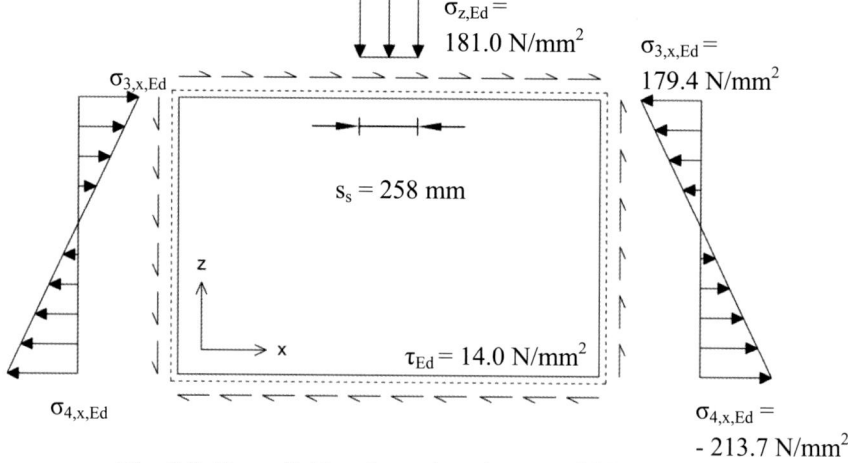

Fig. 3.9: Stress field acting at location $x_1 = 6.375$ m

The equivalent design stress in the panel becomes:

$$\sigma_{eq,Ed} = \sqrt{179.4^2 + 181^2 - 179.4 \cdot 181 + 3 \cdot 14.0^2} = 181.8 \text{ N/mm}^2$$

3.8 FLANGE INDUCED BUCKLING VERIFICATION

Two load amplifiers need to be calculated in order to determine the plate slenderness. The minimum load amplifier α_{cr} for the design loads to reach the elastic critical load of the plate under the complete stress field can be either determined in one step by using appropriate software, e.g. *EBPlate* (EBplate, 2007), or on the basis of each component of the stress field, e.g. by hand-calculation according to 10(6), EN 1993-1-5. However, the advantage of this procedure can be utilised if appropriate software is used. With *EBPlate* (EBplate, 2007), assuming hinged boundary conditions at all four edges, α_{cr} becomes:

$$\alpha_{cr} = 2.043$$

The first buckling mode under the complete stress field is shown in Fig. 3.10.

The minimum load amplifier $\alpha_{ult,k}$ for the design loads to reach the characteristic value of resistance becomes:

$$\alpha_{ult,k} = \frac{f_y}{\sigma_{eq,Ed}} = \frac{235}{181.8} = 1.293$$

From this, the slenderness can be calculated:

$$\overline{\lambda}_p = \sqrt{\frac{\alpha_{ult,k}}{\alpha_{cr}}} = \sqrt{\frac{1.293}{2.015}} = 0.801$$

The determination of the reduction factors is done based on different buckling curves for each basic loading. For bending stress with $\psi = -1.192$, no reduction is necessary, i.e. $\rho_x = 1.0$, because according to clause 4.4(2), EN 1993-1-5:

$$\overline{\lambda}_p = 0.801 \quad < \quad 0.5 + \sqrt{0.25 - 0.055 \cdot (3+\psi)} = 0.888$$

For transverse stress, the reduction factor for plate-like buckling according to Annex B.1, EN 1993-1-5 (CEN, 2006a) becomes:

$$\rho_z = \frac{1}{\varphi_p + \sqrt{\varphi_p^2 - \overline{\lambda}_p}} \leq 1$$

3. CRANE RUNWAY BEAM EXAMPLE

$$\rho_z = \frac{1}{0.897 + \sqrt{0.897^2 - 0.795}} = 1.0$$

with

$$\varphi_p = 0.5 \cdot \left[1 + \alpha_p \cdot \left(\overline{\lambda}_p - \overline{\lambda}_{p0}\right) + \overline{\lambda}_p\right]$$

$$\varphi_p = 0.5 \cdot \left[1 + 0.34 \cdot (0.795 - 0.8) + 0.80\right] = 0.897$$

with $\alpha_p = 0.34$ and $\overline{\lambda}_{p0} = 0.8$ (see Table 2.9)

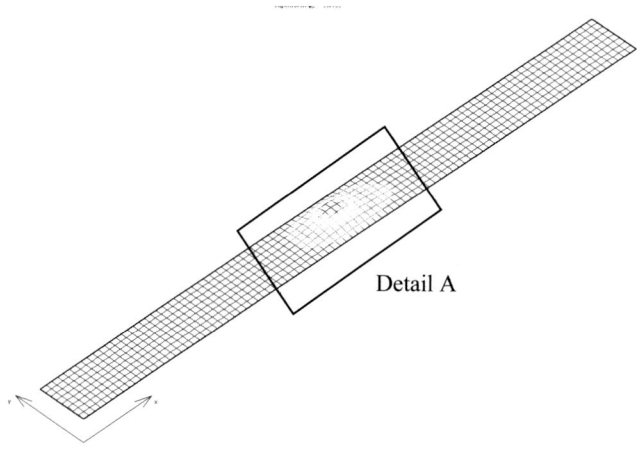

a) Whole web panel

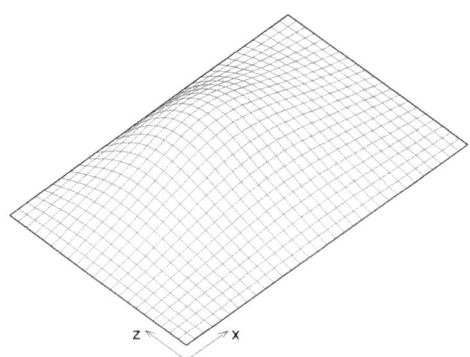

b) Detail A
Fig. 3.10: Buckling mode at location $x_1 = 6.375$ m under the complete stress field (EBplate, 2007)

3.8 FLANGE INDUCED BUCKLING VERIFICATION

Column-like behaviour in the transverse direction should be checked. The system, which considers only the stress state induced by the transverse stress, is used to determine the critical plate- and column-buckling stresses. With *EBPlate* (EBplate, 2007), assuming hinged boundary conditions at all four edges, the critical plate-buckling stress becomes:

$$\sigma_{cr,p,z} = 404.1 \text{ N/mm}^2$$

Due to the nonlinear distribution of transverse stresses in the web, the determination of the critical column-buckling stress was done here most accurately based on the energy method which takes into account the nonlinear stress distribution. A Finite-Element-based calculation gives:

$$\sigma_{cr,c} = 87.9 \text{ N/mm}^2$$

Although the determination of $\sigma_{cr,c}$ in the transverse direction should take into account the nonlinear stress distribution in the web, no suitable hand-calculation method exists at the moment. A common approach is to assume a linearly varying stress distribution for a pin-ended strut instead, which is zero at one end. Then, $\sigma_{cr,c}$ can be calculated according to DIN 4114 (DIN 4114, 1953) as follows:

$$\sigma_{cr,c} = 1.88 \cdot \sigma_E = 1.88 \cdot 189800 \cdot \left(\frac{t}{b}\right)^2 =$$

$$= 1.88 \cdot 189800 \cdot \left(\frac{16}{1200}\right)^2 = 63.4 \text{ N/mm}^2$$

It should be noted that this simplification may lead to unsafe results because $\sigma_{cr,c}$ is underestimated and in turn the ratio $\sigma_{cr,p}/\sigma_{cr,c}$ is overestimated so that column-like behavior is not detected correctly. The shorter the loading lengths become, the larger is the deviation. Here, both values are calculated and compared:

$$\xi_{hand-calculation} = \frac{\sigma_{cr,p,z}}{\sigma_{cr,c}} - 1 = \frac{404.1}{63.4} - 1 = 5.374$$

3. CRANE RUNWAY BEAM EXAMPLE

$$\xi_{energy\ method} = \frac{\sigma_{cr,p,z}}{\sigma_{cr,c}} - 1 = \frac{404.1}{87.9} - 1 = 3.597$$

Because $\xi > 1.0$ in both cases, column-like behaviour does not have to be considered according to the definition in clause 4.5.4(1), EN 1993-1-5.

For shear stress, the reduction factor according to Table 5.1, EN 1993-1-5 for a non-rigid end post becomes:

$$\chi_w = \frac{0.83}{\overline{\lambda}_w} \quad \text{for } \overline{\lambda}_w \geq \frac{0.83}{\eta}$$

$$\chi_w = \frac{0.83}{0.801} = 1.036 \quad \text{for } \overline{\lambda}_w \geq 0.692$$

Since all reduction factors are equal, i.e. $\rho_x = \rho_z = \chi_w = 1.0$, the verification at location $x_1 = 6.375$ m can be simplified:

$$\alpha_{Rd} = \frac{\rho \cdot \alpha_{ult,k}}{\gamma_{M1}} \geq 1$$

$$\alpha_{Rd} = \frac{1.0 \cdot 1.293}{1.0} = 1.293 \quad > \quad 1 \quad \text{OK.}$$

3.8 FLANGE INDUCED BUCKLING VERIFICATION

To prevent buckling of the compression flange in the plane of the web, the following criterion should be fulfilled according to section 8, EN 1993-1-5:

$$\frac{h_w}{t_w} \leq k \cdot \frac{E}{f_{yf}} \sqrt{\frac{A_w}{A_{fc}}}$$

where
$$A_w = h_w \cdot t_w = 1200 \cdot 16 \cdot 10^{-2} = 192 \text{ cm}^2$$
$$A_{fc} = b_{fc,eff} \cdot t_f = 400 \cdot 40 \cdot 10^{-2} = 160 \text{ cm}^2$$

Factor k accounts for the utilisation of the rotation capacity. Here, the elastic moment resistance is utilized, so that $k = 0.55$.

$$\frac{1200}{16} \leq 0.55 \cdot \frac{210\,000}{225} \cdot \sqrt{\frac{192}{160}}$$

$$75.0 < 562.3 \quad \text{OK.}$$

3.9 STIFFENER VERIFICATIONS

3.9.1 Bearing stiffeners

Bearing stiffener consists of a single double-sided stiffener (non-rigid end post). It is laterally supported at both ends, see Fig. 3.3. The effective cross section of the stiffener is shown in Fig. 3.11. It comprises the area of the double-sided stiffener and a width of the web equal to $15 \cdot \varepsilon \cdot t_w = 240$ mm. On the safe side, the smallest dimension of the transverse stiffener is taken. Due to the given outstand, the width of the web at the end of the beam is limited to 120 mm.

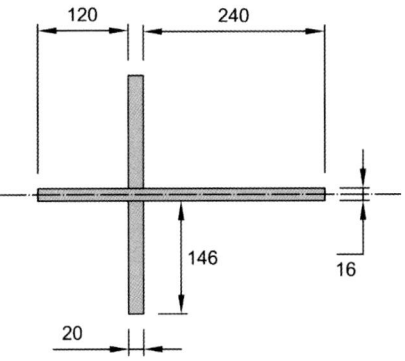

$A_{st} = 117.6 \text{ cm}^2$; $I_{st} = 4512 \text{ cm}^4$;
$I_T = 38.9 \text{ cm}^4$ (stiffener alone, one-sided);
$I_p = 528.4 \text{ cm}^4$ (stiffener alone, one-sided)

Fig. 3.11: Effective cross section of the bearing stiffener

3. Crane Runway Beam Example

The maximum design reaction force at the support is composed of the reaction forces due to self-weight $V_{g,k} = 37.5$ kN as well as wheel loads $V_{Q,k} = 387.8$ kN and $Q_{r,max} = 554$ kN, see Fig. 3.12. The reaction force R_{Ed} becomes:

$$R_{Ed} = \gamma_G \cdot V_{g,k} + \gamma_Q \cdot (V_{Q,k} + Q_{r,max}) =$$

$$= 1.35 \cdot 37.5 + 1.35 \cdot (387.8 + 554) = 1322 \text{ kN}$$

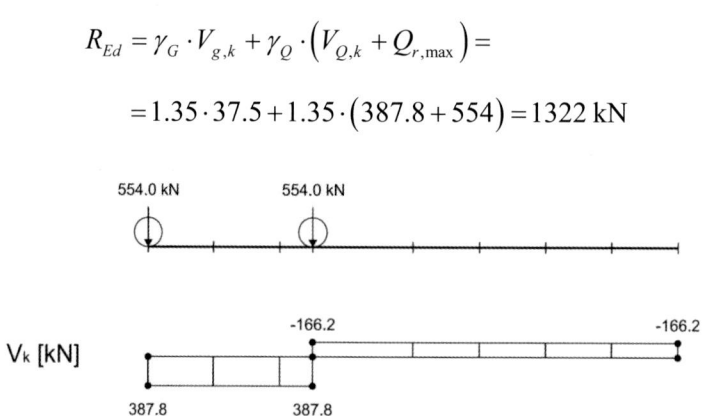

Fig. 3.12: Characteristic internal forces due to wheel loads at the support

Firstly, the buckling resistance of the bearing stiffener is verified. According to clause 9.4(2), EN 1993-1-5, the buckling length L_{cr} of the stiffener is taken as:

$$L_{cr} = \ell = 0.75 \cdot h_w = 0.75 \cdot 1200 = 900 \text{ mm}$$

Thus, the slenderness $\bar{\lambda}$ can be determined:

$$i = \sqrt{\frac{I_{st}}{A_{st}}} = \sqrt{\frac{4512 \cdot 10^4}{117.6 \cdot 10^2}} = 61.9 \text{ mm}$$

$$\lambda = \frac{L_{cr}}{i} = \frac{900}{61.9} = 14.5$$

$$\lambda_1 = \pi \cdot \sqrt{\frac{E}{f_y}} = \pi \cdot \sqrt{\frac{210000}{235}} = 93.9$$

$$\bar{\lambda} = \frac{\lambda}{\lambda_1} = \frac{14.5}{93.9} = 0.155$$

3.9 Stiffener Verifications

The reduction factor χ should be determined based on European Buckling Curve c according to clause 6.3.1.2, EN 1993-1-1. Because $\overline{\lambda} < 0.2$, the reduction factor is $\chi = 1.0$ and the cross sectional check governs. The design resistance becomes:

$$N_{c,Rd} = N_{b,Rd} = \frac{\chi \cdot A_{st} \cdot f_y}{\gamma_{M1}} = \frac{1.0 \cdot 117.6 \cdot 10^2 \cdot 235}{1.0} \cdot 10^{-3} = 2764 \text{ kN}$$

The buckling resistance of the bearing stiffener is verified when the support reaction force R_{Ed} is less than or equal to the design buckling resistance $N_{b,Rd}$.

$$\frac{R_{Ed}}{N_{b,Rd}} \leq 1.0$$

$$\frac{1322}{2764} = 0.478 < 1.0 \quad \text{OK.}$$

Secondly, to prevent torsional buckling of the stiffener, the following criterion should be fulfilled according to clause 9.2.1(8), EN 1993-1-5 for stiffeners with open cross sections:

$$\frac{I_T}{I_p} \geq 5.3 \cdot \frac{f_y}{E}$$

$$\frac{38.9}{528.4} \geq 5.3 \cdot \frac{235}{210000}$$

$$73.6 \cdot 10^{-3} > 5.9 \cdot 10^{-3} \quad \text{OK.}$$

3. Crane Runway Beam Example

Chapter 4

BOX-GIRDER BRIDGE EXAMPLE

4.1 DESCRIPTION OF THE BRIDGE

4.1.1 Longitudinal elevation

The bridge is a symmetrical composite box-girder structure with five spans, 90 m long, three times 120 m long and 90 m long (i.e. a total length between abutments equals 540 m). The structural steel depth is constant and equals 4000 mm. For simplification reasons, the bridge is straight (no curvature in plane) and the top face of the deck is transversally and longitudinally horizontal.

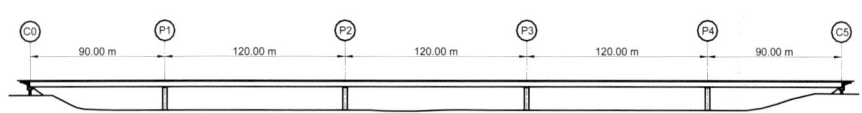

Fig. 4.1: Bridge elevation

4.1.2 Cross section of the composite deck

A four-lane traffic road passes over the bridge. Each lane is 3.5 m wide and the two outside ones are bordered with a 2.06 m wide safety lane on the right-hand side. Normalised safety barriers are located outside the traffic lanes and in the middle of the slab width (see Fig. 4.2).

4. Box-Girder Bridge Example

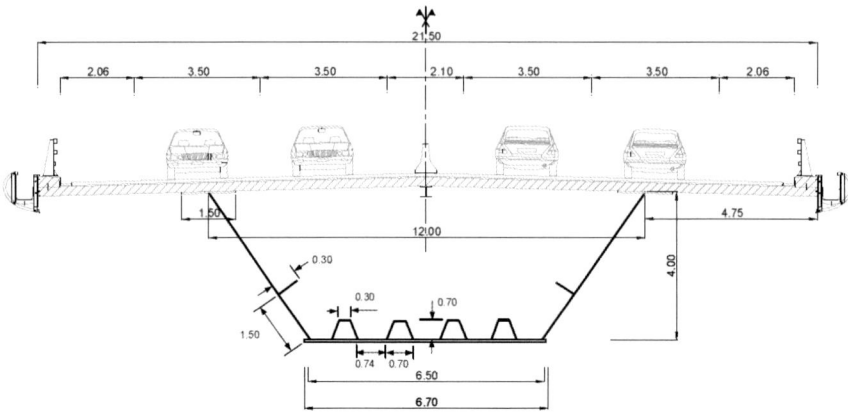

Fig. 4.2: Cross section with traffic data

The cross section of the concrete slab with the non-structural equipments is symmetrical with respect to the axis of the bridge. The 21.5 m wide slab has been modelled with a theoretical constant thickness equal to 0.325 m. The centre-to-centre spacing between main girders is equal to 12.0 m and the slab cantilever on either side of the cross section is 4.75 m wide.

The concrete slab is connected to an open steel box-section with the following features:

- 4 trapezoidal closed longitudinal stiffeners welded on the bottom flange and equally spaced
- Transverse frames at supports and every 4.0 m in spans
- Centre-to-centre distance between webs in the lower part: 6.50 m
- Width of upper flanges: 1500 mm
- Width of lower flange: 6700 mm

4.1.3 Material properties and partial factors

4.1.3.1 Structural steel

Steel grade S355 was used. Its mechanical properties are given in EN10025 (CEN, 2004) and are summarized in Table 4.1. The quality is chosen according to EN1993-2, Table 3.1 (which can be modified by the

National Annex) and EN1993-1-10. The structural steel modulus of elasticity is equal to $E_a = 210000$ N/mm²

Table 4.1: Decrease of f_y and f_u according to plate thickness t

t (mm)	f_y (N/mm²)	f_u (N/mm²)	Quality
$t < 16$	355	470	K2
$16 \leq t < 30$	345	470	N
$30 \leq t < 40$	345	470	N
$40 \leq t < 63$	335	470	N
$63 \leq t < 80$	325	470	N
$80 \leq t < 100$	315	470	NL
$100 \leq t$	295	450	NL

4.1.3.2 Reinforced concrete

Normal concrete of class C35/45 is used for the reinforced slab, with a characteristic compressive cylinder strength f_{ck} at 28 days equal to 35 N/mm² and a mean modulus of elasticity equal to $E_{cm} = 34000$ N/mm².

The reinforcing steel bars used in this project are class B high bond bars with a yield strength $f_{sk} = 500$ N/mm². According to EN1994-2, the modulus of elasticity is taken as equal to that of structural steel, $E_s = E_a = 210000$ N/mm².

4.1.3.3 Partial factors

At ULS, the recommended values from EN1993-2, Table 6.1, are used for the structural steel which means $\gamma_{M0} = 1.0$ and $\gamma_{M1} = 1.1$. Note that these values can be modified by the National Annex.

For the concrete and the reinforcing bars, the partial factors are given by EN1994-2 with $\gamma_C = 1.5$ and $\gamma_S = 1.15$.

4.1.4 Structural steel distribution

The structural steel distribution was designed for the permanent situation (normal use under traffic loads) according to Eurocodes 1, 3 and 4, and is illustrated in Fig. 4.3 below for half length of the bridge.

To maintain the total box-girder depth equal to 4000 mm, the variation of the flange thickness is compensated with variable web depths. Due to a quite large concrete slab width (21.5 m), a very thick upper flange is required above the internal supports. For this reason this flange is made of two plates welded together. The width of this additional upper flange is equal to 1400 mm.

An additional longitudinal steel rolled I-girder (located right in the middle of the bridge cross section, see Fig. 4.2) is also connected to the concrete slab. It helps in the slab concreting phases. Transverse frames stiffen the box-section on abutments and on internal supports, as well as every 4.0 m in spans.

The bottom flange longitudinal trapezoidal stiffeners are continuous with a plate thickness equal to 15 mm. The single flat web longitudinal stiffener is discontinuous when crossing the transverse frames of the box-girder. Its plate thickness is equal to 30 mm. In the zones surrounding the internal supports, this stiffener is located at one third of the total web depth in the compressed part of the web, see Fig. 4.2.

The discontinuity of this web stiffener means that it is neglected in the box-girder stiffness for the global analysis and for the calculation of stresses, but taken into account for the web buckling verification (cross section classification, calculation of the elastic critical stresses and calculation of the effective^p widths of the sub-panels). See EN1993-1-5, clause 9.2.2.

4.1 DESCRIPTION OF THE BRIDGE

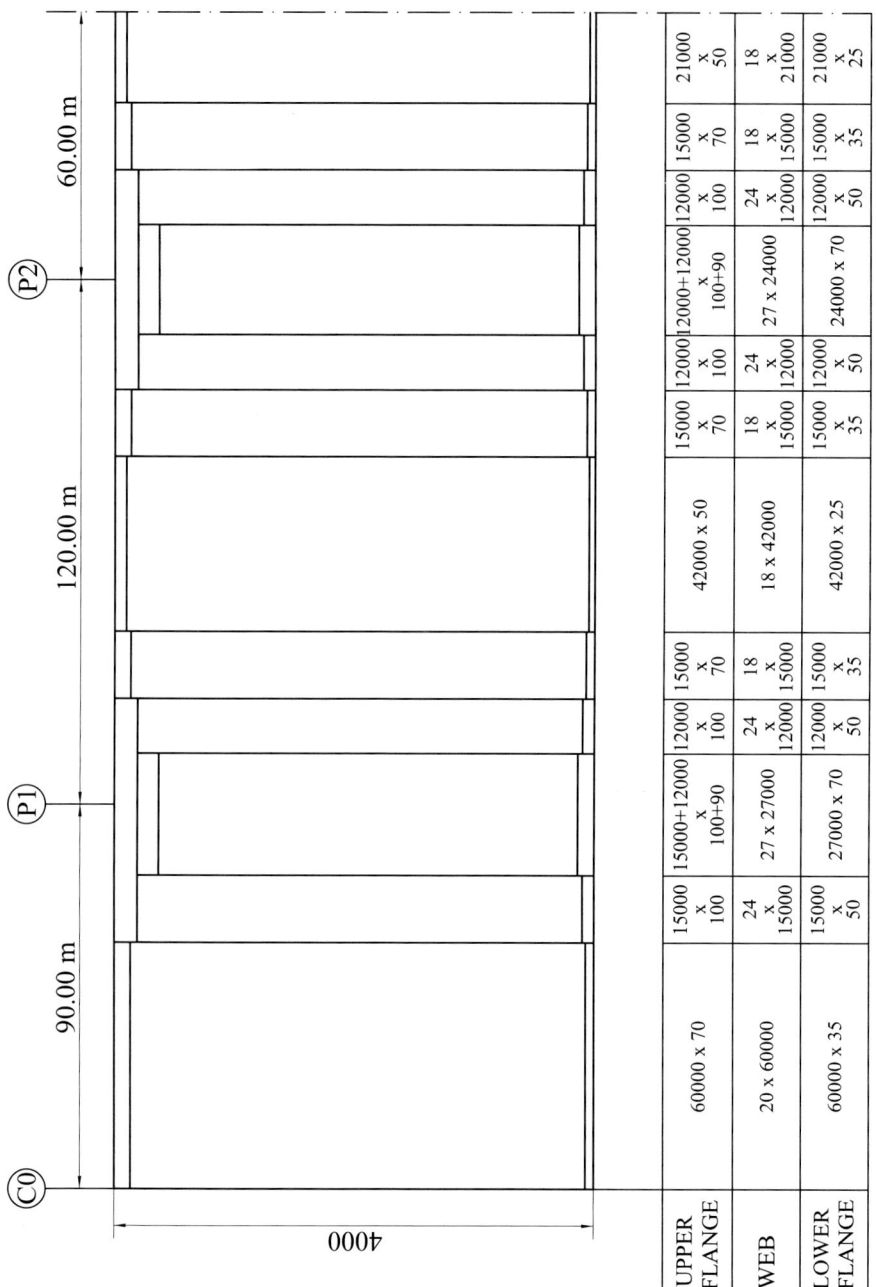

Fig. 4.3: Structural steel distribution (half bridge length)

4. BOX-GIRDER BRIDGE EXAMPLE

4.2 INTERNAL FORCES AND MOMENTS, STRESSES

4.2.1 Actions and load partial factors

The following actions were considered in the cracked global analysis of the box-girder bridge according to EN1994-2:

- Self-weight of the steel structure (after the launching phases),
- Self-weight of the reinforced concrete slab (applied with respect to the concreting phases),
- Self-weight of the non-structural equipments (safety barriers, waterproofing layer, asphalt layer, cornice, ...),
- Concrete shrinkage,
- Concrete creep (taken into account by using different modular ratios according to EN1994-2)
- Traffic loads according to Load Model 1 (*LM1*) from EN1991-2.

These actions were combined according to Annex A2 of EN1990 for calculating the stresses and the internal forces and moments at Ultimate Limit State (ULS) as follows:

$$1.35\ G_{max} + 1.0\ S + 1.35\ LM1,$$

where G_{max} and S represent the total unfavourable permanent loads and the concrete shrinkage, respectively.

The cracked global analysis of this box-girder bridge according to EN1994-2 is out of the scope of this Design Manual. Consequently, it is not detailed and the results are given directly in the two sections below in terms of bending moment, shear force and stresses.

Two different design situations were identified, for which the structural steel part of the cross section will be justified according to EN1993-1-5:

- The transient design situation corresponding to the launching phase just before the launching nose reaches the end support C5 - the patch loading verification of the web at the internal support P4, see section 4.2.2,

- The ULS permanent design situation (normal use under traffic load) at internal support P1, see section 4.2.3.

4.2.2 Transient design situation (launching phase)

The steel structure of the bridge is launched by using a 30 m long launching nose. When this nose is about to reach the end support C5, the cross section which is finally located at 60 m from this end support C5 is provisionally located on support P4. Fig. 4.4 below gives the bending moment and the shear force distribution at that launching time, for a half cross section. The support reactions are summarized in the included table.

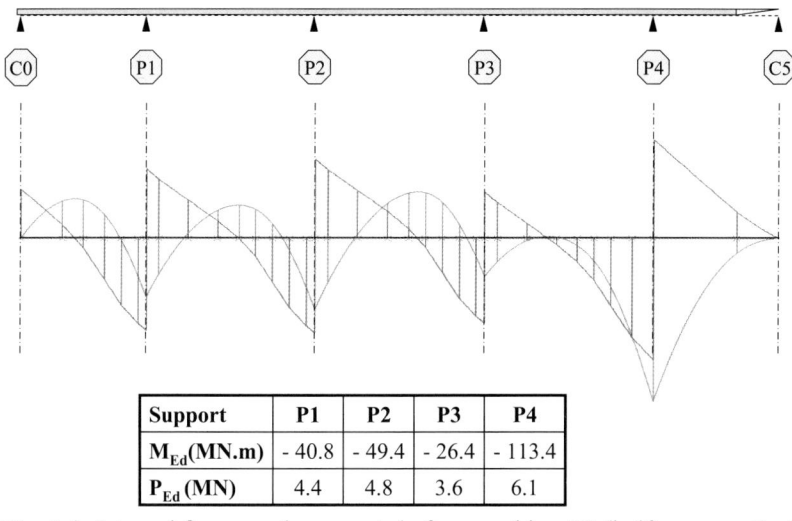

Support	P1	P2	P3	P4
M_{Ed}(MN.m)	-40.8	-49.4	-26.4	-113.4
P_{Ed} (MN)	4.4	4.8	3.6	6.1

Fig. 4.4: Internal forces and moments before reaching C5 (half cross section)

The cross section provisionally at support P4 has a 35 mm thick bottom flange and a 70 mm thick upper flange. Its web is 20 mm thick. Below only this launching situation will be checked, even if it is not necessarily the worst case.

4.2.3 Permanent design situation

Under traffic loads, during normal use of the bridge, the bending

4. Box-Girder Bridge Example

moment and the shear force at ULS (calculated by a cracked global analysis according to EN1994-2) on internal support P1 are as follows:

$$M_{Ed} = 653.3 \text{ MNm}$$
$$V_{Ed} = 24.7 \text{ MN}$$

These values apply to the total box-girder section. V_{Ed} is a vertical force that should be recalculated to a shear force in the inclined plane of one of the main web:

$$V_{Ed,w} = \frac{V_{Ed}}{2 \cdot \sin(\theta_w)} = 15.0 \text{ MN}$$

where $\theta_w = 55.5°$ is the angle between the inclined web and the bottom flange of the box-girder section.

In order to calculate the normal stresses at the internal support P1, the bending moment M_{Ed} should be split into $M_{a,Ed} = -369.3$ MNm and $M_{c,Ed} = -284.0$ MNm, respecting the construction phases (values extracted from the cracked global analysis according to EN1994-2). $M_{a,Ed}$ is resisted by the structural steel part only (induced before the concrete slab becomes active) and $M_{c,Ed}$ is resisted by the composite cross section as soon as the reinforced slab becomes active following the construction steps.

$$\sigma_{Ed} = M_{a,Ed} \frac{v_a}{I_a} + M_{c,Ed} \frac{v_2}{I_2} \tag{4.1}$$

where I_a/v_a (resp. I_2/v_2) is the gross elastic section modulus for the structural steel part only (resp. for the cracked composite steel and concrete cross section).

$$I_a = 4.383 \times 10^{12} \text{ mm}^4$$

$$I_2 = 4.706 \times 10^{12} \text{ mm}^4$$

$v_{a,inf} = 1927$ mm ; $v_{2,inf} = 2032$ mm (mid-plane of the bottom flange)

$v_{a,sup} = 1946$ mm ; $v_{2,sup} = 1841$ mm (mid-plane of the upper flange)

For the composite cross section, the concrete slab is cracked and only the reinforcing bars are taken into account as two identical layers (with a section equal to 0.5% of the concrete area and a concrete cover equal to 6.5 cm including the longitudinal bar half diameter (20 mm) and the outside transverse bar diameter (20 mm)). Finally normal stresses in the mid-plane of the flanges at ULS are as follows:

$$\sigma_{Ed,\inf} = 162.4 + 122.6 = 285.0 \text{ N/mm}^2 \text{ (compression)} \quad (4.2)$$

$$\sigma_{Ed,sup} = -163.9 - 111.1 = -275.0 \text{ N/mm}^2 \text{ (tension)} \quad (4.3)$$

4.3 WEB BUCKLING VERIFICATION FOR THE LAUNCHING PHASE

The dimensions of the web panel which is provisionally located at support P4 when the box-girder (with its 30 m long launching nose) is about to reach the end support C5, are shown in Fig. 4.5 below.

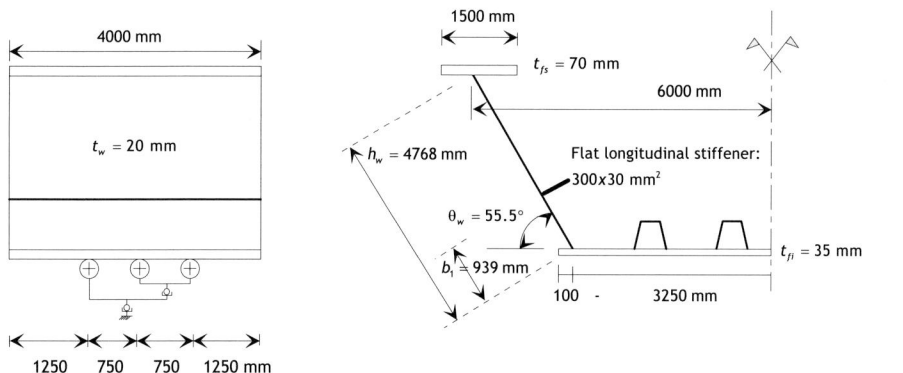

Fig. 4.5: Web panel geometry

For this specific panel, the web is stiffened by a single flat stiffener 300 x 30 mm², located at one fifth of the web depth. Note that this location of the stiffener is different from the one used for the closest web panel to the internal support, see sub-chapter 4.5. This was done to show the way of taking into account the effect of a longitudinal stiffener in the patch loading calculation.

4. BOX-GIRDER BRIDGE EXAMPLE

Considering the web inclination of the box-girder cross section, the support reaction P_{Ed} in the web plane is equal to 6.1/sin(55.5°) = 7.4 MN (and a transverse force equal to 6.1/tan(55.5°) = 4.2 MN is applied to the stiffened bottom flange). This reaction is introduced in the web plane through the launching device which is assumed to be a rolling shoe with 3 equally spaced wheels and a total length s_s = 1500 mm between external wheel axis. The half box-girder cross section also resists a concomitant bending moment M_{Ed} = -113.4 MNm which is due to the cantilever part of the box-girder bridge about to reach the C5 end support.

The launching device centres the web panel between two transverse frames of the box-girder.

4.3.1 Patch loading verification

The longitudinal stiffener is associated with a part of the web according to Figure 9.1 from EN1993-1-5, i.e. $15\varepsilon t_w = 15 \cdot \sqrt{235/345} \cdot 20 = 247.6$ mm on each side of the single flat plate.

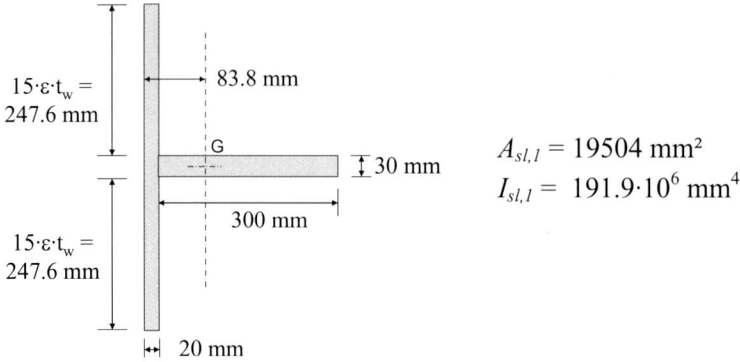

Fig. 4.6: Longitudinal stiffener properties

The flexural rigidity of the web plate and the relative flexural rigidity of the longitudinal stiffener are given by:

$$D = \frac{h_w t_w^3}{12 \cdot (1-v^2)} = 3.493 \times 10^6 \text{ mm}^4$$

4.3 WEB BUCKLING VERIFICATION FOR THE LAUNCHING PHASE

$$\gamma_s = \min\left[\frac{I_{sl,1}}{D}; 13\left(\frac{a}{h_w}\right)^3 + 210\cdot\left(0.3 - \frac{b_1}{a}\right)\right] = \min(54.9;\ 21.4) = 21.4$$

where $a = 4$ m is the spacing between two adjacent transverse frames, $b_1 = h_w/5 - t_{st}/2 = 938.6$ mm is the free depth of the lower web sub-panel (directly loaded), and $h_w = 4768$ mm is the free web depth (in its plane, by taking into account the web inclination).

The buckling coefficient of the stiffened web for patch loading verification is then given by:

$$k_F = 6 + 2\left(\frac{h_w}{a}\right)^2 + \left[5.44\cdot\frac{b_1}{a} - 0.21\right]\cdot\sqrt{\gamma_s} = 8.84 + 4.93 = 13.77$$

This formula is proposed as recommended in EN1993-1-5, clause 6.4(2), but note that it can be modified by the National Annex. Its scope is defined by:

$$0.05 \leq \frac{b_1}{a} = \frac{4768}{5\cdot 4000} = 0.235 \leq 0.3 \text{ and } \frac{b_1}{h_w} = 0.197 \leq 0.3 \text{ (satisfied here)}$$

If one of these criteria is not checked, then the beneficial effect of the longitudinal stiffener cannot be taken into account in the calculation of the buckling coefficient.

The elastic critical resistance for patch loading is obtained by:

$$F_{cr} = 0.9\cdot k_F E \frac{t_w^3}{h_w} = 4.37 \text{ MN}$$

EN1993-1-5, clause 6.5, defines the effective loaded length l_y used to calculate the yield resistance F_y. For box-girders, the loaded bottom flange width should be limited to $15\varepsilon t_f = 15\cdot(235/345)^{0.5}\cdot 35 = 433$ mm on each side of the web, which means $b_f = 100$ mm $+ t_w + 15\ \varepsilon t_f = 553.3$ mm, see Fig. 4.5 above.

$$m_1 = \frac{f_{yf}b_f}{f_{yw}t_w} = 27.7 \text{ and } m_2 = 0.02\cdot\left(\frac{h_w}{t_f}\right)^2 = 371.2$$

4. Box-Girder Bridge Example

4.3.1.1 Resistance load for a single wheel ($s_s = 0$)

$$l_y = s_s + 2t_f\left(1 + \sqrt{m_1 + m_2}\right) = 1468 \text{ mm} \leq a = 4000 \text{ mm}$$

$$F_y = l_y\, t_w\, f_{yw} = 10.1 \text{ MN}$$

is the yield resistance and the slenderness is then given by:

$$\bar{\lambda}_F = \sqrt{\frac{F_y}{F_{cr}}} = 1.52$$

(as $\bar{\lambda}_F \geq 0.5$, the previous calculation of m_2 is valid; if not, F_y and $\bar{\lambda}_F$ should have been recalculated with $m_2 = 0$).

Finally, the reduction factor and the design resistance to local buckling under transverse force are given by:

$$\chi_F = \frac{0.5}{\bar{\lambda}_F} = 0.33 \leq 1.0$$

$$F_{Rd} = \frac{\chi_F F_y}{\gamma_{M1}} = \frac{0.33 \cdot 10.1}{1.1} = 3.03 \text{ MN}$$

4.3.1.2 Resistance load for a patch length $s_s = 1500$ mm

$$l_y = s_s + 2t_f\left(1 + \sqrt{m_1 + m_2}\right) = 2968 \text{ mm} \leq a = 4000 \text{ mm}$$

$$F_y = l_y\, t_w\, f_{yw} = 20.5 \text{ MN}$$

is the yield resistance and the slenderness is then given by:

$$\bar{\lambda}_F = \sqrt{\frac{F_y}{F_{cr}}} = 2.16$$

(as $\bar{\lambda}_F \geq 0.5$, the previous calculation of m_2 is valid; if not, F_y and $\bar{\lambda}_F$ should have been recalculated with $m_2 = 0$.)

Finally, the reduction factor and the design resistance to local buckling under transverse force are given by:

$$\chi_F = \frac{0.5}{\lambda_F} = 0.23 \leq 1.0$$

$$F_{Rd} = \frac{\chi_F F_y}{\gamma_{M1}} = \frac{0.23 \cdot 20.5}{1.1} = 4.28 \text{ MN}$$

4.3.1.3 Patch loading verification

The applied transverse force F_{Ed} is equal to 7.5 MN for the patch length s_s = 1500 mm and equal to 7.5/3 = 2.5 MN for one of the 3 wheels.

$$\eta_2 = \frac{2.50}{3.03} = 0.825 \leq 1.0 \text{ for a single wheel}$$

$$\eta_2 = \frac{7.50}{4.28} = 1.75 \geq 1.0 \text{ for the patch length } s_s$$

The stiffened web is not verified for local buckling under transverse force for this specific launching situation. The best way to improve the resistance is to increase the web thickness (for instance, using t_w = 30 mm instead of 20 mm gives F_{Rd} = 9.62 MN) or to add another roller (usually more cost effective).

4.3.2 Interaction between patch loading and bending moment

The cross section in Fig. 4.5 is also subject to a negative bending moment M_{Ed} = -113.4 MNm for the considered launching phase (the stiffened bottom flange is in compression). The interaction between the transverse reaction and this bending moment should be checked according to the following expression (EN1993-1-5, clause 7.2):

$$\eta_2 + 0.8\eta_1 \leq 1.4 \text{ with } \eta_2 = \frac{F_{Ed}}{F_{Rd}} \text{ and } \eta_1 = \frac{M_{Ed}}{f_y W_{eff}} \cdot \gamma_{M0}$$

4. BOX-GIRDER BRIDGE EXAMPLE

The effective elastic section modulus W_{eff} is calculated exactly in the same way as performed in sub-chapters 4.4 to 4.6 below for the permanent design situation, so that it is not repeated here.

4.4 EFFECTIVE CROSS SECTION OF THE STIFFENED BOTTOM FLANGE AT INTERNAL SUPPORT P1 (UNIFORM COMPRESSION)

The stiffened bottom flange panel closest to the intermediate support P1 is checked for buckling. The Fig. 4.7 illustrates the 4 longitudinal trapezoidal stiffeners which are regularly spaced and welded on the flange and different values for the thicknesses and widths of each sub-panel.

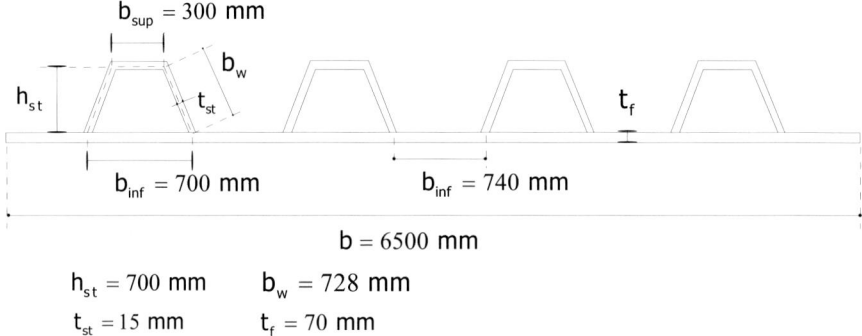

h_{st} = 700 mm b_w = 728 mm
t_{st} = 15 mm t_f = 70 mm

Fig. 4.7: Geometry of the stiffened bottom flange (near the support P1)

This stiffened panel is considered to be under uniform compression with a stress equal to 285.0 N/mm², which has been calculated in the mid-plane of the bottom plate, see section 4.2.3.

4.4.1 First step: shear lag effect according to EN1993-1-5, 3.2 and 3.3

The first step is the calculation of the area A_{sl} of all the longitudinal stiffeners within the half width b_0 of the flange. For example, 2 trapezoidal stiffeners have to be considered:

$$A_{sl} = 2(2b_w + b_{sup})t_{st} = 0.053 \text{ m}^2$$

4.4 EFFECTIVE CROSS SECTION OF THE STIFFENED BOTTOM FLANGE AT INTERNAL SUPPORT P1

$$b_0 = b/2 = 6.5/2 = 3.25 \text{ m}$$

$$\alpha_0 = \sqrt{1 + \frac{A_{sl}}{b_0 t_f}} = 1.11$$

$$L_e = 0.25 \cdot (90 + 120) = 52.5 \text{ m}$$

$$\kappa = \frac{\alpha_0 b_0}{L_e} = 0.069$$

As $0.02 < \kappa \leq 0.7$ the β factor is given by:

$$\beta = \frac{1}{1 + 6 \cdot \left(\kappa - \frac{1}{2500 \cdot \kappa}\right) + 1.6 \cdot \kappa^2} = 0.722$$

$$\beta^\kappa = 0.722^{0.069} = 0.978$$

The effective^s area of the bottom flange is then obtained by multiplying the gross area by β^κ, if the National Annex has adopted the elastoplastic shear lag model according to Note 3 in EN1993-1-5, clause 3.3 (which is the recommended one by the standard). A clever approach to apply β^κ consists in reducing the thicknesses of all sub-panels instead of the widths because it preserves the mean planes of all sub-panels and because it avoids the gap in the variations in the effective^s area along the span when crossing a longitudinal stiffener. As EN 1993-1-5 only indicates that β^κ is applied to the area $A_{c,eff}$ (and not to the width), this recommendation is not contradictory to the standard.

4.4.2 Second step: Critical plate buckling stress according to EN1993-1-5, Annex A

The second step of the checking is the calculation of the critical plate buckling stress of the studied stiffened bottom flange, $\sigma_{cr,p} = k_{\sigma,p} \cdot \sigma_E$. As more than 3 regularly spaced stiffeners are welded on it, they can be smeared

4. BOX-GIRDER BRIDGE EXAMPLE

to get an equivalent orthotropic plate and EN1993-1-5, Annex A, can be applied.

Plate under uniform compression: $\psi = 1$

Aspect ratio: $\alpha = \dfrac{a}{b} = \dfrac{4.0}{6.5} = 0.615 \geq 0.5$

Relative area: $\delta = \dfrac{\sum A_{sl}}{b \cdot t_f} = \dfrac{4(2b_w + b_{sup})t_{sl}}{b \cdot t_f} = 0.232$

Second moment of area of the whole stiffened plate (bottom flange and 4 longitudinal stiffeners):

$$I_{sl} = 2.251 \times 10^{10} \text{ mm}^4$$

Second moment of area of the bottom plate alone:

$$I_p = \dfrac{bt_f^{\,3}}{12(1-v^2)} = 2.042 \times 10^8 \text{ mm}^4$$

$$\gamma = \dfrac{I_{sl}}{I_p} = 110.24 - \text{relative inertia ratio}$$

The buckling coefficient is given by Equation (A.2) from Annex A in EN1993-1-5:

$$k_{\sigma,p} = \dfrac{2\left((1+\alpha^2)^2 + \gamma - 1\right)}{\alpha^2(\psi+1)(1+\delta)} = 238.3 \text{ (case with } \alpha = 0.615 \leq \sqrt[4]{\gamma} = 3.240\text{)}$$

The Euler stress is given by:

$$\sigma_E = \dfrac{\pi^2 E t_f^{\,2}}{12(1-v^2)b^2} = 22.01 \text{ N/mm}^2$$

Finally the use of Annex A gives a critical buckling stress equal to:

4.4 EFFECTIVE CROSS SECTION OF THE STIFFENED BOTTOM FLANGE AT INTERNAL SUPPORT P1

$$\sigma_{cr,p} = k_{\sigma,p} \cdot \sigma_E = 5246 \text{ N/mm}^2$$

It should be noticed that this buckling stress corresponds to the occurrence of a 1-wave global mode in the stiffened plate. EN1993-1-5 also indicates that "appropriate charts or relevant computer simulations" could be used as an alternative. Attention should be paid to the fact that the first mode is not necessarily the 1-wave global mode of the stiffened plate.

4.4.3 Third step: Effective^p cross section

This calculation is organised into 2 steps:

- Step A: local buckling of sub-panels,
- Step B: global buckling of the whole stiffened bottom flange.

It should also be reminded that the determination of this effective^p cross section should be performed after having reduced the thickness of all the sub-panels in the stiffened bottom flange, due to shear lag effect (see clause 4.4(3) in EN1993-1-5). It should be noted that the thickness should not be reduced when calculating the critical stress for plate buckling. If the elastoplastic shear lag model from Note 3 in EN1993-1-5, clause 3.3, is used (factor β^*), then this reduction is generally negligible, which is the case for the example of this Design Manual. Consequently, for simplification, the determination of the effective^p cross section was made below on the basis of the gross cross section.

4.4.3.1 Step A: Local buckling of sub-panels

The bottom flange includes 4 types of different sub-panels. Each of them should be classified and if necessary (i.e. class 4 sub-panel) a reduced effective^p cross section for local buckling should be defined.

- The first sub-panel to be classified is the upper flange of the trapezoidal stiffener which is an internal panel under uniform compression:

4. Box-Girder Bridge Example

$$\frac{b_{sup}}{t_{st}} = \frac{300}{15} = 20 \leq 33\varepsilon = 33\sqrt{\frac{235}{355}} = 26.85$$

resulting in a class 1 sub-panel

- The second sub-panel to be classified is the part of the bottom flange between the webs of a single trapezoidal stiffener, which is an internal panel under uniform compression:

$$\frac{b_{inf}}{t_f} = \frac{700}{70} = 10 \leq 33\varepsilon = 33\sqrt{\frac{235}{325}} = 28.06$$

resulting in a class 1 sub-panel

- The third panel to be classified is the part of the bottom flange between the webs of two adjacent trapezoidal stiffeners, which is an internal panel under uniform compression:

$$\frac{b - 4 \cdot b_{inf}}{5 \cdot t_f} = \frac{740}{70} = 10.6 \leq 33\varepsilon = 33\sqrt{\frac{235}{325}} = 28.06$$

resulting in a class 1 sub-panel

- The fourth sub-panel to be classified is the web of the trapezoidal stiffener. This sub-panel is theoretically in bending, but it is usually accepted (and adopted here) to consider that the whole stiffened flange is under uniform compression (this can be justified by comparing the stiffener depth with the depth of the complete cross section).

$$\frac{b_w}{t_{st}} = \frac{728}{15} = 48.5 \geq 42\varepsilon = 42\sqrt{\frac{235}{355}} = 34.17$$

resulting in a class 4 sub-panel

As intermediate conclusion of this step A, only the webs of the stiffeners should be reduced for taking local buckling effect into account. EN1993-1-5, clause 4.4, deals with the calculation of this effective^p area:

Plate under uniform compression: $\psi = 1$ (as simplification)

4.4 Effective Cross Section of the Stiffened Bottom Flange at Internal Support

Buckling coefficient: $k_\sigma = 4$ (Table 4.1 in EN1993-1-5)

$$\text{Euler's stress: } \sigma_E = \frac{\pi^2 E t_{st}^2}{12(1-\nu^2)b_w^2} = 80.6 \text{ N/mm}^2$$

$$\text{Slenderness: } \overline{\lambda}_p = \sqrt{\frac{f_y}{k_\sigma \sigma_E}} = \sqrt{\frac{355}{4 \cdot 80.6}} = 1.049 \geq 0.673$$

$$\text{Reduction factor: } \rho = \frac{\overline{\lambda}_p - 0.055 \cdot (3+\psi)}{\overline{\lambda}_p^2} = 0.753$$

According to Table 4.1 in EN1993-1-5, the area of each web of the trapezoidal stiffeners is reduced by considering an effective width $b_{e1} = 0.5 \cdot 0.753 \, b_w = 274$ mm attached to the bottom flange, and an effective width $b_{e2} = b_{e1}$ attached to the upper flange of the trapezoidal stiffeners.

The bottom flange should be split into 2 parts according to Figure 4.4 in EN1993-1-5 in order to define $A_{c,eff,loc}$. See Figure below:

$$b_{edge,eff} = 740/2 = 370 \text{ mm}$$

$A_{c,eff,loc} = 48.7 \cdot 10^4$ mm² by reducing the gross area $A_c = 50.8 \cdot 10^4$ mm² for local buckling of sub-panels

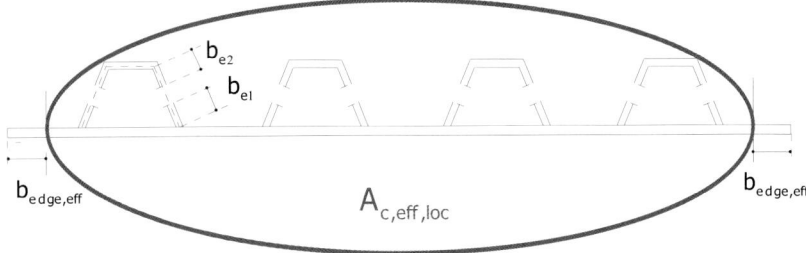

Fig. 4.8: Effective^p area for local buckling in the bottom flange

4.4.3.2 Step B: Global buckling of the whole stiffened bottom flange

The area $A_{c,eff,loc}$ should now be reduced by a factor ρ_c for global buckling of the stiffened bottom flange. This factor is obtained by an

4. Box-Girder Bridge Example

interpolation between a plate-like behaviour and a column-like behaviour. The *plate-like behaviour* is dealt with in clause 4.5.2 of EN1993-1-5:

$$\beta_{A,c} = \frac{A_{c,eff,loc}}{A_c} = 0.958$$

$$\overline{\lambda}_p = \sqrt{\frac{\beta_{A,c} f_y}{\sigma_{cr,p}}} = \sqrt{\frac{0.958 \cdot 325}{5246}} = 0.244$$

As $\overline{\lambda}_p \leq 0.673$, there is no reduction due to the plate-like behaviour, which means $\rho = 1$. This reduction factor is calculated according to clause 4.4(2) in EN1993-1-5.

The *column-like behaviour* is dealt with in clause 4.5.3 of EN1993-1-5. The column is defined by the gross cross section of one of the longitudinal stiffeners associated with a part of the main bottom plate. This part is defined by Figure A.1 from Annex A of EN1993-1-5. Figure A.1 is drawn in a very general way for any value of the ψ ratio. For the common case $\psi = 1$, the figure can be simplified. Fig. 4.9 shows the definition of the effective cross section of the column.

The gross mechanical properties of this column are as follows (with the notations of EN1993-1-5): $A_{sl,1} = 12.7 \times 10^4$ mm^2 and $I_{sl,1} = 5.522 \times 10^9$ mm^4. The distances between the centre of gravity of the column and of the stiffener alone (e_1) on one side, and that of the main bottom plate (e_2) on the other side are equal to: $e_1 = 352.6$ mm and $e_2 = 92.1$ mm. Taking into account the reduction for local buckling (see step A), the effective^p area of the column is equal to $A_{sl,1,eff} = 12.1 \times 10^4$ mm^2.

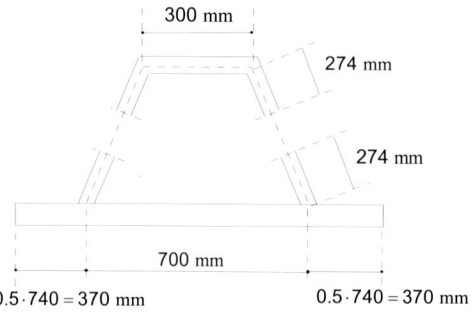

Fig. 4.9: Column cross section for the column-like behaviour of the flange

4.4 Effective Cross Section of the Stiffened Bottom Flange at Internal Support P1

The critical column buckling stress is given by the classic Euler formula, considering that the length of the column is equal to the spacing between transverse frames of the box-girder bridge, i.e. the length a (=4 m in this the example) of the considered bottom flange:

$$\sigma_{cr,c} = \frac{\pi^2 EI_{sl,1}}{A_{sl,1} a^2} = 5626 \text{ N/mm}^2$$

Using the equations in 4.5.3(4) and 4.5.3(5) of EN1993-1-5, the reduction factor χ_c for the column-like behaviour is obtained as follows:

$$\beta_{A,c} = \frac{A_{sl,1,eff}}{A_{sl,1}} = 0.957$$

$$\overline{\lambda}_c = \sqrt{\frac{\beta_{A,c} f_y}{\sigma_{cr,c}}} = \sqrt{\frac{0.957 \cdot 355}{5626}} = 0.246$$

As $\overline{\lambda}_c \geq 0.2$, the reduction factor χ_c is given by the European Buckling Curves using a modified imperfection factor:

$$\alpha_e = \alpha + \frac{0.09}{i/e}$$

with:
- $\alpha = 0.34$ (closed section stiffeners)
- $e = \max(e_1, e_2)$
- $i = \sqrt{I_{sl,1} / A_{sl,1}} = 208.4$ mm for the radius of gyration of the column

Finally:

$$\alpha_e = 0.492$$

$$\phi = \frac{1}{2}\left[1 + \alpha_e \left(\overline{\lambda}_c - 0.2\right) + \overline{\lambda}_c^2\right] = 0.542$$

$$\chi_c = \frac{1}{\phi + \sqrt{\phi^2 - \overline{\lambda}_c^2}} = 0.977$$

4. BOX-GIRDER BRIDGE EXAMPLE

The interaction between the plate-like and the column-like behaviour is dealt with in clause 4.5.4 of EN1993-1-5:

$$\frac{\sigma_{cr,p}}{\sigma_{cr,c}} - 1 = \frac{5246}{5626} - 1 = -0.067 \leq 0 \text{ so } \xi = 0$$

It should be noted that theoretically the critical plate buckling stress is always higher than the critical column buckling stress. This is not the case for this example due to some approximation hidden in the used formulae.

$$\rho_c = (\rho - \chi_c)\xi(2-\xi) + \chi_c = \chi_c = 0.977$$

The effective^p area of the stiffened bottom flange is given by:

$$A_{c,eff} = \rho_c A_{c,eff,loc} + 2 \cdot b_{edge,eff} \cdot t_f = 52.74 \times 10^4 \text{ mm}^2$$

and the final effective area taking account of plate buckling – shear lag interaction by:

$$A_{eff} = A_{c,eff} \beta^\kappa = 52.74 \times 10^4 \cdot 0{,}978 = 51.58 \times 10^4 \text{ mm}^2$$

4.5 EFFECTIVE CROSS SECTION OF THE STIFFENED WEB AT INTERNAL SUPPORT P1 (BENDING)

The previous stiffened bottom flange is part of a box-girder bridge cross section located at an internal support. The web of this cross section is under bending (upper part in tension), so that buckling can occur in its compressed bottom part. For this numerical example, the web is assumed to be stiffened longitudinally by a single flat longitudinal stiffener (300 x 30 mm^2), located at one third of its depth from the bottom flange. The stiffener is not continuous at the intersection with the transverse stiffeners. Consequently, it only increases the buckling resistance of the web but is not taken as a part of the cross section. For detailed geometry and dimensions of the half cross section, see Fig. 4.10 (h_w = 4647 mm, $h_{w,sup}$ = 3117 mm, $h_{w,inf}$ = 1500 mm).

4.5 Effective Cross Section of the Stiffened Web at Internal Support P1

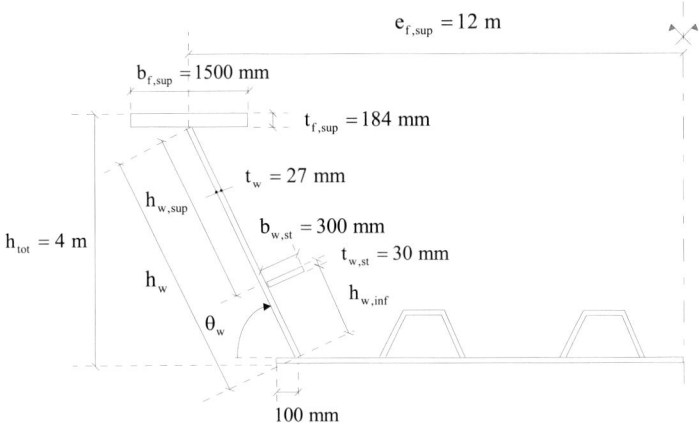

Fig. 4.10: Geometry of the stiffened web

Note that the upper flange (1500x100 mm²) and its additional plate (1400x90 mm²) were replaced by a single theoretical plate (1500x184 mm²).

EN1993-1-5, clause 4.4(3), indicates that the effective^p area of the web should be determined using the effective^{p+s} area of the bottom flange including buckling plate and shear lag effects and the gross area of the web. Regarding the upper flange in tension, no plate buckling occurs, but the shear lag can eventually introduce an effective^s reduction. It is first verified that it is not the case for the example, because $b_0 = (1500 - 27)/2 = 736$ mm $\leq L_e/50 = 0.25 \cdot (90 + 120) \cdot 10^3 / 50 = 1050$ mm according to EN1993-1-5, clause 3.1(1).

The first step of the calculation consists in the determination of the mechanical properties of the cross section composed of the effective^{p+s} area of the stiffened bottom flange (taking into account buckling and shear lag effects) and the gross area of the web and of the upper composite flange. This is a tedious work (especially for the second moment of inertia), but without specific difficulties. The results are directly given below (subscript 1 is used to indicate that these effective properties are intermediate values and not the definitive effective properties of the cross section):

- for the structural steel part only:

$$A_{a,eff,1} = 1.351 \times 10^6 \text{ mm}^2$$

$$I_{a,eff,1} = 4.245 \times 10^{12} \text{ mm}^4$$

4. BOX-GIRDER BRIDGE EXAMPLE

$z_{a,eff,1}$ = 2018 mm (location of the centre of gravity with respect to the bottom face of the bottom flange)

- for the cracked composite steel and concrete cross section:

$$A_{eff,1} = 1.421 \times 10^6 \text{ mm}^2$$

$$I_{eff,1} = 4.552 \times 10^{12} \text{ mm}^4$$

$z_{eff,1}$ = 2123 mm (location of the centre of gravity with respect to the bottom face of the bottom flange)

Finally the stress distribution in the main web can be calculated. It will be used to classify the different web panels for the buckling check in the following:

$$\sigma_{1,\text{inf}} = 297.6 \text{ N/mm}^2 \text{ (web-to-bottom flange junction)}$$

$$\sigma_{1,\text{sup}} = 112.9 \text{ N/mm}^2 \text{ (lower web-to-stiffener junction)}$$

$$\sigma_{2,\text{inf}} = 109.2 \text{ N/mm}^2 \text{ (stiffener-to-upper web junction)}$$

$$\sigma_{2,\text{sup}} = -262.1 \text{ N/mm}^2 \text{ (web-to-top flange junction)}$$

4.5.1 Local buckling of sub-panels

With the previous stress calculations, the position of the longitudinal flat stiffener (in the compression zone of the web) and the web depth, it becomes possible to calculate the ψ ratios and the class for the web sub-panels:

- Outstand plate corresponding to the flat stiffener in uniform compression:

$$\psi = 1$$

$$\frac{b_{w,st}}{t_{w,st}} = \frac{300}{30} = 10 \leq 14\varepsilon = 14\sqrt{\frac{235}{345}} = 11.55 \text{ resulting in a class 3 sub-panel}$$

4.5 Effective Cross Section of the Stiffened Web at Internal Support P1

- Bottom web sub-panel in bending and entirely in the compression zone:

$$\psi_{inf} = \frac{\sigma_{1,sup}}{\sigma_{1,inf}} = 0.379$$

$$\frac{h_{w,inf}}{t_w} = \frac{1500}{27} = 55.5 \geq \frac{42\varepsilon}{0.67 + 0.33\psi_{inf}} = 43.6$$

resulting in a class 4 sub-panel

- Upper web sub-panel in bending and partially in the tensile zone:

$$\psi_{sup} = \frac{\sigma_{2,sup}}{\sigma_{2,inf}} = -2.421$$

$$\frac{h_{w,sup}}{t} = \frac{3117}{27} = 115.4 \leq 62\varepsilon\left(1-\psi_{sup}\right)\sqrt{-\psi_{sup}} = 272 \text{ resulting in a class 3 sub-panel}$$

As an intermediate conclusion the plate buckling should be studied for the lower web sub-panel. EN 1993-1-5, clause 4.4, deals with the calculation of this effective^p area:

Buckling coefficient (Table 4.1 in EN1993-1-5):

$$k_\sigma = \frac{8.2}{1.05 + \psi} = 5.74$$

Critical buckling stress:

$$\sigma_{cr} = k_\sigma \frac{\pi^2 E t_w^2}{12(1-v^2)h_{w,inf}^2} = 353.0 \text{ N/mm}^2$$

Slenderness:

$$\overline{\lambda}_p = \sqrt{\frac{f_y}{\sigma_{cr}}} = 0.989 \geq 0.673$$

4. BOX-GIRDER BRIDGE EXAMPLE

Reduction factor:

$$\rho = \frac{\overline{\lambda}_p - 0.055 \cdot (3 + \psi_{inf})}{\overline{\lambda}_p^2} = 0.821$$

Effective widths:

$$b_{e1} = \rho \frac{2}{5-\psi} h_{w,inf} = 533.2 \text{ mm and } b_{e2} = \rho h_{w,inf} - b_{e1} = 698.6 \text{ mm}$$

According to Table 4.1 from EN1993-1-5, a width b_{e1} of the web sub-panel should be attached to the bottom flange and a width b_{e2} should be attached to the longitudinal stiffener.

4.5.2 Global buckling of the whole stiffened web in bending

As for the bottom flange, the global buckling of the stiffened web in bending is studied by an interpolation between a plate-like and a column-like behaviour.

4.5.2.1 Column-like behaviour

The column is made of the longitudinal stiffener and its adjacent parts from the main web. The compressed part of the upper web sub-panel has a depth equal to:

$$\frac{0.4}{\sin(\theta_w)} \left(z_{eff,1} - t_f - \frac{1}{3}(h_{tot} - t_{f,sup} - t_f) - \frac{t_{w,st}}{2} \sin(\theta_w) \right) = 366.7 \text{ mm}$$

This depth is not reduced for local buckling, as the upper web sub-panel is not a class 4 panel.

The mechanical properties of the gross area of this column are given by $A_{sl,1} = 4.268 \times 10^4$ mm^2 and $I_{sl,1} = 2.594 \times 10^9$ mm^4. The center of gravity G of the gross column is located at 48 mm from the external face of the main web, and then, $e_1 = 129$ mm between G and the center of gravity of the

4.5 EFFECTIVE CROSS SECTION OF THE STIFFENED WEB AT INTERNAL SUPPORT P1

stiffener alone, $e_2 = 34.5$ mm between G and the center of gravity of the main web alone.

The mechanical properties of the effective area of this column (local buckling studied in section 4.5.1) are given by $A_{sl,eff,1} = 3.857 \times 10^4$ mm^2 and $I_{sl,eff,1} = 2.538 \times 10^8$ mm^4.

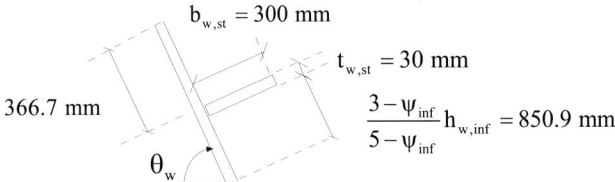

Gross area of the column

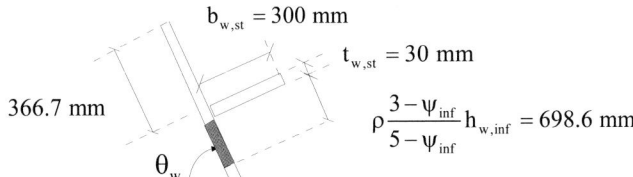

Effective area of the column for local buckling

Fig. 4.11: Column-like behaviour in the main web

The critical column buckling stress is given by the classic Euler's formula, considering that the length of the column is equal to the spacing between transverse frames of the box-girder bridge, i.e. the length $a=4$ m in this example:

$$\sigma_{cr,sl} = \frac{\pi^2 E I_{sl,1}}{A_{sl,1} a^2} = 787.2 \text{ N/mm}^2$$

This value should be extrapolated to the compressed edge of the lower web sub-panel (see Figure A.1 from Annex A and clause 4.5.3(3) in EN1993-1-5):

$$\sigma_{cr,c} = \sigma_{cr,sl} \frac{2 \cdot \sigma_{1,inf}}{\sigma_{1,sup} + \sigma_{2,inf}} = 2109.8 \text{ N/mm}^2$$

4. BOX-GIRDER BRIDGE EXAMPLE

Using the equations in clauses 4.5.3(4) and 4.5.3(5) of EN1993-1-5, the reduction factor χ_c for the column-like behaviour is obtained as follows:

$$\beta_{A,c} = \frac{A_{sl,1,eff}}{A_{sl,1}} = 0.904$$

$$\overline{\lambda}_c = \sqrt{\frac{\beta_{A,c} f_y}{\sigma_{cr,c}}} = \sqrt{\frac{0.904 \cdot 345}{2109.8}} = 0.384 \geq 0.2$$

The modified imperfection factor is given by:

$$\alpha_e = \alpha + \frac{0.09}{i/e}$$

with:

$\alpha = 0.49$ (open section stiffeners)

$e = \max(e_1, e_2) = 129$ mm

$i = \sqrt{I_{sl,1}/A_{sl,1}} = 246.5$ mm for the radius of gyration of the column

Finally:

$$\alpha_e = 0.639$$

$$\phi = \frac{1}{2}\left[1 + \alpha_e\left(\overline{\lambda}_c - 0.2\right) + \overline{\lambda}_c^{\,2}\right] = 0.632$$

$$\chi_c = \frac{1}{\phi + \sqrt{\phi^2 - \overline{\lambda}_c^{\,2}}} = 0.881$$

4.5.2.2 Plate-like behaviour

In case of a single stiffener welded on the web, the plate-like behaviour is modelled by the buckling of the previous column, embedded by a plate effect (beam on elastic foundation). This model is given in Annex A.2.2 from EN1993-1-5.

4.5 Effective Cross Section of the Stiffened Web at Internal Support P1

$$a_c = 4.33 \sqrt[4]{\frac{I_{sl,1} \left(h_{w,\text{inf}} + \frac{t_{w,st}}{2}\right)^2 \left(h_{w,\text{sup}} + \frac{t_{w,st}}{2}\right)^2}{t_w^3 \left(h_{w,\text{inf}} + t_{w,st} + h_{w,\text{sup}}\right)}} = 12241 \text{ mm}$$

As $a \leq a_c$ ($a = 4$ m), the column buckles in a 1-wave mode and the buckling stress is obtained by adding a term representing the elastic foundation restraint to the previous critical buckling stress obtained with Euler's formula:

$$\sigma_{cr,sl} = \frac{\pi^2 E I_{sl,1}}{A_{sl,1} a^2} + \frac{E t_w^3 \left(h_{w,\text{inf}} + t_{w,st} + h_{w,\text{sup}}\right) a^2}{4\pi^2 \left(1-\nu^2\right) A_{sl,1} \left(h_{w,\text{inf}} + \frac{t_{w,st}}{2}\right)^2 \left(h_{w,\text{sup}} + \frac{t_{w,st}}{2}\right)^2}$$

$$\sigma_{cr,sl} = 796.1 \text{ N/mm}^2$$

The critical plate buckling stress is obtained by extrapolating $\sigma_{cr,sl}$ to the compressed edge of the lower web sub-panel (see Figure A.1 from Annex A and clause 4.5.3(3) in EN1993-1-5):

$$\sigma_{cr,p} = \sigma_{cr,sl} \frac{2 \cdot \sigma_{1,\text{inf}}}{\sigma_{1,\text{sup}} + \sigma_{2,\text{inf}}} = 2133.7 \text{ N/mm}^2$$

Slenderness:

$$\overline{\lambda}_p = \sqrt{\frac{A_{sl,eff,1}}{A_{sl,1}} \frac{f_y}{\sigma_{cr,p}}} = \sqrt{\frac{3.857}{4.268} \frac{345}{2133.7}} = 0.382 \leq 0.673$$

As $\overline{\lambda}_p \leq 0.673$, the reduction factor ρ for the plate-like behaviour is equal to 1 (Eq. (4.2) in EN1993-1-5).

4.5.2.3 Interpolation between plate-like and column-like behaviour

The interaction between the plate-like and the column-like behaviours is dealt with in clause 4.5.4 of EN1993-1-5:

4. Box-Girder Bridge Example

$$\xi = \frac{\sigma_{cr,p}}{\sigma_{cr,c}} - 1 = \frac{2133.7}{2109.8} - 1 = 0.011$$

$$\rho_c = (\rho - \chi_c)\xi(2 - \xi) + \chi_c = \chi_c = 0.883$$

Because the longitudinal stiffener is discontinuous, only the effective widths of the web on both sides of the stiffener need to be reduced by ρ_c.

4.5.3 Torsional buckling of the longitudinal web stiffener

The web longitudinal stiffener is:

- discontinuous (which means not welded to the transverse frames of the box-girder),
- an open cross section (single flat 300x30 mm²),
- and axially loaded (because located in the compression zone of the main web).

Consequently it has to be design against torsional buckling according to EN1993-1-5, clause 9.2.1(8) and (9). Unlike a T-shape stiffener, a single flat does not possess warping stiffness. The following requirement should be fulfilled (see also section 2.9.4 of this Manual):

$$\frac{I_t}{I_p} \geq 5.3 \frac{f_y}{E}$$

where I_t is the St. Venant torsional stiffness of the stiffener alone and I_p is the polar second moment of area of the stiffener alone around the edge fixed to the web plate.

$$I_t = \frac{b_{w,st} \cdot t_{w,st}^3}{3} = 2700000 \text{ mm}^4$$

$$I_p = \frac{b_{w,st} t_{w,st}^3}{12} + \frac{b_{w,st}^3 t_{w,st}}{12} + b_{w,st} t_{w,st} \left(\frac{b_{w,st}}{2}\right)^2 = 0.271 \times 10^9 \text{ mm}^4$$

Finally the criterion is verified:

$$\frac{I_t}{I_p} = 0.00998 \geq 5.3\frac{f_y}{E} = 0.00896$$

4.6 CHECKING OF THE BOX-GIRDER SECTION UNDER BENDING AT SUPPORT P1

To conclude the calculations from sub-chapters 4.4 and 4.5, the stresses in the cross section should be re-calculated by using the effective properties of the structural steel part only (taking buckling effects and shear lag effects into account). The construction phases should also be considered, which means that the cracked composite mechanical properties (effective section of the structural steel + reinforcement) should also be evaluated.

According to the previous calculations:

- the webs of the trapezoidal stiffeners of the bottom flange are reduced for local buckling,
- the stiffened bottom flange is reduced for global buckling and for shear lag effect,
- the lower web sub-panel is reduced for local buckling.

The longitudinal stiffener of the web is discontinuous (i.e. not welded to the transverse frame of the box-girder bridge) which means that its resistance area should not be taken into account in the resistance area of the whole box-girder cross section. The mechanical properties of the effective structural steel cross section and of the composite effective cross section are given below (all calculations done):

$$I_{a,eff} = 4.169 \times 10^{12} \text{ mm}^4$$

$$I_{2,eff} = 4.468 \times 10^{12} \text{ mm}^4$$

$v_{a,inf,eff} = 2010$ mm ; $v_{2,inf,eff} = 2117$ mm (mid-plane of the bottom flange)

$v_{a,sup,eff} = 1863$ mm ; $v_{2,sup,eff} = 1756$ mm (mid-plane of the upper flange)

4. BOX-GIRDER BRIDGE EXAMPLE

Finally, the stresses at ULS in the mid-plane of the flanges are verified (i.e. the box-girder cross section resists to the applied ULS bending moment):

$$\sigma_{Ed,\text{inf,eff}} = M_{a,Ed} \cdot \frac{v_{a,\text{inf,eff}}}{I_{a,\text{eff}}} + M_{c,Ed} \cdot \frac{v_{2,\text{inf,eff}}}{I_{2,\text{eff}}}$$

$$\sigma_{Ed,\text{inf,eff}} = 369.3 \cdot \frac{2010}{4.169 \times 10^3} + 284.1 \cdot \frac{2117}{4.468 \times 10^3}$$

$$\sigma_{Ed,\text{inf,eff}} = 178.0 + 134.1 = 312.6 \text{ N/mm}^2$$

$$\sigma_{Ed,\text{inf,eff}} \leq f_{yf} = 325 \text{ N/mm}^2 \text{ for } t_{\text{inf}} = 70 \text{ mm}$$

$$\sigma_{Ed,\text{sup,eff}} = M_{a,Ed} \cdot \frac{v_{a,\text{sup,eff}}}{I_{a,\text{eff}}} + M_{c,Ed} \cdot \frac{v_{2,\text{sup,eff}}}{I_{2,\text{eff}}}$$

$$\sigma_{Ed,\text{sup,eff}} = -369.3 \cdot \frac{1863}{4.169 \times 10^3} - 284.1 \cdot \frac{1756}{4.468 \times 10^3}$$

$$\sigma_{Ed,\text{sup,eff}} = -165.0 - 111.7 = -276.7 \text{ N/mm}^2$$

$$\sigma_{Ed,\text{sup,eff}} \geq -f_{yf} = -295 \text{ N/mm}^2 \text{ for } t_{\text{sup}} = 100 + 90 \text{ mm}$$

4.7 SHEAR RESISTANCE OF THE STIFFENED WEB PANEL CLOSEST TO THE INTERNAL SUPPORT P1

The previous cross section was studied for the bending resistance and will now be checked for the shear resistance according to section 5 from EN1993-1-5.

According to Figure 5.3 from EN1993-1-5, the longitudinal single flat stiffener should be associated with a part of the main web before calculating the shear buckling coefficient according to A.3 from EN1993-1-5, Annex A. Fig. 4.12 summarizes the retained geometry.

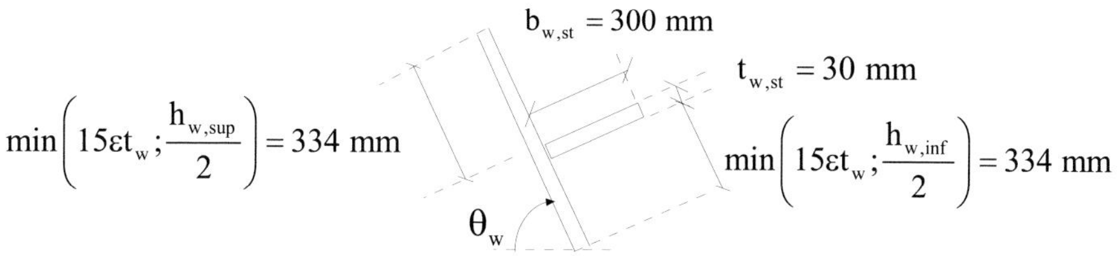

4.7 Shear Resistance of the Stiffened Web Panel Closest to The Internal Support P1

$$\min\left(15\varepsilon t_w;\frac{h_{w,sup}}{2}\right) = 334 \text{ mm}$$

$b_{w,st} = 300$ mm

$t_{w,st} = 30$ mm

$$\min\left(15\varepsilon t_w;\frac{h_{w,inf}}{2}\right) = 334 \text{ mm}$$

θ_w

Fig. 4.12: Longitudinal stiffener acting with the main web for shear buckling

The mechanical properties of this stiffener are as follows (all calculations done): $A_{sl} = 2.786 \times 10^4$ mm² and $I_{sl} = 2.315 \times 10^8$ mm⁴. As the aspect ratio of the whole web is equal to $a/h_w = 4000/4647 = 0.861 < 3$, the shear buckling coefficient is given by A.3(2), Eq. (A.6), from Annex A in EN1993-1-5:

$$k_\tau = 4.1 + \frac{6.3 + 0.18\dfrac{I_{sl}}{t_w^3 h_w}}{\left(\dfrac{a}{h_w}\right)^2} + 2.2 \cdot \sqrt[3]{\dfrac{I_{sl}}{t_w^3 h_w}} = 16.22$$

According to clause 5.1(2) in EN1993-1-5, the shear buckling in the main stiffened web should be checked if the following criterion is satisfied:

$$\frac{h_w}{t_w} \geq \frac{31}{\eta}\varepsilon\sqrt{k_\tau}$$, which is the case for the example (172.1 ≥ 85.9).

The recommended value $\eta = 1.2$ was used (up to steel grade S460). The critical shear buckling stress and the slenderness are then expressed by:

$$\tau_{cr} = k_\tau \sigma_E = k_\tau \frac{\pi^2 E}{12(1-\nu^2)}\left(\frac{t_w}{h_w}\right)^2 = 16.22 \cdot 6.407 = 103.9 \text{ N/mm}^2$$

$$\overline{\lambda}_w = \sqrt{\frac{f_{yw}}{\tau_{cr}\sqrt{3}}} = 1.385$$

This slenderness was calculated for the whole web but should not be lower than the slenderness of each web sub-panel (as un-stiffened plate).

4. BOX-GIRDER BRIDGE EXAMPLE

- for the upper web sub-panel:

$$k_{\tau,sup} = 5.34 + 4\left(\frac{h_{wsup}}{a}\right)^2 = 7.769 \text{ (because } a/h_{w,sup} = 1.283 > 1\text{)}$$

$$\sigma_{E,sup} = \frac{\pi^2 E}{12(1-v^2)}\left(\frac{t_w}{h_{wsup}}\right)^2 = 14.244 \text{ N/mm}^2$$

$$\tau_{cr,sup} = k_{\tau,sup}\sigma_{E\,sup} = 110.7 \text{ N/mm}^2$$

$$\overline{\lambda}_{w,sup} = \sqrt{\frac{f_{yw}}{\tau_{cr,sup}\sqrt{3}}} = 1.342$$

- for the lower web sub-panel:

$$k_{\tau,inf} = 5.34 + 4\left(\frac{h_{winf}}{a}\right)^2 = 5.903 \text{ (because } a/h_{w,inf} = 2.666 > 1\text{)}$$

$$\sigma_{E,inf} = \frac{\pi^2 E}{12(1-v^2)}\left(\frac{t_w}{h_{winf}}\right)^2 = 61.47 \text{ N/mm}^2$$

$$\tau_{cr,inf} = k_{\tau,inf}\sigma_{E\,inf} = 362.8 \text{ N/mm}^2$$

$$\overline{\lambda}_{w,inf} = \sqrt{\frac{f_{yw}}{\tau_{cr,inf}\sqrt{3}}} = 0.741$$

Finally the web slenderness that should be used for calculating the reduction factor χ_w is equal to max (1.385 ; 1.347 ; 0.748) = 1.385 (see clause 5.3(5), from EN1993-1-5). As $\overline{\lambda}_w = 1.385 \geq 1.08$, for a rigid and post Table 5.1 in EN1993-1-5 gives:

$$\chi_w = \frac{1.37}{0.7 + \overline{\lambda}_w} = 0.657$$

It is also assumed that the vertical web stiffeners (located every 4.0 m and corresponding to the transverse frames of the box-girder bridge) act as rigid supports for the web panel loaded in shear. This is verified by giving a minimum second moment of area I_{st} to these vertical stiffeners, according to clause 9.3.3(3) from EN1993-1-5 (case with $a/h_w = 4000/4647 < \sqrt{2}$):

$$I_{st} \geq 1.5 \frac{h_w^3 t_w^3}{a^2} = 1.5 \frac{4647^3 \cdot 27^3}{4000^2} = 185.2 \cdot 10^6 \text{ mm}^4$$

Designing a vertical T-shaped stiffener with a flange 500x60 mm² and a web 300x30 mm², the main web is taken into account for a width $2 \cdot 15 \cdot \varepsilon \cdot t_w$ + $t_{w,st}$ = $30 \cdot (235/345)^{0.5} \cdot 27$ + 30 = 698.5 mm and then $I_{st} = 1461.1 \times 10^6$ mm⁴, which is enough to fulfil the criterion. Note that these dimensions were not chosen with respect to this specific criterion, but to avoid the torsional buckling of the vertical stiffener according to EN1993-1-5, clause 9.2.1(8), as follows:

$$\frac{I_t}{I_p} = 0.0098 \geq 5.3 \frac{f_y}{E} = 0.00085$$

- St. Venant torsional constant of the stiffener alone :

$$I_t = \frac{500 \cdot 60^3}{3} + \frac{300 \cdot 30^3}{3} = 38.7 \times 10^6 \text{ mm}^4$$

- Polar second moment of area of the stiffener alone around the edge fixed to the plate :

$$I_p = I_{Gy} + I_{Gz} + A_{st} d^2 = 3.95 \times 10^9 \text{ mm}^4$$

As an alternative to EN1993-1-5, clause 9.2.1(8), for a T-stiffener, it could be interesting to apply EN1993-1-5, clause 9.2.1(9), which takes the warping stiffness of the stiffener into account in the torsional buckling stress as follows:

$$\sigma_{cr,T} = G \frac{I_t}{I_p} + \frac{\pi^2 E_a I_w}{h_w^2 I_p} \geq 6 \cdot f_y = 6 \cdot 335 = 2010 \text{ N/mm}^2$$

4. Box-Girder Bridge Example

$$I_w = \frac{b_{st,f}^3 t_{st,f}}{12} \cdot \left(b_{st,w} + \frac{t_{st,f}}{2}\right)^2 = \frac{500^3 \cdot 60}{12} \cdot \left(300 + \frac{60}{2}\right)^2$$

$$I_w = 6.81 \times 10^{13} \text{ mm}^6$$

$$\sigma_{cr,T} = \frac{210000}{2 \cdot (1+0.3)} \cdot \frac{38.7 \times 10^6}{4.17 \times 10^9} + \frac{\pi^2 \cdot 210000 \cdot 6.81 \times 10^{13}}{4768^2 \cdot 4.17 \times 10^9}$$

$$\sigma_{cr,T} = 749.6 + 1488.9 = 2238.5 \text{ N/mm}^2 \geq 2010 \text{ N/mm}^2$$

This second criterion seems to be more favourable to the vertical stiffener because of the warping stiffness term increasing the buckling stress. But this is not always the case because the first criterion in EN1993-1-5, clause 9.2.1(8) is obtained from the second one by neglecting the warping stiffness and by using the limit of 2 f_y instead of 6 f_y. In this case a very strong flange was needed to fulfil the first requirement.

Finally, with the recommended value of the partial factor $\gamma_{M1} = 1.1$ for bridges, the contribution from the web to the shear resistance of the cross section is given by:

$$V_{bw,Rd} = \frac{\chi_w f_{yw} h_w t_w}{\gamma_{M1} \sqrt{3}} = 14.93 \text{ MN}$$

For evaluating the contribution from flanges, it was considered in the following that no concomitant bending moment is applied to the cross section. This means that Eq. (5.8) from EN1993-1-5 becomes:

$$V_{bf,Rd} = \frac{b_f t_f^2 f_{yf}}{c \gamma_{M1}}$$

Of course this formula should be modified if a concomitant bending moment is applied and in particular when studying the interaction criterion. This formula gives the maximum value of the contribution from flanges and it will be shown that it is negligible.

b_f, t_f and f_{yf} are taken for the flange which provides the least axial resistance, with b_f being taken as not larger than $15 \cdot \varepsilon t_f$ on each side of the

4.7 SHEAR RESISTANCE OF THE STIFFENED WEB PANEL CLOSEST TO THE INTERNAL SUPPORT P1

web. The text of EN1993-1-5 does not really apply to a box-girder stiffened flange, so the axial resistances of each flange were assumed as follows:

- $(100 + \beta^* \cdot \rho_c \cdot 370) \cdot 70 \cdot 325 = 10.3$ MN for the effective bottom flange (with shear lag effect $\beta^* = 0.978$, see section 4.4.1, and plate buckling reduction $\rho_c = 0.977$, see sub-section 4.4.3.2),
- $t_w + \min [15 \cdot \varepsilon \cdot t_{f,sup} ; (b_{fsup} - t_w)/2] \cdot 2 \cdot 140 \cdot 295 = 62.0$ MN for the effective top flange.

Thus, it can be concluded that the bottom flange produces a smaller axial resistance and that its dimensions should be used for the contribution from flanges in the shear resistance.

$$c = a \left(0.25 + \frac{1.6 b_f t_f^2 f_{yf}}{t_w h_w^2 f_{yw}} \right) = 1023 \text{ mm}$$

$$V_{bf,Rd} = 0.642 \text{ MN}$$

As conclusion, the design resistance for shear of the cross section is equal to:

$$V_{b,Rd} = V_{bw,Rd} + V_{bf,Rd} = 15.57 \text{ MN} \le \frac{\eta f_{yw} h_w t_w}{\gamma_{M1} \sqrt{3}} = 27.26 \text{ MN}$$

$$\eta_3 = \frac{V_{Ed}}{V_{b,Rd}} = \frac{15.0}{15.57} = 0.96 \le 1.0$$

It should be noticed that the maximum percentage of the flange contribution is equal to $0.642/14.93 = 4\%$ of the shear resistance. If the concomitant bending moment is considered, this percentage is lower. Moreover, to consider the flange contribution, the welds between web and flanges should satisfy clause 9.3.5 from EN1993-1-5. Therefore, it is usually admitted that this flange contribution can be normally neglected in bridge design.

4.8 INTERACTION BETWEEN BENDING AND SHEAR AT SUPPORT P1

$$\bar{\eta}_3 = \frac{V_{Ed}}{V_{bw,Rd}} = \frac{15.0}{14.93} = 1.005 > 0.5$$

Interaction between bending and shear should be considered in accordance with clause 7.1 from EN1993-1-5.

$$\bar{\eta}_1 = \frac{M_{Ed}}{M_{pl,Rd}} = \frac{M_{a,Ed} + M_{c,Ed}}{M_{pl,Rd}} = \frac{369.3 + 284.1}{892.6} = 0.732$$

$$\bar{\eta}_1 \leq \frac{M_{f,Rd}}{M_{pl,Rd}} = \frac{665.3}{892.6} = 0.745$$

$M_{f,Rd}$ (resp. $M_{pl,Rd}$) is the design value of the plastic resistance bending moment of the flanges only (resp. of the whole cross section). One of these flanges is steel-concrete composite in the example. The calculation of these plastic resistance bending moments is not difficult, so the numerical values are directly given here:

$$M_{f,Rd} = 665.3 \text{ MNm}$$

$$M_{pl,Rd} = 892.6 \text{ MNm}$$

Considering the $\bar{\eta}_1$ value calculated with the total bending moment, the interaction criterion from EN1993-1-5, clause 7.1, does not have to be verified any more because the bending moment can be resisted by the flanges only, whereas the shear force can be resisted by the web only. Nevertheless, the numerical calculation is done below:

$$\bar{\eta}_1 + \left(1 - \frac{M_{f,Rd}}{M_{pl,Rd}}\right)\left(2\bar{\eta}_3 - 1\right)^2 = 0.992 \leq 1.0$$

4.9 INTERMEDIATE TRANSVERSE STIFFENER DESIGN

4.9.1 Transverse web stiffeners

In sub-chapter 4.7, the transverse web stiffener has been designed as a one-sided T-shape stiffener with a flange area equal to 500 x 60 mm² and a web area equal to 300 x 30 mm². Two criteria have been checked for verifying that no torsional buckling occurs and that this transverse stiffener acts as rigid support for the shear verification in the adjacent web panels.

In addition, it should be considered that this intermediate transverse web stiffener gets transverse deviation forces from adjacent compressed panels (see also sub-section 2.9.2.1) and axial forces from the tension field action (see also sub-section 2.9.2.2).

4.9.1.1 Axial forces from the tension field action

The axial force from the tension field action can usually occur in the first intermediate transverse stiffener near support (where the shear force is maximum) and according to EN1993-1-5, clause 9.3.3 (3), it is given by:

$$N_{st,ten} = V_{Ed} - \frac{1}{\bar{\lambda}_w} t_w h_w \frac{f_{yw}}{\sqrt{3} \cdot \gamma_{M1}}$$

V_{Ed} is the shear force at a distance 0.5 h_w from the edge of the panel with the largest shear force. For simplification, it has been taken equal to the value on support, 15.0 MN. Sub-chapter 4.7 gives the values $\bar{\lambda}_w = 1.385$; $t_w = 27$ mm ; $h_{w,sup} = 3.117$ m ; $f_{yw} = 345$ N/mm² Finally, the axial force from the tension field action is equal to $N_{st,ten} = 4.0$ MN.

4.9.1.2 Transverse deviation forces from adjacent compressed panels

These deviation forces are modelled by an additional axial force given by (see also sub-section 2.9.2.3):

$$\Delta N_{st,Ed} = \frac{\sigma_m h_w^2}{\pi^2} \text{ with } \sigma_m = \frac{\sigma_{cr,c}}{\sigma_{cr,p}} \cdot \frac{N_{Ed}}{h_w} \cdot \left(\frac{1}{a_1} + \frac{1}{a_2} \right)$$

4. BOX-GIRDER BRIDGE EXAMPLE

From the previous study of the global buckling in the whole web (see section 4.5.2), $\sigma_{cr,c} = 2109.8$ N/mm² and $\sigma_{cr,p} = 2133.7$ N/mm² and:

$$\frac{\sigma_{cr,c}}{\sigma_{cr,p}} = 0.989 \sim 1.0$$

N_{Ed} is the maximum compressive force of both adjacent panels, not less than the maximum compressive stress at the edge of the panel (=285.0 N/mm²) times half of the effective compressive area of the panel $A_{c,eff}$. With the calculations from sub-chapter 4.5, we get:

$A_{c,eff}$ = 27 mm · (366.7 mm + 30 mm + 0.821·1500 mm) + 30 mm · 300 mm
= 52 961.4 mm²

$$N_{Ed} = 0.5 \cdot 52961.4 \text{ mm}^2 \cdot 285.0 \text{ N/mm}^2 = 7.55 \text{ MN}$$

$$h_w = 4647 \text{ mm}$$

$$a_1 = a_2 = 4000 \text{ mm (transverse frames spacing)}$$

Finally the additional axial force modelling the transverse deviation forces is equal to $\Delta N_{st,Ed} = 1.76$ MN.

4.9.1.3 Verification of the transverse stiffener

To provide rigid support to the adjacent plates, the intermediate transverse stiffener should be checked on the basis of a second order analyses by fulfilling at ULS the two following criteria:

- maximum stress in the stiffener at ULS:

$$\sigma_{max} \leq \frac{f_y}{\gamma_{M1}} = 335/1.1 = 304.5 \text{ N/mm}^2$$

- additional lateral deflection w at ULS:

$$w \leq \frac{h_w}{300} = 15.5 \text{ mm}$$

4.9 INTERMEDIATE TRANSVERSE STIFFENER DESIGN

A fairly accurate approximation of the maximum stress and the additional deflection taking into account the second order effect, is given in sub-section 2.9.2.3 in case of a single-sided stiffener.

$$I_{st} = 1461.1 \times 10^6 \text{ mm}^4 \text{ (see 4.7 above)}$$

$$A_{st} = 57860 \text{ mm}^2$$

The distance between the centroid of the stiffener (with the adjacent part of the main web) and the mid-plane of the main web is $e_1 = 203.5$ mm.

$$N_{cr,st} = \frac{\pi^2 E I_{st}}{h_w^2} = 140.23 \text{ MN}$$

$$\sum N_{st,Ed} = N_{st,ten} + \Delta N_{st,Ed} = 4.0 \text{ MN} + 1.76 \text{ MN} = 5.76 \text{ MN}$$

$$w_0 = \min\left(\frac{h_w}{300}; \frac{a_1}{300}; \frac{a_2}{300}\right) = 13.3 \text{ mm}$$

$$\delta_m = \frac{N_{st,ten} \cdot e_1}{\sum N_{st,Ed} \cdot w_0} = 10.63$$

The additional lateral deflection is less than $h_w/300$:

$$w = w_0 \cdot \frac{1}{\frac{N_{cr,st}}{\sum N_{st,Ed}} - 1} \cdot (1 + 1.25 \cdot \delta_m) = 8.2 \text{ mm} \leq 15.9 \text{ mm}$$

The value of the maximum stress taking into account the second order effect is given by the following approximate equation:

$$\sigma_{max} = \frac{N_{st,ten}}{A_{st}} + \frac{\sum N_{st,Ed} \cdot e_1}{I_{st}} \cdot w_0 \cdot \frac{1}{1 - \frac{\sum N_{st,Ed}}{N_{cr,st}}} \cdot (1 + 1.11 \cdot \delta_m)$$

$$\sigma_{max} = 69.13 + 142.42 = 211.55 \text{ N/mm}^2 \leq 335/1.1 = 304.55 \text{ N/mm}^2$$

4. Box-Girder Bridge Example

4.9.2 Lower flange transverse stiffeners

The transverse stiffeners are located at every 4.0 m to provide a support to longitudinal stiffeners and to take the deviation force from direct stresses in the lower flange panel.

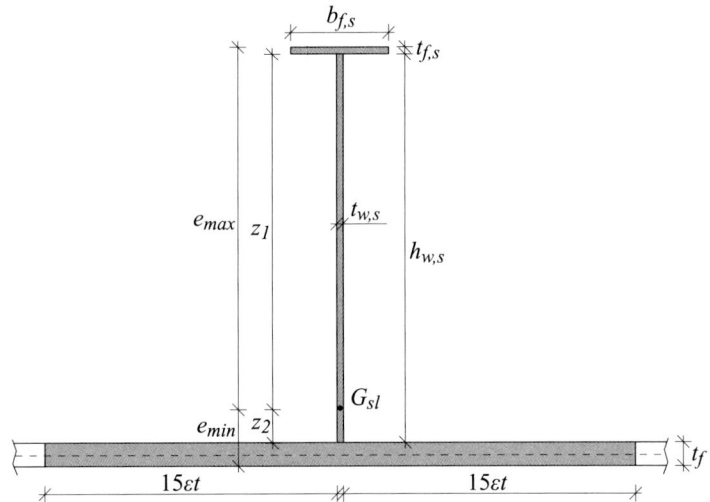

Fig. 4.13: Gross cross section of the transverse stiffener

Material: steel grade S355 M

$f_{y,f} = 325\,\text{kN/mm}^2 \; (t_f = 70\,\text{mm})$

$f_{y,s} = 345\,\text{kN/mm}^2 \; (t_{w,s} = t_{f,s} = 25\,\text{mm})$

Geometric characteristics of the gross cross section of the transverse stiffener:

$b_{f,s} = 300\,\text{mm}$ $\qquad t_f = 70\,\text{mm}$

$t_{f,s} = 25\,\text{mm}$ $\qquad e_{min,gross} = 197.7\,\text{mm}$

$h_{w,s} = 1150\,\text{mm}$ $\qquad e_{max,gross} = 1047.3\,\text{mm}$

$t_{w,s} = 25\,\text{mm}$ $\qquad I_{s,gross} = 2.036 \cdot 10^{10}\,\text{mm}^4$

4.9 Intermediate Transverse Stiffener Design

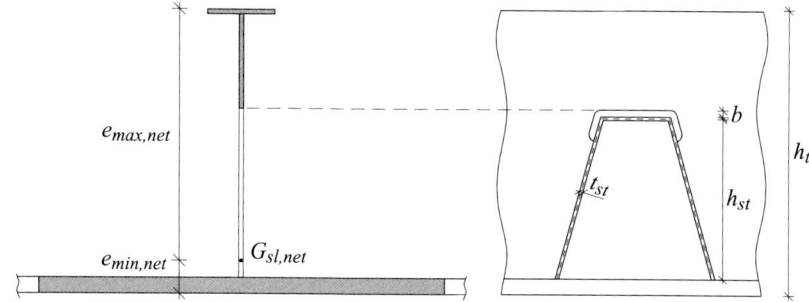

Fig. 4.14: Net cross section of the transverse stiffener

Geometric characteristics of the net cross section of the transverse stiffener:

$h_t = 1245 \, \text{mm}$

$h_{st} = 700 \, \text{mm}, \; t_{st} = 15 \, \text{mm}$ (see 4.4)

$b \geq 2 t_{st} = 2 \cdot 15 = 30 \, \text{mm} > 25 \, \text{mm}$ (acc. to EN 1993-2, C.1.3.5.2(4))

$e_{min,net} = 166.9 \, \text{mm}$

$e_{max,net} = 1078.1 \, \text{mm}$

$I_{s,net} = 1.832 \cdot 10^{10} \, \text{mm}^4$

According to EN 1993-1-5, clause 9.2.4(4), the cut-out height is limited to $0.6 h_t$:

$$h_{st} + t_{st}/2 + b = 700 + 15/2 + 30$$
$$= 737.5 \, \text{mm} < 0.6 h_t = 0.6 \cdot 1245 = 747.0 \, \text{mm} \quad \checkmark$$

4.9.2.1 Cross section class check

Flange (compression):

$$\varepsilon = \sqrt{\frac{235}{f_{y,s}}} = \sqrt{\frac{235}{345}} = 0.825$$

4. BOX-GIRDER BRIDGE EXAMPLE

$$\frac{b_{f,s}/2 - t_{f,s}}{t_{f,s}} = \frac{300/2 - 25}{25} = 5 < 14\varepsilon = 14 \cdot 0.825 = 11.6 \text{ (Class 3)}$$

Web (bending):

$$z_1 = e_{max,gross} - t_{f,s} = 1047.3 - 25 = 1022.3 \text{ mm}$$

$$z_2 = e_{min,gross} - t_f = 197.7 - 70 = 127.7 \text{ mm}$$

$$\psi = -\frac{z_2}{z_1} = -\frac{127.7}{1022.3} = -0.12 > -1$$

$$\frac{h_{w,s}}{t_{w,s}} = \frac{1150}{25} = 46.0 < \frac{42\varepsilon}{0.67 + 0.33\psi} = \frac{42 \cdot 0.825}{0.67 - 0.33 \cdot 0.12} = 55.1 \text{ (Class 3)}$$

Gross cross section of the transverse stiffener is in Class 3.

4.9.2.2 Strength and stiffness check of the stiffener

$$a_1 = a_2 = 4000 \text{ mm}, \ b = 6500 \text{ mm}$$

$$A^p_{c,eff} = 52.74 \cdot 10^4 \text{ mm}^2 \text{ (see 4.4.3.2)}$$

$$\sigma_{c,max} = \sigma_{Ed,inf,eff} = 312.6 \text{ N/mm}^2 \text{ (see 4.4)}$$

$$N_{Ed} = A^p_{c,eff} \cdot \sigma_{c,max} = 52.74 \cdot 10^4 \cdot 312.6 = 1.649 \cdot 10^8 \text{ N} > \frac{A^p_{c,eff}}{2} \cdot \sigma_{c,max}$$

$$\sigma_{cr,c} = 5626 \text{ N/mm}^2 \text{ (see sub-section 4.4.3.2)}$$

$$\sigma_{cr,p} = 5246 \text{ N/mm}^2 \text{ (see section 4.4.2)}$$

$$\frac{\sigma_{cr,c}}{\sigma_{cr,p}} = \frac{5626}{5246} = 1.072 > 1.0 \rightarrow \frac{\sigma_{cr,c}}{\sigma_{cr,p}} = 1.0$$

$$\sigma_m = \frac{\sigma_{cr,c}}{\sigma_{cr,p}} \frac{N_{Ed}}{b}\left(\frac{1}{a_1}+\frac{1}{a_2}\right) = 1.0 \cdot \frac{1.649 \cdot 10^8}{6500}\left(\frac{2}{4000}\right) = 12.68\,\text{N/mm}^2$$

$$u_{gross} = \frac{\pi^2 \cdot E \cdot e_{max}}{\dfrac{f_{y,s} \cdot 300 \cdot b}{\gamma_{M1}}} = \frac{\pi^2 \cdot 210000 \cdot 1047.3}{\dfrac{345 \cdot 300 \cdot 6500}{1.1}} = 3.549 \geq 1.0$$

$$w_0 = \min\left[\frac{b}{300}, \frac{a_1}{300}, \frac{a_1}{300}\right] = \min\left[\frac{6500}{300}, \frac{4000}{300}, \frac{4000}{300}\right]$$

$$= \frac{4000}{300} = 13.3\,\text{mm}$$

$$I_{s,act} \geq I_{s,gross} = \frac{\sigma_m}{E}\left(\frac{b}{\pi}\right)^4\left(1 + w_0 \frac{300}{b} u_{gross}\right)$$

$$= \frac{12.68}{210000}\left(\frac{6500}{\pi}\right)^4\left(1 + 13.3\frac{300}{6500} 3.549\right) = 3.524 \cdot 10^9\,\text{mm}^4$$

$$I_{s,act,gross} = 2.036 \cdot 10^{10}\,\text{mm}^4 \geq I_{s,req,gross} = 3.524 \cdot 10^9\,\text{mm}^4 \checkmark$$

The transverse stiffener fulfils the minimum requirement for the second moment of area.

4.9.2.3 Shear resistance of the stiffener web

According to EN 1993-1-5, clause 9.2.4(5), the web of the gross cross section adjacent to the cut-out should resist a shear force V_{Ed}:

$$V_{Ed} = \frac{I_{s,net}}{e}\frac{f_{yw}}{\gamma_{M0}}\frac{\pi}{b_G},$$

where
$$e = e_{max,net} = 1078.1\,\text{mm}$$

b_G is the length of the transverse stiffener between the inclined webs:

$$b_G = b = 6500 \text{ mm}$$

$$V_{Ed} = \frac{I_{s,net}}{e} \frac{f_{y,s}}{\gamma_{M0}} \frac{\pi}{b_G} = \frac{1.832 \cdot 10^{10}}{1078.1} \frac{345}{1.0} \frac{\pi}{6500} = 2.833 \cdot 10^6 \text{ N}$$

$$\overline{\lambda}_{w,s} = \frac{h_{w,s}}{86.4 t_{w,s} \varepsilon} = \frac{1150}{86.4 \cdot 25 \cdot 0.825} = 0.65 < 0.83$$

$$V_{bw,s,Rd} = \frac{f_{y,s} h_{w,s} t_{w,s}}{\sqrt{3} \gamma_{M1}} = \frac{345 \cdot 1150 \cdot 25}{\sqrt{3} \cdot 1.0} = 5.206 \cdot 10^6 \text{ N}$$

$$\eta_3 = \frac{V_{Ed}}{V_{bw,s,Rd}} = \frac{2.833 \cdot 10^6}{5.206 \cdot 10^6} = 0.54 < 1.0 \checkmark$$

4.10 BUCKLING VERIFICATIONS AT INTERNAL SUPPORT P1 ACCORDING TO SECTION 10, EN 1993-1-5

4.10.1 General

In this sub-chapter, the verification method according to section 10, EN 1993-1-5, is explained for the cross section at the internal support P1. Note that this procedure is an alternative method to sub-chapters 4.3 to 4.9.

4.10.2 Stiffened bottom flange

4.10.2.1 General

The stress field acting on the bottom flange, which is stiffened by four longitudinal stiffeners with trapezoidal cross section, closest to the internal support P1 is shown in Fig. 4.15.

4.10 BUCKLING VERIFICATIONS AT INTERNAL SUPPORT P1 ACCORDING TO SECTION 10, EN 1993-1-5

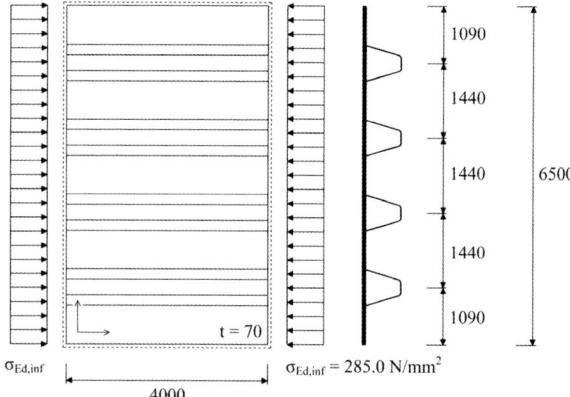

Fig. 4.15: Stress field field acting on the stiffened bottom flange panel closest to the internal support P1. Dimensions in [mm]

The bottom flange is only subjected to uniform compression so that the equivalent design stress $\sigma_{eq,Ed}$ in the panel is equal to the direct stress $\sigma_{Ed,inf}$, see section 4.2.3.

$$\sigma_{eq,Ed} = \sigma_{Ed,inf} = 285.0 \text{ N/mm}^2$$

The verification of the bottom flange considers the complete stress field acting at the stiffened panel assuming hinged boundary at all four edges. During the verification procedure, the determination of two load amplifiers is required in order to calculate the plate slenderness. The minimum load amplifier $\alpha_{ult,k}$ for the design loads to reach the characteristic value of resistance becomes:

$$\alpha_{ult,k} = \frac{f_y}{\sigma_{eq,Ed}} = \frac{325}{285.0} = 1.140$$

The minimum load amplifier α_{cr} for the design loads to reach the elastic critical load of the plate under the complete stress field can be either determined in one step by using appropriate software, e.g. *EBPlate* (EBPlate, 2007), or on the basis of each component of the stress field, e.g. by hand-calculation according to 10(6), EN 1993-1-5. However, the advantage of this procedure can be utilised if appropriate software is used. A stiffened panel may show either local buckling of the sub-panels or global buckling of the stiffened panel, which are addressed in sub-section 4.10.2.2 and sub-section 4.10.2.3.

As determined in sub-section 4.4.3.1, the webs of the longitudinal stiffeners are Class 4 so that local buckling has to be considered in the calculations. The reduction factor for the webs of the closed longitudinal stiffeners is $\rho_{st} = 0.753$.

4.10.2.2 Determination of ρ_{loc} to account for local buckling

The objective of modelling the panel with discrete stiffeners is the determination of local buckling in sub-panels. With *EBPlate* (EBPlate, 2007) and assuming hinged boundary conditions at all four edges the relevant buckling modes under the complete stress field are shown in Fig. 4.16.

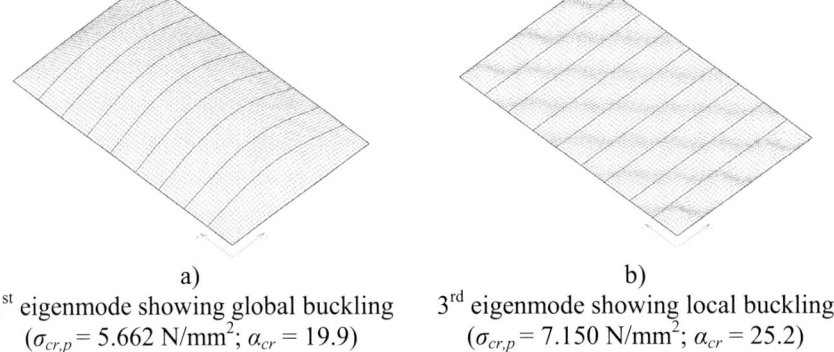

a)
1st eigenmode showing global buckling
($\sigma_{cr,p} = 5.662$ N/mm^2; $\alpha_{cr} = 19.9$)

b)
3rd eigenmode showing local buckling
($\sigma_{cr,p} = 7.150$ N/mm^2; $\alpha_{cr} = 25.2$)

Fig. 4.16: Buckling modes of the stiffened bottom flange with discretely modelled stiffeners under the complete stress field (EBPlate, 2007)

It can be seen from Fig. 4.16 that the first eigenmode is associated with a global buckling mode for which column-like buckling is checked in sub-section 4.10.2.3. Local buckling of the sub-panels is firstly found in the third eigenmode. While for local buckling post-critical strength can be usually accounted for, the resistance against global buckling is affected by column-like buckling in most cases, which further reduces the resistance. That is why in the end a reduction due to global buckling may govern, even if local buckling is found in the first eigenmode. Because here global buckling governs already in the system which is intended to account for local buckling, global buckling will also govern the verification in the end.

4.10 BUCKLING VERIFICATIONS AT INTERNAL SUPPORT P1 ACCORDING TO SECTION 10, EN 1993-1-5

For the sake of completeness, the slenderness corresponding to local buckling is calculated below based on the third eigenmode, see Fig. 4.16b).

$$\overline{\lambda}_p = \sqrt{\frac{\alpha_{ult,k}}{\alpha_{cr}}} = \sqrt{\frac{1.140}{25.2}} = 0.213$$

Because $\overline{\lambda}_p < 0.673$, the reduction factor is $\rho_{loc} = 1.0$ in case of direct stress. This is in agreement with sub-section 4.4.3.1, in which the sub-panels were determined as Class 1 cross sectional element.

4.10.2.3 Determination of ρ_c to account for global buckling

Global buckling could be already determined with the modelling of the panel with discrete stiffeners. For the sake of completeness, an alternative modelling of the panel with smeared stiffeners - in case of plates with at least three stiffeners - is given below in order to determine global buckling of the stiffened panel. With *EBPlate* (EBPlate, 2007) and assuming hinged boundary conditions at all four edges, the first buckling mode under the complete stress field is shown in Fig. 4.17 and α_{cr} is equal to 20.7.

Table 4.2 shows a comparison of the critical values for global buckling which were determined with different methods. It can be shown that the hand-calculation method, see section 4.4.2, gives the most conservative value. However, all results are plausible and of similar magnitude. In the following calculations, the smallest values are chosen, i.e. $\sigma_{cr,p} = 5246$ N/mm^2 and $\alpha_{cr} = 18.5$.

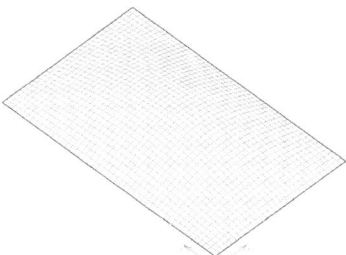

Fig. 4.17: First buckling mode of the stiffened bottom flange with smeared modelled stiffeners under the complete stress field
($\sigma_{cr,p} = 5.874$ N/mm^2; $\alpha_{cr} = 20.7$) (EBPlate, 2007)

4. Box-Girder Bridge Example

Table 4.2: Comparison of critical values for global buckling

Method	$\sigma_{cr,p}$ [N/mm^2]	α_{cr} [-]
Software-based (EBPlate, 2007), model with discrete stiffeners	5.662	19.9
Software-based (EBPlate, 2007), model with smeared stiffeners	5.874	20.7
Annex A.1, EN 1993-1-5; see section 4.4.2	5.246	18.5

The plate slenderness can be calculated:

$$\overline{\lambda}_p = \sqrt{\frac{\alpha_{ult,k}}{\alpha_{cr}}} = \sqrt{\frac{1.140}{18.5}} = 0.248$$

Column-like behaviour should be checked in the relevant direction. In sub-section 4.4.3.2 the critical column buckling stress was determined as $\sigma_{cr,c} = 5626$ N/mm^2. Evaluating the interpolation function, it turns out that pure column-like buckling governs:

$$\frac{\sigma_{cr,p}}{\sigma_{cr,c}} - 1 = \frac{5246}{5626} - 1 = -0.067 < 0 \quad \text{so that } \xi = 0$$

Thus, it is sufficient to determine only the reduction factor χ_c for column-like behaviour. The interpretation of section 10, EN 1993-1-5 (CEN, 2006a), is that the reduction factor χ_c for column-like behaviour is also determined with $\overline{\lambda}_p = 0.248$. According to sub-section 4.4.3.2, the imperfection factor α_e is equal to 0.492. The reduction factor χ_c is given by the general format of the European Buckling Curves using the modified imperfection factor α_e.

$$\varphi = 0.5 \cdot \left[1 + \alpha_e \cdot \left(\overline{\lambda}_p - 0.2\right) + \overline{\lambda}_p^2\right]$$

$$\varphi = 0.5 \cdot \left[1 + 0.492 \cdot (0.248 - 0.2) + 0.248^2\right] = 0.543$$

$$\chi_c = \frac{1}{\varphi + \sqrt{\varphi^2 - \overline{\lambda}_p^2}} \leq 1$$

4.10 Buckling Verifications at Internal Support P1 according to Section 10, EN 1993-1-5

$$\chi_c = \frac{1}{0.543 + \sqrt{0.543^2 - 0.248^2}} = 0.975$$

Because $\xi = 0$, column-like behavior is governing according to the definition in clause 4.5.4(1), EN 1993-1-5, and ρ_c becomes:

$$\rho_c = (\rho - \chi_c) \cdot \xi \cdot (2 - \xi) + \chi_c = \chi_c = 0.975$$

Finally, the verification of the bottom flange is governed by the smallest reduction factor of the stiffener, local buckling and global buckling:

$$\rho = \min(\rho_{st}; \rho_{loc}; \rho_c) = \min(0.753; 1.0; 0.975) = 0.753$$

Since there is only one loading direction, the verification of the bottom flange can be simplified:

$$\alpha_{Rd} = \frac{\rho \cdot \alpha_{ult,k}}{\gamma_{M1}} \geq 1$$

$$\alpha_{Rd} = \frac{0.753 \cdot 1.144}{1.1} = 0.783 \ < \ 1 \quad \text{Not fulfilled!}$$

The characteristic of section 10, EN 1993-1-5 (CEN, 2006a) ("reduced stress method") is that the weakest cross sectional element governs the design of the whole cross section, which is the web of the stiffener in this example. A load shedding from highly utilized cross sectional elements in less utilized cross sectional elements is not assumed although this may be the case. The Class 4 stiffener governs this example and leads to the large difference between the calculation according to the effective width method and the reduced stress method.

When at least a Class 3 stiffener is chosen, global buckling would govern and the reduction factor would be around the calculated value of $\rho_c = 0.975$, which brings the results of both calculation methods closer together.

4. BOX-GIRDER BRIDGE EXAMPLE

4.10.3 Stiffened web

4.10.3.1 General

The stress field acting on the web panel, which is stiffened by a flat bar stiffener (300 mm x 30 mm; Class 3), closest to the internal support P1 is shown in Fig. 4.18. Stresses are taken from sub-chapter 4.5 for the web-to-flange junctions of the upper and lower edge of the web panel.

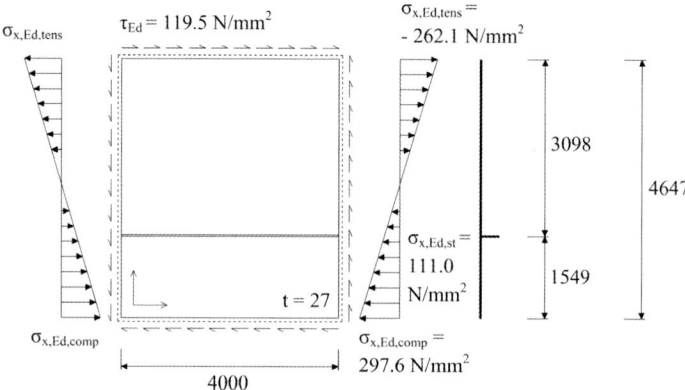

Fig. 4.18: Stress field acting on the stiffened web panel closest to the internal support P1. Dimensions in [mm]

The equivalent design stress in the panel becomes:

$$\sigma_{eq,Ed} = \sqrt{297.6^2 + 3 \cdot 119.5^2} = 362.5 \text{ N/mm}^2$$

The verification of the web panel considers the complete stress field acting at the stiffened panel assuming hinged boundary at all four edges. During the verification procedure, the determination of two load amplifiers is required in order to calculate the plate slenderness. The minimum load amplifier $\alpha_{ult,k}$ for the design loads to reach the characteristic value of resistance becomes:

$$\alpha_{ult,k} = \frac{f_y}{\sigma_{eq,Ed}} = \frac{345}{362.5} = 0.952$$

The value of $\alpha_{ult,k}$ is already smaller than 1.0, i.e. the verification according to the reduced stress method would not be fulfilled. The difference to the effective width method is based on the fact that section 10, EN 1993-1-5, does not consider a partial plastic stress redistribution which is more favourable and permitted in elastic design, see clause 6.2.1(5) note, EN 1993-1-1. Using the effective width method, it was shown in sub-chapter 4.8 that the bending moment is resisted by the flanges alone so that the web resistance can be fully utilised by the shear force. In contrast to the interaction criterion of the effective width method, bending moment and shear force cannot be primarily allocated to the cross sectional elements flanges and web when using the reduced stress method. However, for the sake of completeness the calculation is continued.

The minimum load amplifier α_{cr} for the design loads to reach the elastic critical load of the plate under the complete stress field can be either determined in one step by using appropriate software, e.g. (EBPlate, 2007), or on the basis of each component of the stress field, e.g. by hand-calculation according to 10(6), EN 1993-1-5. However, the advantage of this procedure can be utilized if appropriate software is used. A stiffened panel may show either local buckling of the sub-panels or global buckling of the stiffened panel, which are addressed in sub-section 4.10.3.2 and sub-section 4.10.3.3.

4.10.3.2 Determination of ρ_{loc} to account for local buckling

The objective of modelling the panel with discrete stiffeners is the determination of local buckling in sub-panels. With *EBPlate* (EBPlate, 2007) and assuming hinged boundary conditions at all four edges, the first buckling mode under the complete stress field is shown in Fig. 4.19.

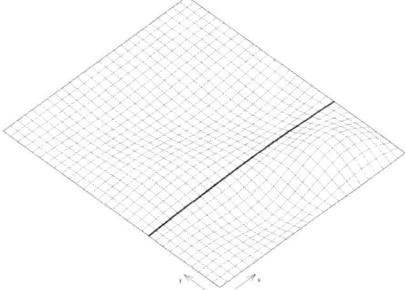

Fig. 4.19: First buckling mode of the stiffened web with discretely modelled stiffeners under the complete stress field ($\alpha_{cr} = 1.136$) (EBPlate, 2007)

4. Box-Girder Bridge Example

It can be seen from Fig. 4.19 that the first eigenmode is associated with a local buckling shape which is dominated by the bending stress in the small sub-panel. The plate slenderness can be calculated:

$$\bar{\lambda}_p = \sqrt{\frac{\alpha_{ult,k}}{\alpha_{cr}}} = \sqrt{\frac{0.952}{1.136}} = 0.915$$

For bending stress with a stress ratio of $\psi = 112.9/297.6 = 0.379$ in the small sub-panel, the reduction factor according to Eq. (4.2), EN 1993-1-5 becomes:

$$\rho = \frac{\bar{\lambda}_p - 0.055 \cdot (3+\psi)}{\bar{\lambda}_p^2} \quad \text{for } \bar{\lambda}_p > 0.5 + \sqrt{0.25 - 0.055 \cdot (3+\psi)}$$

$$\rho = \frac{0.915 - 0.055 \cdot (3+0.379)}{0.915^2} = 0.871 \quad \text{for } \bar{\lambda}_p > 0.753$$

For shear stress, the reduction factor according to Table 5.1, EN 1993-1-5 for a rigid end post becomes:

$$\chi_w = \frac{0.83}{\bar{\lambda}_p} \quad \text{for } \bar{\lambda}_p \geq \frac{0.83}{\eta} \text{ and } \bar{\lambda}_p < 1.08$$

$$\chi_w = \frac{0.83}{0.915} = 0.907 \quad \text{for } \bar{\lambda}_p \geq 0.692 \text{ and } \bar{\lambda}_p < 1.08$$

4.10.3.3 Determination of ρ_c to account for global buckling

For global buckling the panel has to be modelled with a discrete stiffener, because the determination with smeared stiffeners presumes at least three stiffeners. The linear bifurcation analysis in sub-section 4.10.3.2 showed only local buckling shapes even for high eigenvalues, so that below global buckling is accounted for by the hand-calculation formulas of EN 1993-1-5. Similar to section 4.5.2 and sub-chapter 4.7, the critical values for the stiffened panel according to Table 4.3 were determined.

4.10 Buckling Verifications at Internal Support P1 according to Section 10, EN 1993-1-5

Table 4.3: Critical values for global buckling

Critical value	[N/mm²]	[-]
Plate-like behaviour; Annex A.1, EN 1993-1-5; cp. section 4.5.2.2	$\sigma_{cr,p} = 2134$	$\alpha_{cr,x} = 7.171$
Colum-like behaviour; Annex A.1, EN 1993-1-5; cp. section 4.5.2.1	$\sigma_{cr,c} = 2110$	-
Annex A.1, EN 1993-1-5; cp. section 4.7	$\tau_{cr} = 103.9$	$\alpha_{cr,\tau} = 0.869$

With $\psi_x = -262.1/297.6 = -0.880$ the minimum load amplifier α_{cr} becomes:

$$\alpha_{cr} = \frac{1}{\frac{1+\psi_x}{4\cdot\alpha_{cr,x}} + \sqrt{\left(\frac{1+\psi_x}{4\cdot\alpha_{cr,x}}\right)^2 + \frac{1-\psi_x}{2\cdot\alpha_{cr,x}^2} + \frac{1}{\alpha_{cr,\tau}^2}}}$$

$$\alpha_{cr} = \frac{1}{\frac{1-0.880}{4\cdot 7.171} + \sqrt{\left(\frac{1-0.880}{4\cdot 7.171}\right)^2 + \frac{1+0.880}{2\cdot 7.171^2} + \frac{1}{0.869^2}}} = 0.860$$

The plate slenderness can be calculated:

$$\bar{\lambda}_p = \sqrt{\frac{\alpha_{ult,k}}{\alpha_{cr}}} = \sqrt{\frac{0.952}{0.860}} = 1.052$$

Column-like behaviour should be checked in the relevant direction. Evaluating the interpolation function, it turns out that almost pure column-like buckling governs:

$$\frac{\sigma_{cr,p}}{\sigma_{cr,c}} - 1 = \frac{2.134}{2.110} - 1 = 0.011$$

For bending stress with a stress ratio of $\psi = \psi_x = -0.880$, the reduction factor according to Eq. (4.2), EN 1993-1-5 becomes:

4. Box-Girder Bridge Example

$$\rho = \frac{\overline{\lambda}_p - 0.055 \cdot (3+\psi)}{\overline{\lambda}_p^2} \quad \text{for } \overline{\lambda}_p > 0.5 + \sqrt{0.25 - 0.055 \cdot (3+\psi)}$$

$$\rho = \frac{1.052 - 0.055 \cdot (3 - 0.880)}{1.052^2} = 0.845 \quad \text{for } \overline{\lambda}_p > 0.865$$

The interpretation of section 10, EN 1993-1-5, is that the reduction factor χ_c for column-like behaviour is also determined with $\overline{\lambda}_p = 1.052$. According to sub-section 4.5.2.1, the imperfection factor α_e is equal to 0.639. The reduction factor χ_c is given by the general format of the European Buckling Curves using the modified imperfection factor α_e.

$$\varphi = 0.5 \cdot \left[1 + \alpha_e \cdot (\overline{\lambda}_p - 0.2) + \overline{\lambda}_p^2\right]$$

$$\varphi = 0.5 \cdot \left[1 + 0.639 \cdot (1.052 - 0.2) + 1.052^2\right] = 1.326$$

$$\chi_c = \frac{1}{\varphi + \sqrt{\varphi^2 - \overline{\lambda}_p^2}} \leq 1$$

$$\chi_c = \frac{1}{1.326 + \sqrt{1.326^2 - 1.052^2}} = 0.469$$

Because $\xi = 0.011$, column-like behavior is the governing failure mode according to the definition in clause 4.5.4(1), EN 1993-1-5.

$$\rho_c = (\rho - \chi_c) \cdot \xi \cdot (2 - \xi) + \chi_c$$

$$\rho_c = (0.845 - 0.469) \cdot 0.011 \cdot (2 - 0.011) + 0.469 = 0.477$$

For shear stress, the reduction factor according to Table 5.1, EN 1993-1-5 for a rigid end post becomes:

$$\chi_w = \frac{0.83}{\overline{\lambda}_p} \quad \text{for } \overline{\lambda}_p \geq \frac{0.83}{\eta} \text{ and } \overline{\lambda}_p < 1.08$$

4.10 Buckling Verifications at Internal Support P1 according to Section 10, EN 1993-1-5

$$\chi_w = \frac{0.83}{1.052} = 0.789 \quad \text{for } \overline{\lambda}_p \geq 0.692 \text{ and } \overline{\lambda}_p < 1.08$$

Finally, the verification of the stiffened web panel is governed by the smallest reduction factor. In this case, global buckling governs:

$$\rho = \min(\rho_{loc}; \rho_c) = \min(0.871; 0.477) = 0.477$$

$$\chi = \min(\chi_{loc}; \chi_{glob}) = \min(0.907; 0.789) = 0.789$$

The resistance is determined in a single verification step. The verification of the plate subjected to the complete stress field is:

$$\sqrt{\left(\frac{\sigma_{x,Ed}}{\rho_x \cdot f_y / \gamma_{M1}}\right)^2 + 3 \cdot \left(\frac{\tau_{Ed}}{\chi_w \cdot f_y / \gamma_{M1}}\right)^2} \leq 1$$

$$\sqrt{\left(\frac{297.6}{0.477 \cdot 345 / 1.1}\right)^2 + 3 \cdot \left(\frac{119.5}{0.789 \cdot 345 / 1.1}\right)^2} \leq 1$$

$$\sqrt{1.989^2 + 3 \cdot 0.483^2} \leq 1$$

$$2.158 > 1 \quad \text{Not fulfilled!}$$

The characteristic of section 10, EN 1993-1-5 ("reduced stress method"), is that no partial plastic stress redistribution is allowed, as it is the case e.g. for the interaction criterion according to section 7, EN 1993-1-5. Internal forces such as bending moment and shear force cannot be primarily allocated to the cross sectional elements: flanges and web. However, using the effective width method, it can be assumed that the bending moment is resisted by the flanges alone so that the web resistance can be fully utilised by the shear force which gives a much more favourable interaction. As a result the verification of the web panel according to the reduced stress method, based on the Mises criterion, already fails with the determination of $\alpha_{ult,k}$. Besides that, the nature of this example did not allow to determine α_{cr} in one step by using e.g. appropriate software. Instead, α_{cr} had to be

4. BOX-GIRDER BRIDGE EXAMPLE

calculated with conservative hand-calculation formulas and the global plate slenderness is entirely influenced by shear buckling. Since column-like buckling prevails over plate-like buckling, and the reduction factor is calculated with the global plate slenderness $\overline{\lambda}_p = 1.052$ instead of $\overline{\lambda}_c = 0.384$ according to sub-section 4.5.2.1, it results in a very low final reduction factor for column-like buckling. Another aspect is that the reduced stress method consistently uses γ_{M1}. In contrast to this, the effective width method uses γ_{M0} for the direct stress verification and γ_{M1} for the shear stress verification. All effects together lead to the large difference between the reduced stress method and the effective width method.

REFERENCES

"ABAQUS FEA", D S Simulia, (2007). *Dassault Systemes*, Version 6.7.

Basler K, Yen BT, Mueller J, Thurlimann B, (1960). *Web buckling tests on welded plate girders*, Welding Research Council Bulletin Series No. 64, New York.

Beg D, Dujc J, (2007). *On stability of transverse stiffeners*. SSRC Annual Stability Conference, April 18-21, 2007, New Orleans, USA, Proceedings, pp. 375-389.

Braun B, Kuhlmann U, (2009). *Bemessung und Konstruktion von aus Blechen zusammengesetzten Bauteilen*, Stahlbau-Kalender 2009, Verlag Ernst & Sohn.

Davaine L, Raoul J, Aribert JM, (2004). *Patch loading resistance of longitudinally stiffened bridge girders*, Proceedings of the conference Steel Bridge 2004, Millau.

Davaine L, (2005). *Formulation de la résistance au lancement d'une âme métallique de pont raidie longitudinalement*, Doctoral Thesis D05-05, INSA de Rennes, France.

DIN 536-1 (1991). Crane rails – Part 1, Dimensions, sectional properties, steel grades for crane rails with foot flange, form A, *Deutches Institut Für Normung*.

DIN 4114 Blatt 2, (1953). Stahlbau – Stabilitätsfälle (Knickung, Kippung, Beulung), *Deutches Institut Für Normung*.

DIN-Fachbericht 103, (2009). Stahlbrücken, 3rd edition, *Deutches Institut Für Normung*.

EBPlate, (2007). A piece of software developed in the frame of the COMBRI research project. Its aim is to assess the elastic critical stresses of

REFERENCES

plates. EBPlate is free of charge and can be downloaded from the web site of cticm: www.cticm.com

ECCS, (1977). *Second international colloquium on stability*, Introductory Report, Chapter 2, Tokyo 1976, Liège 1977, Washington 1977.

CEN (1993). ENV 1993-1-1:1993 - Eurocode 3: Design of steel structures – Part 1-1: General rules and rules for buildings. *European Committee for Standardization*, Brussels.

CEN (2002). EN 1990: Eurocode:2002. – Basis of structural design, *European Committee for Standardization*, Brussels.

CEN (2004). EN 10025-2:2004 - Hot rolled products of structural steels – Part 2: Technical delivery conditions for non-alloy structural steels, *European Committee for Standardization*, Brussels.

CEN (2005). EN 1993-1-1:2005 - Eurocode 3: Design of steel structures – Part 1-1: General rules and rules for buildings, *European Committee for Standardization*, Brussels.

CEN (2006a). EN 1993-1-5:2006 - Eurocode 3: Design of steel structures – Part 1-5: Plated structural elements, *European Committee for Standardization*, Brussels.

CEN (2006b). EN 1993-2:2006 - Eurocode 3: Design of steel structures – Part 2: Steel Bridges, *European Committee for Standardization*, Brussels.

CEN (2006c). EN 1991-3: Eurocode 1:2006 - Actions on structures – Part 3: Actions induced by cranes and machinery, *European Committee for Standardization*, Brussels.

CEN (2007). EN 1993-6:2007 - Eurocode 3: Design of steel structures – Part 6: Crane supporting structures, *European Committee for Standardization*, Brussels.

CEN (2008). EN 1090-2: 2008 - Execution of steel structures and aluminium structures, Part 2: Technical requirements for the execution of steel structures, *European Committee for Standardization*, Brussels.

CEN (2009). EN 1993-1-5:2006/AC:2009 - Corrigendum to Eurocode 3: Design of steel structures – Part 1-5: Plated structural elements, *European Committee for Standardization*, Brussels.

Evans HR, Tang KH, (1981). *A report on five tests carried out on a large-scale transversely stiffened plate girder – TRV3,* Transaction ASCE, Vol. 112, p.p. 527-544.

Gozzi J, (2007). *Patch Loading Resistance of Plated Girders - Ultimate and serviceability limit state*, Doctoral Thesis 2007:30, Division of Steel Structures, Luleå University of Technology, Sweden.

Graciano C, (2002). *Patch loading - Resistance of longitudinally stiffened girder webs.* Doctoral Thesis 2002:18D, Division of Steel Structures, Luleå University of Technology, Sweden.

Graciano C, Johansson B, (2003). *Resistance of longitudinally stiffened I-girders subjected to concentrated loads*, Journal of Constructional Steel Research 59, No. 5, pp. 561-586.

Höglund T, (1972). *Design of thin plate I-girders in shear and bending with special reference to web buckling*, Bulletin N°. 94, Division of Building Statics and Structural Engineering, Royal Institute of Technology, Stockholm, Sweden.

Iyengar NGR, (1988). *Structural stability of columns and plates*, John Wiley & Sons.

Johansson B, Maquoi R, Sedlacek G, Müller C, Beg D, (2007). *Commentary and worked examples to EN 1993-1-5, Plated Structural Elements"*, 1st Edition, ECCS-JRC Report No. EUR 22898 EN.

Johansson B, Veljkovic M, (2009). Review of plate buckling rules in EN 1993-1-5. Steel Construction - Design and Research 2, No. 4, pp. 228-234.

Klöppel K, Scheer J, (1960). *Beulwerte ausgesteifter Rechteckplatten* (Band I), Ernst & Sohn Verlag, Berlin.

Klöppel K, Möller KH, (1968). *Beulwerte ausgesteifter Rechteckplatten* (Band II). Ernst & Sohn Verlag, Berlin.

REFERENCES

Kuhlmann U, Braun B, Detzel A, Feldmann M, Naumes J, Oppe M, Galéa Y, Martin PO, Raoul J, Davaine L, Johansson B, Clarin M, Gozzi J, Degée H, Boissonnade N, Chica J, Rey F, (2007). *Competitive Steel and Composite Bridges by Improved Steel Plated Structures* (COMBRI). Final Report, RFS-CR-03018, European Commission - Research Fund for Coal and Steel.

Kuhlmann U, Braun B, (2009). *Bestimmung der Sicherheits- elemente zur Anwendung von DIN EN 1993-1-5.* DIBt Final Report, Project ZP 52-5-16.117.1-1130/04 and -1155/05, 2009.

Lagerqvist O, (1994). *Patch loading - Resistance of steel girders subjected to concentrated forces.* Doctoral Thesis 1994:159D, Division of Steel Structures, Luleå University of Technology, Sweden.

Lagerqvist O, Johansson B, (1996). *Resistance of I-girders to concentrated loads*, Journal of Constructional Steel Research 39, No. 2, pp. 87-119.

Müller C, (2003). *Zum Nachweis ebener Tragwerke aus Stahl gegen seitliches Ausweichen*, Doctoral Thesis D82, RWTH Aachen, Germany.

Pavlovčič L, Beg D, Kuhlmann U, (2007). *Shear resistance of longitudinally stiffened panels*, Part 2, Numerical parametric study, Journal of Constructional Steel Research, 63 (2007), pp. 351-364.

Presta F, (2007). *Post-buckling behaviour of transversely stiffened plate girders,* Doctoral Thesis, Univrsita degli studi della Calabria, Cosenza.

Roberts TM, Rockey KC, (1979). *A mechanism solution for predicting the collapse loads of slender plate girders when subjected to in-plane patch loading*, Proceedings of the Institution of Civil Engineers, Part 2, 67, pp. 155-175.

Scheer J, Nölke H, (2001). *Zum Nachweis der Beulsicherheit von Platten bei gleichzeitiger Wirkung mehrerer Randspannungen,* Stahlbau 70, No. 9, pp. 718-729.

Sedlacek G, Eisel H, Hensen W, Kühn B, Paschen M, (2003). *Leitfaden zum DIN-Fachbericht 103*, Verlag Ernst & Sohn.

Sedlacek G, Feldmann M, Naumes J, Mueller C, Kuhlmann U, Braun B, Mensinger M, Ndogmo J, (2008). *Entwicklung und Aufbereitung wirtschaft-licher Bemessungsregeln für Stahl- und Verbundträger mit schlanken Stegblechen im Hoch- und Brückenbau, DASt Bericht 1/2008*, Deutscher Ausschus für Stahlbau, Project AiF 14771, Düsseldorf, Germany.

Winter G, (1947). *Strength of Thin Steel Compression Flanges*, Transaction ASCE, Vol. 112, p.p. 527-544.

Zienkiewicz O, Taylor R, Zhu J, (2005). *The finite element method – Its basis and fundamentals*, Elsevier, 6th edition.